FROM
ATOMOS
TO
ATOM

HARPER TORCHBOOKS / The Cloister Library

(Continued on next page)

HARPER TORCHBOOKS / The Academy Library

HARPER TORCHBOOKS / The Science Library

FROM ATOMOS TO ATOM

The History of the Concept *Atom*

ANDREW G. VAN MELSEN

HARPER TORCHBOOKS / The Science Library

HARPER & BROTHERS, NEW YORK

CONTENTS

_____

TRANSLATOR'S FOREWORD

From the moment modern science made its entrance into history and began to reshape intellectual life and civilization, the relationship between philosophy and science has been a subject of discussion among philosophers and scientists. This book intends to contribute to this discussion through a study of the historical relationship between science and philosophy, by tracing the history of the concept *atom,* which plays such an important role in both philosophic and scientific theories, from its earliest beginnings down to our time.

The present study is not the first work of the author on the history of the concept *atom.* In an earlier work[1] he traced the origin and development of the *philosophic* atomic theories of the past, and made clear that there is a historical connection between philosophic and physical atomic theories. In the course of this earlier work he had opportunity to show that the atomic theory, as it developed in the seventeenth century, was an outgrowth not only of the revived atomic theory of Democritus, but also of Aristotle's minima theory, which had survived in medieval philosophic circles. The present study may be considered, partly as a revision and abbreviation of this earlier work, but in addition the author considers the history of the *physical* atomic theory, and offers a profound confrontation of the philosophic and physical atomic theories.[2]

At a time when the atom bomb has created an almost universal interest in the fascinating problem of the atom, this study should not fail to arouse the interest of those who have some acquaintance with science and philosophy. The book does not require any profound insight into either scientific or philosophic problems, but a certain amount of elementary knowledge is presupposed.

A few words may be added here concerning the author. Dr. Andrew G. van Melsen was born in 1912 in the Netherlands. At the youthful age of thirty-four he became professor of natural philosophy and of philosophy of science at the Charlemagne University of Nijmegen. His brilliant studies in the sciences of chemistry, physics, and philosophy at the University of Utrecht, which culminated in his dissertation on the philosophic past of the atomic theory, had given

---

[1]*Het wijsgerig verleden der atoomtheorie,* Amsterdam 1941, (*The Philosophic Past of the Atomic Theory*).

[2]In another work Dr. van Melsen offers a general confrontation of philosophy and physical science. This work was published under the title *Natuurwetenschap en Wijsbegeerte,* Utrecht-Brussels 1946, (*Physical Science and Philosophy*).

him an excellent preparation for this arduous position. Since the re-opening of the Netherlands universities after the war, Dr. van Melsen has published numerous articles and several books on philosophico-scientific problems. The present work appeared in Dutch in 1949 as the second volume of the Dutch *Scientific and Philosophic Library*,[3] and was widely acclaimed by the critics as an outstanding contribution to both science and philosophy. It has since then appeared in German, Spanish and Italian editions, as well as in English. In 1951 the author came to the United States as a visiting professor to lecture on the philosophy of nature and science at Duquesne University, where he published a treatise on the philosophy of nature. This work has been reprinted three times. A Dutch edition has already appeared, and Italian and Polish translations are in preparation.

A few minor changes have been made in this reprint to bring the work up to date.

HENRY J. KOREN, C.S.Sp.

Duquesne University
Pittsburgh, December 15, 1959.

---

[3]*Wetenschappelijk-Wijsgerige Bibliotheek,* edited by A. de Froe, W. Hel-linga, and H. Groot, and published by J. M. Meulenhoff, Amsterdam.

INTRODUCTION

Having a history is generally considered a mark of distinction. And justly so, for whatever has a history shows that its importance transcends the ephemeral temporariness which is the lot of so many things. It has proved its resistance to the forces of destruction which experience shows at work in everything. Of course, having a history can never be the sole standard of importance, because there are too many things whose sole value for the present time seems to lie in the fact that they have a history.

However enticing it may be to speculate upon the general importance of having a history, we will not pursue this line of thought, but restrict ourselves at once to the object of our study, the concept *atom*. This is a concept which can pride itself both on a long history and eminently actual importance. We first encounter it as the central concept of Greek philosophy. Although later it withdrew somewhat into the background, nevertheless it maintained itself through almost all centuries till again it began to occupy the center of attention in the scientific discussions of the seventeenth centry, when physical science, in the modern sense of the word, clearly began to take shape. Immediately it became one of the fundamental concepts of this science and it has remained so until this very day.

This brief sketch not only indicates the importance of the concept *atom,* but also reveals a serious difficulty in the study of its history. Its history, so to speak, does not run in a straight line. If, for instance, in our historical investigations we base ourselves upon the knowledge of the concept *atom* as it has become familiar to us through the study of modern physical science, we will easily lose track of it in the more distant past. We would expect to find in the past a concept which is less complicated, perhaps, and simpler in structure, but at any rate built along the same lines as the concept familiar to us. But we would be disappointed in our expectations, because among the Greeks the concept *atom* was seen in the frame of a different problem which is wider and more embracing than that of our contemporary physical science. The physicist who is interested in the history of his science encounters among the Grecian thinkers many considerations which seem to him beside the point, and he fails to find others which he considers of the greatest importance. Thus he is easily tempted to conclude that the Greeks did not really understand very much of the essential problem. Yet this conclusion would involve a grave injustice

1

to the Greeks, because our physicist would have left out of consideration that the Grecian approach to the problem is, partly at least,
different from his own.

A similar danger faces the philosopher who, ignorant of the proper
setting of modern physical science, would start with the distant past
and after a study of Greek atomic theory devote his attention to the
modern conception of the atom. Most likely he would not evaluate the
contemporaneous setting of the atomic problem at its proper value.

After this double warning the reader will be inclined, perhaps, to
conclude that the Grecian and the modern atomic concept do not have
so very much in common. This, however, likewise would be a serious
misconception, for notwithstanding the difference there is an unmistakable historic connection. But to sketch this connection here in
the Introduction to this book would be presumptuous. It would con-
fuse the proper functions of an Introduction and an Epilogue. This
entire study is precisely an endeavor to determine as accurately as
possible the nature of this connection. From the whole work it
should become clear to the reader that the title FROM ATOMOS TO
ATOM intends to indicate more than the mere time limits of the period
considered in this survey. By distinguishing in the title between the
Greek word ATOMOS and the modern word ATOM we intend to convey
also the distinctive spheres of Grecian and modern *thought,* as well as
their unmistakable continuity. Moreover, the use of the Greek and
the modern variation of the term *atom* makes it clear that we do not
want to limit the meaning of the term to its strictly technical sense:
it stands for modern concepts such as molecule and electron as well as
for the so-called *natural minima* by which medieval scholastics used
to indicate the idea of smallest parts.

Concerning the connection between the concepts of *smallest parts*
as used in modern physical science and those which played a role
in the philosophic theories of the past, it should be sufficient for the
purposes of this introduction if we point out that this connection
is the same as that between physical science and philosophy in
general. For it is a matter of fact that the former has come forth
from the latter. Among many other questions ancient philosophy
gave its attention to those problems which are now considered to
belong exclusively to physical science. Not before the seventeenth
century did physical science and philosophy separate, or rather,
it was in that century that their ways began to lead in different
directions. The very titles of many classical works of the past

clearly bear witness to that intimate relation. For instance, the work in which Newton published the Laws of Gravitation bears the title: PHILOSOPHIAE NATURALIS PRINCIPIA MATHEMATICA[1] (1687). Again, Dalton's study of atomic theory, A NEW SYSTEM OF CHEMICAL PHILOSOPHY, (1808) still shows in its title the origin of chemistry from philosophy. Moreover, even nowadays it is not unusual, at least in European Universities, to refer to the Faculty of Mathematics and Science as the Faculty of Natural Philosophy[2]. Finally, it is not only physical science which developed from ancient philosophy, the same is true of practically all other sciences.

This unity of science in former ages should not surprise us. The study of science had the same meaning in the past as it has in our times, namely the creation of intellectual order in a multitude of experiences. Originally the total of data in which order had to be created was rather small; as a matter of fact, it did not embrace more than the data of common experience. Hence it seemed possible to master this total with a single scientific grasp. There was only one science, and that was philosophy, only one method, the philosophic method. Thus this unique science could pretend to embrace the whole of human knowledge in one common setting. True, within this unique science, distinctions were made according to the different fields of knowledge; for instance, the knowledge of celestial bodies, of inorganic and organic nature. This, however, did not imply any violation of the essential unity of science, because the inner connection was never lost sight of. Neither was the unity destroyed by the fact that this unique science knew different *methods,* because the latter were, characteristically, variations of one and the same method rather than really entirely distinct methods. Apart from the more or less different branches of philosophy which were the prototypes of future autonomous sciences, attention was also given within this philosophic whole to those problems which nowadays still form the object of philosophic speculation, namely, the fundamental speculation about human knowledge and human being.

Thus the scientific study of a particular branch of knowledge presupposed a general schooling. No doubt, a mathematician differed from a physician or a physicist; but nevertheless they all envisaged their science as an integral part of *the* science. For the ancients *the* science was no abstract collective concept in the sense in which we

---

[1]The Mathematical Principles of Natural Philosophy.

[2]We may add that in the United States the title of Doctor of Philosophy is still the customary title for a doctorate in any of the natural sciences . Transl.

nowadays speak of science-in-general, but a real unity in which no part was seen separately from the whole.

Slowly, however, the steady growth of knowledge in each branch, both in extension and in depth, gave rise to scientific theories which intended nothing more than to put order in the data of one particular field. Thus was laid the foundation of separate sciences, each with its own methods adapted to its own specific purpose. It was precisely on account of this that it became impossible for one man to retain a mastery of science in its entirety. What made the continuation of a single all-embracing view impossible was not so much that the steadily growing mass of experimental data exceeded the capacity of *one* man, because every science has the means of keeping its data within easy reach of the interested scholar; rather it was the fact that the settings of the problems became more and more disconnected, the fact that the various sciences began to consider the phenomena under widely divergent aspects and adopted methods suitable for their own specific purpose. For, after all, it is clear that no man is able to make simultaneously his own, the distinct mental attitudes which characterize the economist, the physician, the philologist, the physicist, the mathematician, the jurist, etc.

Thus we are at once faced with the question: What, then, has become of philosophy? Does it still make sense to consider it as a special branch of scientific investigation? Or has its function been wholly parceled out to other sciences in the steady development of separate branches of human knowledge? This is, indeed, a very fundamental question which will continue to hold our attention throughout this study. The fact that philosophy still survives does not really mean very much, for it could be one of those things to which we referred in the beginning of this Introduction: a thing whose value consists solely in its history.

We will not anticipate here the answer to the question as to whether philosophy retains the right to existence, because the whole of our study will provide the answer. The nature of our subject will force us continually to give an accurate account of the difference between philosophy and physical science, and this difference contains the answer to the point in question.

The investigation of the function which the concept *atom* fulfilled in Grecian thought will readily bring us into touch with both the scientific and the philosophic setting of the problem. For although we find that the Greeks were interested also in those problems which are now called scientific, nevertheless it will become clear that their attention was focused upon philosophical problems. This will be the case not only with the Greeks, but also with their successors till the seventeenth century. Only at that time did attention become focused upon the scientific setting; perhaps, we may even say that then for the first time the scientific setting of problems was seen as something separate and specifically distinct. The transition, of course, was a gradual one. Perhaps it can be best expressed as follows: in Grecian philosophy and science the philosophic setting of problems stood in the foreground and the scientific setting in the background. Gradually a shift took place, and from the seventeenth century on the scientific setting moved forward and pushed the philosophic setting into the background, although the latter remained on the stage. We may illustrate this very inadequate metaphor still in another way. Greek thinkers, as Aristotle and Democritus, belong primarily to the history of philosophy, but they also have a place in the history of physical science. The same is true of medieval thinkers such as Avicenna, Averroes, Albert the Great, and Albert of Saxony, to name only a few. Names belonging to the seventeenth century, as Descartes and Leibnitz, are still encountered in the history of both sciences, but their contemporaries Newton and Boyle figure almost exclusively in the history of physical science, although it is certainly possible and not without importance to say something about their philosophic views. After the seventeenth century, however, it will be very exceptional to find the same name mentioned in both science and philosophy.

Thus a history of the concept *atom* will necessarily have to be divided into two characteristically different parts. The first part will be of a philosophic nature, because in the period covered by this part the concept *atom* was preponderantly considered from a philosophic point of view. This period embraces up to the seventeenth century, and is divided into three chapters. The first deals with Grecian philosophy; the second with the Middle Ages and the Renaissance; and the third with the seventeenth century. Moreover, the third chapter will form the link between the first period, which was primarily philosophic, and the second period, which is primarily scientific in outlook. For it was in this century that the concept *atom* evolved into a physical concept. Hence it is especially the growth of the physical atomic theory which will occupy our attention in the second part of this book. In turn, this part is divided into three chapters. The first considers the origin and the initial development of the physical or scientific atomic theory as a distinct autonomous structure.

The second deals with the subsequent evolution of this atomic theory, which so profoundly enriched the concept *atom*. The demarcation of this and the preceding chapter is marked by the turn in the evolution of the concept through the discovery of the phenomena which led to the quantum theory. In the third chapter of this second series we will try to answer some philosophic questions which spontaneously arise in the course of our historical survey. As already mentioned, the most important of these questions will be whether alongside physical science there remains room for the special science which hitherto was called philosophy. That question concerns the specific nature of both science and philosophy. To some extent the answer will be prepared by the philosophical considerations which in the course of this work will interrupt our historical explanations.

Finally, in a last chapter we will reconsider the whole history of the concept *atom*.

PART ONE

THE CONCEPT *ATOM* BEFORE THE ORIGIN

OF THE

PHYSICAL ATOMIC THEORY

CHAPTER ONE

THE PHILOSOPHY OF GREECE

1. INTRODUCTION

After reading in the Introduction our remarks about the history of the concept *atom* the reader will not be surprised to notice that the title of this chapter is not "The Concept *Atom* Among the Greeks," or some similar title, but the more general "The Philosophy of Greece." We do not intend to limit our attention in this chapter to those thinkers who had some concept of *atom,* or at least of *smallest part.* Were we to limit ourselves in this way, we would get a false picture of the importance attached to the concept by those thinkers; that is, we would not see it in the frame of the problems wherein it played its role. For instance, we would certainly understand very little of Democritus' atoms if we did not know anything about the fundamental problem which Democritus sought to solve with his atomic theory. At most, we would observe some vague relationship to our modern atomic concept, in comparison with which that of Democritus would reveal itself as rather primitive. This, of course, would not surprise us in view of the centuries which separate the two concepts. It cannot be disputed that Democritus' concept is indeed primitive, especially when we evaluate it exclusively according to its usefulness in the explanation of physical phenomena, such as evaporation. Undoubtedly, even from this point of view the concept *atom* as found in Democritus possesses a certain value, but only insofar as it is the first step in a direction in which modern science has made so much headway that it hardly seems to make sense to look back as far as Democritus. However, by taking this view of the matter we would do Democritus a great injustice, because from an intellectual point of view his primitive concept may have been an achievement equally important for his time as the surprising turn given to the atomic theory by de Broglie or Bohr in our times. But we would also do an injustice to Democritus for another reason already hinted at in the Introduction, namely that we would not evaluate his atomic theory in its most essential characteristics. For his atomic theory was intended to solve a fundamental difficulty encountered by adolescent Grecian thought, a difficulty which had first to be solved in order

9

to make possible any progress at all in science. This rather startling statement may astonish the reader, but it will, we hope, rouse his interest not only in the Grecian ideas of *smallest parts,* but also in the over-all value of Greek philosophy for Western intellectual life in general and for science in particular. It would be difficult to over-estimate this value, as will become clear from the rest of this chapter.

2. THE IMPORTANCE OF GRECIAN PHILOSOPHY

We may suppose man's quest of knowledge to be as old as man himself, at least as far as the West is concerned. The systematic method, however, by which a harmonious body of concepts and theses was obtained originated in Greece. We children of the twentieth century who possess a cultural language which allows us from our early youth to express our thoughts in suitable terms, realize too little how rich we are in the possession of such a treasure. We have come to accept it as quite natural and see nothing unusual in the fact that our language enables us to express correctly scientific data and demonstrations. Yet to a large extent we owe this possibility to the philosophers of Greece who, so to speak, discovered, preserved, and developed the terms which appear most suited for the expression of scientific data. To give some examples: essential and accidental, material and formal, quantitative and qualitative, cause, condition, capacity, potency, necessary, contingent, substance, property, individual, species, theory, hypothesis, purpose, definition, demonstration, deduction, induction, premise, conclusion, and many others.

Perhaps the objection will be made that these terms are relatively of minor importance in physical science, because the language used by this science is not an ordinary but an artificial language, borrowed, at least in part, from mathematics. This remark is true, no doubt, but it does not weaken our argument. For apart from the fact that even in physical science ordinary language still plays an important role, every artificial language has to be determined by means of ordinary language, either directly or through some other artificial language. Moreover, these artificial languages could only be developed when science had already reached a certain degree of perfection. For one of the primary requirements of an artificial language is to give the best possible representation of that for which it is supposed to stand. For instance, proper symbolic writing in chemistry could not be developed before a sufficient understanding of chemical phenomena had been obtained. Furthermore, it is not without importance to point out that even the Greeks made use of artificial language in a limited way, as appears from the well-known fact that Aristotle used symbols in his logical writings. Thus to a certain extent the Greeks are our masters even in the creation of symbolic language. That they used it precisely in logic is understandable in the light of the observation just made: logic in their time had already reached a very high degree of perfection, witness Aristotle.

Therefore, we may conclude that the Greeks laid the foundations of western science, not only because so many sciences were successfully studied in Greece, although this alone is already a very important factor, but also and especially because science in later times is indebted to the Greeks as the creators of a scientific language and a scientific method. This language and this method originated when Grecian thought was confronted with the fundamental problems which center around the apparent contradiction between the data of experience and the postulates of reason. It was the aim of their great philosophers to solve this contradiction, an aim which they constantly kept in mind, even when they turned their attention to more specific problems.

The question now arises whether or not the development of a scientific method had of necessity to take place in a philosophic setting; or, to express the same idea in different words, whether or not it would have been possible to develop such a method whenever some particular problem received its solution. For it may seem somewhat strange that we find attention given to all-embracing problems at the very beginning of scientific thought, when practically no solution yet had been offered for any particular problem. Later we will return to this question and we will see that it could not have been otherwise: the first science had to be *philosophic,* even though afterwards it would become clear that the solution of the philosophic problems was not necessary in order to solve the specific problems posed by the sciences in later times. Only gradually did man discover that we can avoid the problems of philosophy and still apply ourselves to science.

Thus it is clear that the concept *atom* developed within the frame of philosophic problems. Although we must, therefore, consider these problems, it goes without saying that we cannot treat them as extensively as they deserve. We will have to restrict ourselves to those aspects which have an immediate bearing upon the subject of our study. Fortunately, however, this will bring us right to the core of the main problems in Grecian philosophy. Thus we may hope that many points to which we could only vaguely refer in this introduction will become clear in the course of this study.

3. THE FIRST GRECIAN PHILOSOPHERS

Thales of Miletus. It is remarkable that the first Grecian philosophers about whom something is known generally came from the colonized regions of Asia Minor. We may, therefore, ask ourselves whether philosophy originated there. Burnet considers this very likely.[1] For in order to advance in the direction of philosophy, of more scientific conceptions of sense experiences, the Greeks had to cut themselves loose from myths and fables which give arbitrary solutions of phenomena and thus can never lead to a rational explanation. Now "a myth is essentially a local thing," tied to a certain region with its own peculiarities. Hence the colonization which brought the Greeks in contact with other myths about the same phenomena could easily have shaken their belief in any myths. Myths and fables were concerned chiefly with natural phenomena, so that it is not surprising that, if their authority gradually was undermined, the first efforts towards philosophy were made in the domain of the philosophy of nature, i.e. that they were efforts to explain nature. However, it remains obviously subject to reasonable doubt whether the loss of faith in myths and fables was the principal factor in the birth of philosophy. It is even highly probable that colonization brought the Greeks in contact with valuable data of ancient Asiatic civilizations.[2]

The oldest Greek philosopher whose doctrine is partially known is Thales of Miletus (about 600 B. C.). The problem which held his attention was the problem of unity and multiplicity. Already in him do we find the universal endeavor which characterizes all science to reduce the manifold of the phenomena to a certain unity. Thus Thales thought that there must be one primary matter from which everything has come forth by gradual differentiation. We may call this the *philosophic* aspect of his ideas. However, he does not stop at this general aspect, but indicates water as the primary matter. This we may conveniently consider as the more *scientific* or physical aspect of his theory.

It is not known what phenomena led Thales to his theory nor what line of thought he followed in his speculations. We shall not sug-

[1] J. Burnet, *Early Greek Philosophy,* London[2] 1908, p. 4.
[2] E. Bréhier, *Histoire de la philosophie,* Paris 1945, I, p. 3ff.

gest any conjecture. Likewise, we shall abstain from advancing any opinion about the reasons which possibly led his colleague Anaximenes (about 585-about 528 B. C.), who also came from Miletus, to accept air as the primary matter of all things.

Heraclitus. We must dwell somewhat longer upon Heraclitus (480 B.C.) who considered *fire* as the primary matter of all things, because the considerations which led Heraclitus to this conception are very interesting. Profoundly struck by the continuous change to which all being is subject so that nothing remains identical with itself, Heraclitus thought that the only thing which really *is,* properly speaking, is change itself. To be is *to change.* Therefore, the primary matter from which everything is made must be a principle of change. Now fire fulfills this condition. For fire does not remain identical with itself even for a single instant. It may appear to remain the same, yet it is always in a process of becoming, because it is forever composed of different burning matter. The fact that fire remains *apparently* the same is important for his choice of fire as prime matter. For sense perception will sometimes give the impression of real rest, although there is no real identity, nor real rest. True, this impression may be an illusion, as Heraclitus teaches, but such an appearance of rest requires a foundation. Now this appearance can be explained by the characteristics of primary matter itself in which the same two aspects are found, namely, an appearance of identity with itself and a reality of continuous change. Heraclitus uses a very suggestive comparison to illustrate these two aspects: in a river the water which flows by is forever different so that the river does not for a single moment remain identical with itself; yet it makes an impression of being something permanent.

Parmenides. Radically opposed to the theory of Heraclitus is that of Parmenides (about 500 B.C.), a philosopher of the Eleatic School (so called after the town of Elea in Southern Italy). Parmenides also was concerned with the problem of permanency and change, but while Heraclitus sought the essence of everything in change so that there can be no question of any permanent unchangeable reality, Parmenides' speculations produced exactly the opposite result. According to him reality is unchangeable, and change is nothing but an illusion.

We may ask ourselves how Parmenides came to this conclusion, and also how it is possible that two thinkers could come to such a flagrant contradiction. In order to understand it, at least to a certain extent, we should keep in mind that Heraclitus relied upon sense experience which, indeed, teaches change. He trusted unconditionally in this common experience of the senses. It is not inconsequent that he considered the perception of rest an illusion. For he required an intellectual interpretation of sense experience: "Eyes and ears are bad witnesses for men, if they do not have souls which understand the language of the senses."[3] This explains his critical analysis of rest as the merely apparent identity of something with itself. Parmenides, however, denied *all* value to sense perception, because according to his view everything which we perceive, reflection clearly shows to be impossible. For Parmenides this is the sole criterium: "Only that can really exist which can also be thought."[4]

It will be worth while to pause a moment at this principle of Parmenides, before we examine more closely why change cannot be thought. It may aptly be called the Principle of Intelligibility, because it expresses that only that can exist which does not offer any unsurmountable obstacle to understanding, i.e. which expresses something *intelligible*. Parmenides' principle is of fundamental importance, as we will see presently. If our speculations about reality are to have any sense, they must have a reference to reality. Obviously, this touches one of the most fundamental problems of philosophy.

However, the term *intelligible* should not be misunderstood. It can have two quite different meanings which should be carefully distinguished. The difference can be more easily explained by a consideration of the contradictory of intelligible, unintelligible. To be unintelligible can also have two meanings, which we may call positively and negatively unintelligible. Positively unintelligible means that we positively see that a thing contradicts something else which we hold to be certain. Negatively unintelligible means that we simply do not understand something. Let us illustrate the difference by an example. Somebody is told to drive in six hours from Amsterdam to Paris, a distance of 600 kilometers, with a car capable of a maximum speed of 80 kilometers an hour. After some mental arithmetic he will say: "That is impossible." Why does he say that? Because he perceives *positively* that it cannot be done. Upon the basis of some elementary mathematical and physical insight he applies the principle of Parmenides. Now an example of negative unintelligibility. If we are asked: "Will it be possible to drive from Amsterdam to Paris in one hour?" we will answer: "I do not see how that is possible." This answer is

---

[3]H. Diels, *Fragmente der Vorsocratiker,* Berlin 1934, fragm. 107.
[4]H. Diels, *Ibid.* fragm. 3 and 8, 34.

far less absolute than the preceding one. I do not see that the feat in question is altogether impossible, but I do not very well see any positive possibility. "Not to understand" here means simply that I do not have sufficient data to understand. To express the matter concisely, negative unintelligibility means "*not* to understand that . . .", and positive unintelligibility means "to *understand* that . . . not . .". These two kinds of unintelligibility are quite different, although in practice it will frequently be difficult to distinguish them because we often make mistakes. Sometimes we think that something is positively unintelligible, while in reality our view is based upon a misunderstanding. This may suffice as a first introduction to the principle of Parmenides. We will have plenty of opportunity to come back to it, because many of the most fundamental problems of philosophy are connected with it.

Parmenides is sometimes called the first metaphysician, and justly so. For traditionally metaphysics is the science of being as being. Hence metaphysics, as a science, endeavors to comprehend those theses which apply to everything that is insofar as it has *to be,* and whatever is included in this *to be.* Whether or not there can be any sense in speaking of metaphysics as a science, is again a problem which provisionally must be left alone. At any rate, Parmenides' principle is metaphysical, because it states something about being as being, that is, it expresses a law which according to Parmenides applies to all that is without any restriction. All that is is intelligible, or somehow *being* falls within the grasp of the intellect. Therefore, this principle must apply to every particular *being* or to whatever is considered a being.

Let us return now to Parmenides and see how he applied this principle. Reasoning as follows, Parmenides started with the statement: All that *is,* together forms the being. This statement is historically known as the Principle of Identity, and is also expressed in the following formula: Being is. Now, so reasons Parmenides, that which is must be *one,* i.e. it must possess unity, for if it were manifold there would have to be something which divides it. But outside being, nothing is. Therefore, there is nothing which can divide being, and, therefore, being is *one.* This one being is also unchangeable. For what could be the meaning of change? It could mean either the transition from one kind of being to another kind of being or the transition from non-being to being. There is no other alternative. That is the dilemma which faces the human mind when man investigates the possibility of change. Now, continues Parmenides, both members of the dilemma lead to the same conclusion, namely the impossibility of change. The transition from one kind of being to another kind of being, because there is only one being, so that this part of the dilemma really amounts to being remaining what it is. Hence this part of the dilemma does not describe any real change. The second member of the dilemma likewise does not offer any escape, because non-being *is not;* therefore it cannot become anything. Thus Parmenides' speculations led him to the conclusion that no change is possible. Whatever changes the senses may seem to reveal are nothing but illusions, just as the manifold is an illusion of the reality which can only be *one.*

To modern ears Parmenides' line of thought will sound very strange, and the mind which is trained along the line of physical science will feel irritated, because it is not in the habit of putting problems that way. It does not see any use in such speculations. Let us not be too fast in our judgment. No less a person than Émile Meyerson, the well-known twentieth century French philosopher, after a thorough search of the historical and contemporaneous methods used by the human mind in physical science, arrived at a conclusion which should warn us to be prudent. After asking himself what exactly was meant by scientific explanation Meyerson answered:

> After all, as far as our explanation goes *nothing has happened.* Since the phenomenon is nothing but change, it is clear that in so far as we have explained it, we have caused it to vanish. Every explained part of a phenomenon is a part which is denied.[5]

In other words, the *new,* properly speaking, is not new; it only seems new, but in reality nothing is changed. To illustrate this, he refers to the manner in which, for instance, chemistry explains the phenomena which fall under its observation. When we heat mercuric oxide, a red powder, we obtain, as every tyro in chemistry knows, a metallic liquid and a gas which supports combustion. , Now the chemical explanation, says Meyerson, teaches us that the red powder also is really mercury and oxygen. In other words, that there is here a material reality which remains identical with itself. Of course, by this explanation we have not yet reduced everything to identity, but we have not explained everything completely either. In so far, however, as we have explained the phenomenon, nothing appears changed. Chemistry expresses this with the equation: $HgO \rightarrow Hg + O$.

---

[5]*Identité et Réalité,* Paris[3] 1926, p. 252. G. Heymans (1857-1930) in imitation of Hamilton held a similar view.

When a twentieth century scholar, of whom no one can say that he did not make a searching study of modern physical science, arrives at essentially the same conclusions as Parmenides, it is clear that the latter really did touch a fundamental problem in concluding that, strictly speaking, nothing changes and that observed changes are but illusions. Obviously, we do not intend to justify Parmenides with an appeal to Meyerson nor to propose Meyerson's analysis as the only correct one. We only intended to give the reader some acquaintance with the import of Parmenides' thesis and to make it clear to him that Parmenides did touch a very fundamental problem. For what was applied above to a chemical explanation can be extended to scientific theories in other branches of knowledge. For instance, in psychology two behavior patterns which at first sight seem to be entirely different may be explained as the manifestations of some basically identical characteristic. (See *Note* on p. 48.)

The impression made by Parmenides upon his Grecian contemporaries was profound. We do not mean that they all accepted his view, but all at least took into account the problem formulated by him and his line of reasoning. Moreover, generally speaking it is true that most thinkers after Parmenides tried to bridge the gap between Parmenides and Heraclitus by a higher synthesis which would not only do full justice to the postulates of reason as formulated by Parmenides, but also not contradict the obvious fact of change.

4. DEMOCRITUS

The endeavor to find a solution for Parmenides' dilemma produced also the first atomic theories. We will start with Democritus' theory, which has exercised more influence upon later times than any other Greek atomic theory. Whether or not his theory is also chronologically the oldest cannot be established with certaintly. Democritus, who was born about 460 B.C., is certainly posterior to Empedocles and Anaxagoras (born about 500 B.C.), both of whom also have an atomic theory to their account. However, there is reason to suppose that the father of Democritus' atomism is really a certain Leucippus, who most likely was a little older than Empedocles and Anaxagoras. Therefore, the atomic theory attributed to Democritus would still have to be considered as the first. At any rate, Democritus is the most important of the atomists and, therefore, we have to dwell more extensively upon his theories.

Democritus is described as a universal scholar. "He thought about everything," says Aristotle, his great opponent. It seems that he travelled far and wide, and wrote about the most divergent matters. Unfortunately, none of his works has been saved for posterity. Even his atomic theory is known only through the writings of others. Nevertheless, except for one point, we have a clear idea of it.

The Origin of the Atomic Theory. We have spoken above of the crisis which faced Grecian science in its infancy. Setting out with the purpose of explaining the manifold, it quickly finished with a categorical denial of the obvious manifold. Instead of explaining the manifold changing phenomena it declared change impossible, and thus destroyed any possible basis for a science of nature. Such was the tragic result of the first attempt to give a rational explanation for the phenomena of nature. Hence the first task which Democritus faced was not to explain some particular phenomenon of nature, some concrete change, but to show that changes were possible at all. Or, to express it in the words of Parmenides, Democritus had first to show that change is intelligible. Perhaps we may best describe Democritus' atomism as a subtle attempt to make room for change while retaining as much as possible the principles of Parmenides. We should not forget that Parmenides had made a profound impression, not the least upon Democritus. The latter's atomic theory clearly reveals the constant intention of following Parmenides as closely as possible. As a matter of fact, Democritus took over most of Parmenides' doctrines. There was only one point which Democritus could not accept, namely that all change is nothing but an illusion. Or perhaps it would be better to say: what Parmenides belittled as an illusion was physical reality for Democritus. Even if change were only an illusion, that illusion, at any rate, had to be explained. Thus Democritus' point of departure was, on one hand Parmenides' principle that being is unchangeable, and on the other hand the reality of change. How could these two be reconciled? In order to understand Democritus' line of reasoning we must recall that the reason why Parmenides rejected *all* change was the unintelligibility of change. But, is *every* change really unintelligible? Does this unintelligibility apply even to local motion, to change of place, which offers little obscurity? Such must have been the questions which Democritus asked himself. His answer was of a surprising simplicity: all apparent change ultimately rests upon local motion. Motion of what? The answer to this question led Democritus to the conclusion that the being of

Parmenides is not *one,* but divided into a number of *beings,* each of which, however, in itself is unchangeable and indivisible (ἄτομος, atom). The question may be asked how these atoms are separated from each other, for outside being there is nothing, according to Parmenides; hence being is *one.* Democritus solved this question by stating: "Nothing *is,* just like being is." Taken literally this answer would be very startling. It would seem a glaring contradiction in terms, since nothing by definition is that which *is not.* Democritus, however, did not mean it literally. Nothing, for him, means the void, and being, the full, i.e. what is full of atoms. Thus Democritus' solution practically amounts to a surrender of the absolute uniformity of all being, because for him *to be* means either *to be atom* or *to be void.* By admitting the void Democritus explained not only that the atoms could be separate, but also that they could move. Hence change is nothing but the union or the separation of intrinsically unchangeable atoms. They are capable of juxtaposition, but they can never fuse into a new whole. Neither can they be divided into two parts. The only possible change consists in a differentiation of position of the atoms by union with, or separation from, other atoms in the sense indicated above.

In order to make intelligible the enormous multiplicity of apparent changes Democritus introduced the following hypotheses about the properties of atoms:

1) They are infinite in number, qualitatively absolutely identical, and distinct only by shape and size. Whatever differences we perceive in things are based upon the differences in size and shape of the atoms, but above all upon the differences in their position. A change in a thing is based upon a change in the position of its atoms.

2) Motion is a primitive property of atoms. Like the atoms themselves, it is eternal and incorruptible. Hence the atoms are ceaselessly in motion, but this motion can be changed by pressure and percussion. How exactly Democritus conceived this cannot be established with certainty. Not only the ancient sources of his doctrine, but also the modern students of Greek philosophy differ in their exposition and interpretation of Democritus' theory. However, since this point is relatively unimportant for our purpose, we may omit these various possible interpretations.

Evaluation of Democritus' Atomic Theory. In our critique of Thales of Miletus we distinguished the metaphysical and the physical aspects of his theory, although we did not yet use the term *metaphysical*. In order to do justice to Democritus we must make the same distinction in his atomic theory. By the metaphysical aspect of atomism we mean that aspect which fulfills the conditions of a general law of being, i.e. which applies to all that is. Just as Thales was convinced that it must be possible to reduce all plurality, regardless of its nature, to some unity, so Democritus is of the opinion that *all* change must be based on a shift of intrinsically immutable primordial particles. Both these principles, that of Thales as well as that of Democritus, were conceived by them as rational laws which necessarily apply to all that is.

Let us first evaluate this metaphysical aspect of Democritus' atomic theory. As mentioned, his position is very close to that of Parmenides. At first sight, this may seem subject to serious doubt, because Democritus abandons not only the unity, but also the immutability of being. At close inspection, however, it becomes clear that both thinkers are intimately related. In the first place, in what sense does Democritus abandon the unity of being? It is true that he accepts the void and admits a plurality of beings, even an infinite number of them. Greater discrepancy from unity than this infinite plurality would not seem possible. Nevertheless there are solid reasons to maintain that Democritus' theory is very similar to that of Parmenides. For Democritus' atoms were conceived in such a way that almost no differences can be assigned to them. They differ only in shape and size, and this difference is characterized by *continuity*. There are two points which deserve our attention in this matter. In the first place, all atoms are conceived as consisting of the same matter. Hence there is no qualitative difference, in the sense that one atom would possess some property or quality which another lacks. They all have the same being. Thus we find here something which reminds us of the Eleatic unity of being. In the second place, as regards the differences in size and shape, Democritus explicitly requires continuity. There are no privileged shapes and no privileged sizes. All shapes and sizes exist, but they could be placed in a row in such a manner that there would be no observable difference between successive shapes and sizes. Thus not even the difference in shape and size seems to offer any ground why atoms should be specifically different. Therefore, we may conclude that, although Democritus accepted the plurality of atoms in order to safeguard change, he retained as much as possible the principle that being is *one*.

The same is true as regards the second point, the immutability of being. Democritus' atoms are essentially immutable. He admitted that they are subject to local motion, but this motion does not influence their inner being. Each atom remains what it is and retains its own shape and size.

Thus we see that local motion is the only concession made by Democritus. His justification of this concession is that in his opinion a change in position is intelligible, Parmenides notwithstanding. Democritus' willingness to make this concession will not surprise us, if we keep in mind that mathematics and astronomy had already reached a high degree of development among the Greeks in the school of Pythagoras (about 580-500 B.C.). Now local motion is a concept which is easily accessible to mathematical insight, and does not offer the same amount of difficulty as the concept of qualitative change.[6]

We may conclude therefore that Democritus' atomism is a self-consistent system which is based upon the rational postulate of intelligibility. It is a modification of Parmenides' theories which leaves room for change.

We must now turn our attention to the scientific or physical aspect of Democritus' system. For Democritus did not limit himself to the formulation of a general philosophic theory of the possibility of change. Such a theory was necessary as the foundation for any scientific exposition of physical phenomena. The reason is that the impossibility of change would preclude the possibility of physical science, since physical science is precisely the science of constantly changing material phenomena. The creation, however, of a general philosophic theory of change made the explanation of *particular* physical phenomena possible, and Democritus made a relatively wide use of this possibility. Let us briefly mention some of his explanations.

To begin with the states of aggregation, evaporation consists in the loosening of atomic connections. Therefore, vapor will occupy more space than the liquid before its evaporation. The difference between a liquid and a solid is likewise reduced to a shift in position of the atoms.

Next, Democritus endeavors to indicate exactly what is meant by density. Matter has a high density if it contains many atoms and

---

[6]Among Grecian philosophers the concept *motion* does not exclusively refer to change of place, but can also apply to a change in quality. For this reason we use above the term *local motion*, although the adjective *local* is perhaps superfluous in English. (The word *English* has been substituted for *Dutch* by the translator.)

relatively little void. Generally dense matter will also be hard and difficult to divide, because matter can only be divided where there is a void. If, however, the void is evenly distributed, even matter of high density can be divided.

Another important distinction made by Democritus is that between properties which flow directly from the order of atoms and others. Those of the first kind, of which the states of aggregation are examples, are objective. In later times the English philosopher Locke (1632-1704) will call them primary qualities. The others, which correspond to Locke's secondary qualities, have only subjective value, because they exist only in our senses. For instance, flavor, color, and temperature. By way of illustration Democritus points to the fact that some people experience as bitter what others call sweet. Indirectly he establishes some connection between these secondary qualities and certain atomic dispositions, but this connection remains only vaguely indicated.

Finally, we may point out that Democritus' idea of a primitive and eternal atomic motion contains in germ the later Law of the Conservation of Motion.

It should be clear to anyone who is familiar with the development of physics in later ages that Democritus' atomic theory contained several extremely fruitful thoughts. Of course, we should beware of exaggeration, for everything was still vague and there was no possibility of experimental control insofar as Democritus did not draw any definite conclusions which could be checked by experiments. True, Democritus indicated one experimental datum which could support his theory: a vessel, for instance, which is filled to the brim with ashes can still receive water. Although the amount will be less than if the vessel were not first filled with ashes, yet it is much more than could be expected when the volume proportions of the empty vessel and the vessel filled with ashes are taken into account. This experiment, however, is hardly more than a confirmation, and certainly it is not an apodictic proof. For the phenomenon in question can equally well be explained differently. As a matter of fact, non-atomistic philosophers gave different explanations for it.

Meanwhile it is certain that Democritus' theory was not really based upon similar physical data, even though they must have served as a confirmation of it. The true foundation of his system lies in his reflection on Parmenides' theory with the intention of reconciling the immutability of being with the fact that changes do occur. This is what characterizes the theory of Democritus. Above all, his theory is a philosophic system, although it contains the germ of a physical theory. As a physical theory, however, Democritus atomism is still too vague. It could only become fruitful when theoretical details of its physical aspect had been sufficiently developed to allow an immediate physical interpretation. The times, however, were not yet ready for such a development.

5. THE THEORIES OF ANAXAGORAS AND EMPEDOCLES

We have mentioned above that Democritus' atomic theory was not the only one proposed in the fifth century before Christ. There are two others which probably originated at about the same time, namely the theories of Empedocles and of Anaxagoras (about 450 B.C.). Like Democritus, both retained Parmenides' principle of the immutability of being, but they abandoned its unity. Instead of one immutable being they admitted a plurality of immutable beings.

Empedocles. According to Empedocles the primordial beings are four qualitatively different primitive constituents of everything, namely the four elements air, fire, earth, and water. In his theory all becoming and corruption, all motion and change, can be reduced to *syncrisis* and *diacrisis,* i.e. to the commingling and the separation of these four elements which in themselves remain unchanged. The only thing which really happens is this commingling and separation, everything else is nothing but an illusion. To quote his own words:

> Birth, properly speaking, does not occur in anything mortal nor does any mortal end in a corrupting death. Only commingling takes place and the separation of the commingled. Birth is nothing but the name which man uses to indicate this process.[7]

It is clear that Empedocles' ideas coincide largely with those of Democritus, but there is also an important difference. Empedocles lacks the logic and the consistency of Democritus, but on the other hand he is in closer contact with experience. No matter how strange it may sound to us that water, earth, fire, and air are considered as the building blocks of everything, nevertheless we fully agree with Baeumker when he says that as a first classification of substances the differences of solids, liquids, gases, and fire were bound to strike the

---

[7]H. Diels, *op. cit.,* fragment 8.

first students of nature.[8] For these four *kinds of matter* truly indicate
the most striking perceptible differences in the material world. These
differences are an empirical datum which must be accounted for by
every scientific theory of nature. That we in our modern theory
account for it in a different manner than philosophers in ancient times,
does not take away from the fact that it has been maintained as a most
fundamental datum of experience. The states of aggregation and of
incandescence are still central objects of physical science. Hence it
should not surprise us if Aristotle, who was very empirical-minded,
felt far more for Empedocles' theory of elements than for the system
of Democritus. Especially, because Aristotle thought that he had
succeeded in destroying the very foundation of Democritus' atomism,
namely the unintelligibility of internal change and qualitative differences. However, let us not anticipate history, for we are not yet
concerned with Aristotle, but only with Empedocles and his contemporaries.

Although Empedocles did not arrive at a fully developed theory
of smallest parts, nevertheless there are some indications that he conceived the elements as smallest parts. This is the reason why we
mention him together with Democritus.

Anaxagoras. Anaxagoras, a contemporary of Empedocles, also
accepted a plurality of primitive beings. As for Empedocles, change
for him amounts to commingling and separation. Most likely Anaxagoras took this idea over from Empedocles. However, according to
Anaxagoras the primitive beings are an unlimited number of qualitatively different primitive substances, which he called *seeds*. These
seeds are eternal and incorruptible. Thus his theory, just as those of
Democritus and Empedocles, contains an element borrowed from
Parmenides. A special element added by Anaxagoras is that every
substance contains all possible kinds of seeds, and is named after the
kind of seeds which predominate in it. Since the substance contains
also other kinds of seed, it can change into something else by the
separation of its seeds. It should also be noted that according to
Anaxagoras the seeds are very small, but can always be divided without change of nature. Hence they received the name of *homoiomerics,*
i.e. possessing similar parts. Thus we see that the immutability of
the primitive beings is not as absolute for Anaxagoras as it is for
Empedocles and Democritus, for quantitatively the *homoiomerics* are
not immutable.

---

[8]Cl. Baeumker, *Das Problem der Materie in der Griechischen Philosophie,*
Muenster 1890, p. 69.

Comparison of the Three Atomic Theories. When the systems of Democritus, Empedocles, and Anaxagoras are compared to each other, the following common characteristics can be pointed out. All three thinkers maintain, but each in his own way, Parmenides' fundamental principle that being is immutable. All three abandon the unity of being in order to make change intelligible. All reduce change to the separation and commingling of primitive substances. There are, however, also important differences. Democritus remains closest to the original Eleatic idea of the unity and immutability of being. Moreover, his system is also the most rational of the three. Notwithstanding its later success in physical science, it is less empiric than the two others. On the other hand, it offers more possibilities for mathematical speculations, as we shall see later.

Empedocles stayed closest to experience, although the theory of the four elements retarded the development of physical science during many centuries.

Anaxagoras' speculations offered another solution of the problem of change, but of the three he is the one who proceeded most arbitrarily. At any rate, his following in later times remained insignificant. This may be attributed, perhaps, to the fact that his solution on one hand missed the logical consistency of Democritus, and on the other was not sufficiently supported by experimental evidence.

6. PLATO

The Reaction Against the Materialism of Democritus. Although Plato (427-347 B.C.) also proposed an atomic theory, this is not the main reason why he should be mentioned in the history of the concept *atom.* In order to show this we must first remind the reader of the unity of Grecian science. The Greeks did not know any autonomous theories about particular phenomena, but tried to embrace everything by a single intellectual grasp. Democritus himself provides us with an example. His atomic theory was not merely intended as a hypothetical explanation of evaporation, states of aggregation, and similar phenomena. His aim was to give an ultimate explanation of change as change, and therefore, also of those changes which are implied by man's mental activity. We did not mention it before, but as a consequence of his general theory Democritus admitted a special type of atoms of which the human soul is constructed. Obviously, the special character of these atoms could consist only of a special form and shape.

Souls, says Democritus, are composed of fine round atoms. Because
they are so fine and round, they can penetrate through the whole body,
move it, and thus cause its vital functions. Probably Democritus admitted that even thought must be reduced to the motion of these soul-
atoms. At least his followers in subsequent centuries held this view.
From a general philosophic point of view this is the reason why
Democritus' system must be classified as materialism, for it explained
everything by material principles. The materialistic character of
Democritus' philosophy explains also why thinkers in subsequent centuries reacted so sharply against him. Almost unanimously they
refused to reduce the wealth of the human mind to a system which
knew nothing but moving atoms. Only if we lose sight of the fact
that the Greeks aimed primarily at a universal explanation of the
world, will it surprise us that Democritus' basic ideas could not bear
any fruits in physical science before the seventeenth century. Only
a man who does not understand the import of the Greek systems can
feel resentment against the thinkers who prevented the development
of Democritus' ideas. Such a one would show that he lacks a clear
understanding of the true aim which was foremost in Democritus'
mind. Only gradually did man learn to distinguish methodically the
different problems which are interwoven in Democritus' system. In
his time attention was primarily directed towards fundamental philosophic problems and their solutions. The successors of Democritus
judged his solutions of the problem of being and becoming, of unity
and plurality, to be unsatisfactory, because they considered his theory
too poor in spite of its consistency. They refused to see man's noblest
and most beautiful activity as nothing but an effect which by necessity
of nature flows from a shift in atomic positions.

The limited scope of our study does not allow us to give here a
comprehensive view of Plato, the first philosopher after Democritus
whom we will discuss. His thoughts are too rich and too varied to
be compressed into a few pages. Hence we must limit ourselves again
to some aspect, namely the one which strikes us when we consider
Plato in the light of the problems which caused the opposition of
Parmenides and Heraclitus. As we have seen above, these two
thinkers gave independent and sharply contrasting solutions to the
problem of being and becoming. For Parmenides reality was immutable being, for Heraclitus it was continuous change. Theirs is the
contrast between the world of thought and the world of sense experience. Plato rejected both solutions, because he found them too one-
sided. By using the term *one-sided* we indicate already that he did

not absolutely reject either of them. In order to understand Plato's own theory we have to consider first his master Socrates (469-433 B.C.). True, Socrates was not directly interested in matter, but rather in man, especially in that aspect of man which he believed exempt from the laws of matter. We mean man as an ethical being. However, and this again shows the unity of Grecian science, this does not mean that Socrates falls entirely outside the field of our study. He belongs to it because he is the creator of a general philosophic method, the inductive method of determination of ideas.

When Socrates wants to know, for instance, what goodness is, i.e. the exact thought content of the concept *goodness,* he asks others why they call a thing good in all kinds of concrete examples. In this manner he tried to determine exactly the common element in all these examples in virtue of which they are all called good. By the use of this method he thought it possible to arrive at a definition of goodness.

Plato's Theory of Ideas. Plato acknowledged the exactness of Socrates' method and continued along the same line, but he did not stop there. He tried to explain the remarkable fact that the concept *good* is not found in its pure form in any of the concrete examples of *good.* Again and again the concrete examples are no more than approximations of the *good.* They are all more or less *good,* but never *good* in all aspects. Moreover, Plato realized that this remarkable phenomenon is not limited to ethical concepts, but can be found also in mathematics. The concept *triangle,* for instance, is not present in its pure form in any constructed triangles; the latter are merely approximations of it. There were other things which made Plato wonder. For example, the concept *man* itself is something immutable, because it *remains* while its realizations, the actually living human beings, are born and die. They are corruptible forms of the eternal and immutable concept *man.* The same is true of concepts applying to the vegetable and the animal kingdom. This contrast between the pure incorruptible idea and the imperfect corruptible forms under which we human beings perceive the idea, induced Plato to admit that there are really two worlds: the world of pure *concepts* or *ideas,* and the world of the imperfect *realizations* of these ideas. The latter, according to Plato, are images or shadows of the former. Man, however, participates of both worlds; of the world of pure ideas, by means of his *thoughts* which reveal pure concepts to him, and of the world of shadows, by means of his *senses* which perceive the imperfect realizations of ideas. Thus Plato's vision offered room both for the immutable being of Parmenides in the world of ideas, and for the eternal becoming of Heraclitus in the world of sense experience. Although man shares in both worlds, it is impossible for him to obtain pure concepts from sense experience, because in the world which is open to the senses there are no pure concepts. Somehow these must be borrowed by man from the world of pure ideas. Plato thought he could explain how this happens by the following theory: Before the soul enters the body it dwells in the world of pure ideas where it is able to contemplate them. Although this contemplation is lost when the soul is united to the body, the memory of these ideas remains in it. By the perception of the world of shadows this memory is revived, because the shadows are images of the pure ideas.

Importance of Mathematics. For the purpose of our study it is very important to know that in Plato's system mathematics was to play an outstanding role. If ever, then certainly in mathematics, man is convinced that he is dealing with clearly defined concepts. Even in an imperfect realization of the triangle, for instance, in an imperfect drawing, he is able to read the properties of the perfect triangle. In a certain sense the world of mathematical entities forms a kind of intermediary between the suprasensible world of pure ideas and the world of material reality. Therefore, it was possible for Plato to consider himself justified in taking over the Pythagorian view that the sensible world must be explained by means of mathematics. For this world was formed after the type of the world of pure ideas, and mathematical ideas had determined its proportions. It is said that above the entrance of Plato's Academy was written the text: Ἀγεωμέτρητος μηδεὶς εἰσίτω "Let no non-mathematician enter here." It may be improbable that this text really adorned his Academy, nevertheless the adage characterizes the spirit of Plato's teaching. Many times, perhaps, did the master symbolically express this thought to his pupils. Be this as it was, at any rate mathematics occupied a very important place in Plato's system of philosophy and was strongly encouraged by the Platonic School.

Thus it should not surprise us that Plato was indirectly also a figure of importance in astronomy. For nothing suggested more strongly the idea of being subject to mathematical laws than the phenomena of celestial bodies. According to Plato the orbits of celestial bodies must be circular motions, because circles are the most perfect forms. This induced astronomers, like Eudoxos, to construe a system of circular motions in order to reduce apparently non-circular motions to circles.[9] The importance of this effort, which was successful to a large extent, lies in the fact that it not only forced astronomers to aim at accuracy of observation, but also offered an hypothesis suitable for observation. Although gradually it became clear that the hypothesis of pure circular motion could not be maintained, nevertheless the classification of observational data was made possible by it. Thus these data could acquire real significance in science.

This example clearly illustrates how closely among the Greeks scientific and mathematical considerations were connected with philosophy. The transition from one to the other was almost imperceptible.

Theory of Elements. A few words remain to be said about Plato's theory of elements. He accepted the elements which Empedocles had proposed: fire, air, water, and earth. On mathematical grounds he determined the exact forms which the smallest parts of these elements must have. Fire has the form of a tetrahedron, air of an octahedron, water of an icosahedron, and earth of a cube. As an interesting historical detail it may be mentioned that there are reasons to believe that the Greeks had succeeded only a short time before in the geometrical construction of these bodies.[10] However, Plato's speculations in this matter proved far less fruitful than those referring to astronomy. The reason is not difficult to see. The orbits of celestial bodies can be observed, so that there is an immediate connection between the theoretical idea and the observed phenomena. In the theory of elements, however, such a direct connection is missing. We are able to observe various qualitative properties in the chemical and physical behavior of matter, and perhaps these properties do have some relation to mathematical shapes, but at any rate that relation is less direct. The multiple variety of natural events which is observed by everybody cannot be classified according to mathematical shapes.

Although subsequent times found few supporters for the ingenious method by which Plato construed his theory of elements and atoms, the same cannot be said of the basic idea from which this theory developed. The rapid progress in the mathematical treatment of scientific problems which occurred at the time of the Renaissance is certainly not accidental, for it was coupled with a revival of Platonism.

---

[9]See E. J. Dijksterhuis, *Die Mechanisierung des Weltbildes,* Berlin, 1954, Ch. I, Sect. 42.

[10]See Platon, *Oeuvres Complètes, Tome X, Timée-Critias; Texte Établi par Albert Rivaud,* Paris 1925, pp. 81-83. In the Stephanus' edition (1578) vol. 3, 31b ff. Modern English translations usually indicate the Stephanus' paging. For instance, Jowett. (Transl.)

We must now leave Plato and turn our attention to Aristotle, whose philosophic and scientific ideas have dominated science so much longer than those of Plato. However important Plato may be as a philosopher, however stimulating his ideas may have been in the study of mathematics, he is less important than Aristotle for the development of scientific concepts, because his attention was directed towards the immaterial. Matter occupied but a very inferior place in his speculations. It will be different in Aristotle's philosophy.

7. ARISTOTLE

Aristotle (384-322 B. C.) was born in Stagira where his father practised medicine. The latter's profession is not mentioned merely as a historical detail which otherwise has no connection with the subject of our study, for it is quite possible that Aristotle inherited from his father that great love of nature which characterized him and left its imprint upon his philosophy. The difference between Plato and Aristotle is strikingly expressed by Raphael in his *School of Athens:* Aristotle contemplates the earth, and Plato's gaze is turned towards heaven. The whole philosophy of Aristotle, indeed, shows that he attached a far greater value to terrestrial, sensible things than Plato did. He really took the earth seriously.

Aristotle's philosophical studies extend over almost the entire field of science known in his time. His system united into one imposing whole practically all the scientific results attained by his predecessors. So solidly did he construct his system that it was able to maintain itself for many generations as the framework into which most scientific theories were cast.

Aristotle's influence had remarkable consequences for the concept of *smallest parts.* For Aristotle is the man who blocked the development of Democritus' theory, even more than Plato. Relatively speaking, the latter had applied himself but little to physical science. Although his anti-materialistic philosophy was in perfect contrast to Democritus' atomism, it did not attack this atomism in any details. The systems were too divergent for that. Aristotle, however, explicitly formulated a theory of nature which avowedly tried to solve the problems raised by Democritus. Repeatedly Aristotle mentions Democritus' doctrine, to attack it. Thus Aristotle's works, which are largely preserved, form one of the most valuable sources of Democritus' teachings of which very little is directly known. Just like

Plato, Aristotle directed his attacks primarily against the philosophic background of Democritus' atomic theory and not immediately against the idea of smallest parts in general. As a matter of fact, Aristotle himself held some theory of smallest parts, although he did not develop it to any great extent. His proponents, however, in subsequent centuries worked it out in great detail. Nevertheless in the Aristotelian system the theory of smallest parts occupied a far less central position than in the system of Democritus. Consequently, for some time the role of the concept *smallest parts* remained relatively unimportant in the history of science. Before we can explain all this in detail it will be necessary to study first the fundamental outlines of Aristotle's philosophy; for no detail in the theory of a Greek thinker should be studied without its connection to the whole.

Aristotle's Theory of Knowledge. If we want to understand a philosopher, two things especially must be kept in mind: his predecessors whose thoughts he develops, and the opponents against whom his attacks are primarily directed. To a certain extent Plato played both roles as regards Aristotle, that of predecessor and that of opponent. He had been his master, and Aristotle continued where Plato left off. But at the same time the rejection of Plato's theory of ideas is one of the central points in Aristotle's philosophy. For Aristotle there is but one world, the world of sense experience, and this world is simultaneously the object of our thoughts. Thus Aristotle at once came face to face with the necessity of solving the dilemma of Parmenides. As an *empiricist* Aristotle could not accept the viewpoint that all sensible change is but an illusion. However, before we can follow Aristotle's treatment of the problem of change we must first see how he altered Plato's theory of ideas in order to allot a far more important role to sense experience in the process of knowledge.

Aristotle was profoundly convinced that all human knowledge must be based upon sense experience. That is why he embodied in his system all the experimental data which his predecessors and contemporaries had assembled. In contrast to Plato, for him experience was the sole fount of human knowledge, including the knowledge of abstract concepts. According to Aristotle these concepts are acquired by abstraction from the experience of concrete data. They are not innate and they do not have a separate existence. As universal concepts they exist only in the human mind. The capacity of the human mind to abstract concepts from concrete material things by way of sense experience is explained by the fact that things of the same kind have a common form of being. Such things exhibit, so to speak, the same basic plan, and this basic plan is taken over by the human mind when we form a universal concept. What is individual and concrete is left behind, and only what is universal is admitted into the concept. In this sense Aristotle accepted universal ideas, i. e. insofar as they are concepts. He agrees with Plato that it is the task of science to form pure universal concepts and to discover necessary and eternal truths, but they must be sought where they can be found, i.e. in concrete things. Thus the universal idea *horse* exists only as an abstraction in the human mind, but this abstraction agrees with the basic plan which is found in all horses.

The Possibility of Change. Having safeguarded the reality of the sensible world Aristotle faced the difficulties of Parmenides. First, since the fact of the multiplicity of beings is established by experience, how can we account for the possibility of multiplicity? Secondly, how is an imperfect being possible? For it is clear that not all things are perfect expressions of the idea which is realized in them. Finally, how is change possible? Aristotle was not the man to brush aside Parmenides' speculations with a simple appeal to the sense experience of multiplicity, imperfection, and mutability. Not even for an instant did he lose sight of Parmenides' fundamental principle that all being must be intelligible. This imposed upon him the task of examining critically the speculations which had led Parmenides to reject multiplicity, imperfection, and change. Aristotle formulates his main objection against the analysis of his predecessor in the following words: "False is Parmenides' reasoning because he takes being in only one sense, while it really has several meanings." There is a difference between substantial and accidental being, between things on one hand which have in themselves their own *to be,* as men, animals, and celestial bodies, and on the other hand that which we call properties of these things, as their size, shape, color, etc. The *to be* of a man is just as real as the *to be* of his size; of both we may truthfully say that they *are,* but *to be* in both cases does not mean exactly the same. In the first case it refers to something which is in itself, which is a substance. In the other case it refers to something which is *in* another and *of* another. Size does not exist as such, separated from that which *is* of a certain size. Hence Aristotle thinks that a distinction ought to be made between substantial being and accidental being. It will be well to point out that in making this distinction in being Aristotle does not intend to say that there are several different *beings,* i.e. disconnected beings, such as are the atoms of Democritus. If we want to seek a connection with Democritus, we should rather point to the latter's distinction between what he rather ineptly calls being and non-being. As mentioned already, taken literally, Democritus' words "Non-being exists just as well as being" are an obvious contradition in terms. But, in our opinion, Democritus meant something else, namely, being has two meanings, the full and the void. Taken in this sense, Democritus' critique goes in the same direction as Aristotle's. Therefore, when Aristotle criticizes Parmenides and states that *to be* has several meanings, he is not yet concerned with the question whether or not there is a multiplicity of beings. That problem will receive his attention later. For the time being he merely intends to show that Parmenides' concept of *to be* has several meanings which refer to different aspects of concrete reality. Since for Aristotle every concept corresponds to some aspect of reality, Parmenides' reasoning seems to become consistent if these meanings and their corresponding aspects of reality are not distinguished. Yet it is really inconsistent because it is based upon a concept of being which does not agree with reality. One should not try to apply to reality a univocal concept of being because in reality there are different aspects of being.

A second distinction which, according to Aristotle, must be made is the distinction between what he calls potential and actual being. It is equally right to say that an acorn is an oak and to say that an acorn is not an oak. Both statements make sense. To begin with the last, an acorn is different from a tree, so that it is correct to say that an acorn is not a tree. But the second statement also makes sense because an acorn has a certain capacity or potency to become a tree, which a stone does not have. Hence the mere contrasting of being with non-being is insufficient to cover this case. For this reason Aristotle distinguishes between being-in-capacity or being-in-potency and being-in-perfection or being-in-act. Thus if we say that an acorn is an oak our statement is correct provided we understand it as an oak-in-potency, but false if we mean an oak-in-act.

Hence capacity-for-being is not simply non-being. It is a being-in-potency, distinct on one hand from absolute non-being and on the other hand from being-in-act.

With this distinction in mind Aristotle gives an analysis of change which, according to him, makes change intelligible. As will be recalled, Parmenides' dilemma was intended to show that change is unintelligible and therefore impossible. One member of the dilemma was: from non-being no being can come; and the other: what *is* already cannot come to be. Aristotle wholly concedes the first member if non-being is understood as that which *is* not under any respect. But a thing can very well come to be from something which *is* not yet in some respect. From an acorn an oak can come to be. This is no coming to be from absolute non-being nor a remaining-what-it-is of some existing thing. The latter is excluded by the second member of the dilemma. Hence for Aristotle coming to be, change, is the transition from being-in-potency to being-in-act, from potency to act. In this manner he thought it possible to solve the difficulties of coming to be and change by an analysis of the concept *being*.

All changes are not the same. We have already seen how Aristotle distinguishes between substantial and accidental being. To this distinction corresponds the distinction between substantial and accidental change. In a substantial change the thing as a thing changes, it is no longer what it used to be. In an accidental change the thing remains what it is, only some accident changes. An example of the first kind of change is the death of an animal. After its death the animal *is* no longer. What remains is something entirely different, let us say an accumulation of chemical compounds. Now for an example of accidental change. If an animal changes in size, it does not change as an animal. It remains the same animal it was before the change. Only an accident is changed. Aristotle examines both changes very carefully. He is not satisfied with the general statement that change is a transition from potency to act, but endeavors to indicate exactly what happens in both changes. In the following paragraph we shall follow him in this examination.

Let us begin with the example of the formation of a statue from clay. This is an accidental change, for the clay remains clay. Three things are to be distinguished, namely, the initial state (before the change), the final state (after the change), and that which undergoes the change, the subject. The initial state in this case is the rough shape of clay, the final state is the form of the statue, and the subject is the clay itself. The rough form contains the potency to become the shape of the statue. Hence the elementary condition of all change, the transition from being-in-potency to being-in-act is fulfilled. Now in every change there must be something which changes, something which forms the link between the initial and the final state. Otherwise there would be no question of change, but of annihilation followed by creation. The link in our case is the clay. This material substance has remained the same, so that no substantial change has occurred. However, this statement can easily be misunderstood. In order to avoid misunderstanding we should keep in mind that this "permanent" thing itself also has changed. The form which was there before the change, the rough form, was not something merely glued to the clay, it was a determination of that substance, the determination of its external shape. Even when only a change of external shape takes place, this nevertheless implies a change of some determination of the substance in question, and thus indirectly a change of the substance itself. We could express this by saying: remaining entirely itself, remaining what it is, the clay has changed. We must insist upon this point because we would misunderstand Aristotle if we took the substance too much as a thing to which another thing, an accident, is externally connected without any internal bond. Not even accidental change takes place without affecting the substance. To give another example, becoming older with respect to man is a change which affects his whole being, yet he remains the *same* man. Thus we see that in Aristotle's conception a substance is not something rigid which either remains rigidly the same (in accidental change) or is totally destroyed (in so-called substantial change). On the contrary, it is some determinate fundamental structure which can be further determined in many ways, and needs to be further determined.

After an accurate observation of nature Aristotle considered himself bound to conclude that not only accidental changes occur in nature, but also changes by which the nature of things changes entirely, so-called substantial changes. Plants and animals feed on lifeless matter, elements enter into composition to form new substances, and these in turn decompose or form new compounds. In order to make these substantial changes intelligible Aristotle had to accept something which would form the link between the initial state and the final state in these processes. Now the substance itself cannot be this link because it disappears. When an animal dies it ceases to exist as an animal; hence that which remains must be something else. This *something else* is the common principle of all material being, so-called prime or primary matter (*materia prima*).

Doctrine of Matter and Form. The concept *primary matter* is one of the most subtle concepts of Aristotle's philosophy. To show what he means by it we will use again the example of clay. Clay was the matter which underwent change, a change of external form or shape. In order to see the similarity between primary matter and ordinary matter, such as clay, we must go back to something just mentioned in connection with the concept of substance. The clay does not exist without its external form. It is always determined by *some external form*. Neither does primary matter exist all by itself. It exists always under some *form*. This form, however, should not be understood as an external form, but as a *form of being*, i.e. as a determining factor which makes primary matter be, say, copper, gold, water, marble, or a living being. Thus there is never any primary matter all by itself, but always primary matter which is determined to a certain matter by some form of being. Primary matter is never complete, i.e. a being which is in itself; it is a principle of being, as Aristotle expresses it. Primary matter by itself is nothing but the material potency to several forms of being. By the form of being it is determined to a real material thing, to matter in the ordinary sense of the word.

Few Aristotelian concepts are so mishandled by historians as the concepts of primary matter and form of being. Later on we will have occasion to come back to this. Only by a profound study of the philosophic setting of the problems which gave rise to these concepts is it possible to acquire a correct understanding of them. These problems, as we have seen, originated from the endeavor to make substantial change intelligible. When all kinds of matter can be changed into one another, there must be some common element in all material things. This common element cannot be any being which exists in itself, for otherwise the change would not be a substantial change. Neither can it be a component part which can be separated and continue to exist as such. For otherwise the component part would be a permanent substance, so that there would be no substantial change. Hence Aristotle's conclusion: primary matter is pure being-in-potency, a capacity for material being which is really present in all material beings, but only insofar as actualized in this or that material being. This actualization he calls *form of being* or *substantial form* (*forma substantialis*). Just as primary matter, the substantial form is not a component part which can exist separately, but only a principle of being, namely the determining principle. Although our modern concept of matter is, without doubt, related to the Aristotelian concept of primary matter, the modern term is not equivalent in meaning. When we speak about matter-in-general we do not mean any determined matter, yet we always think of something which exists as such. Perhaps we can best express it by saying that it is primary matter with a kind of *neutral* form. From the above it should be clear that we misunderstand Aristotle if we consider protons and electrons as primary matter.

Aristotle would have answered immediately to such a statement: No, I do not mean that. By primary matter I mean precisely that which equally makes these two primary forms of material being matter, that which makes it possible for them to react in such a way that both cease to be what they were at first.

It is because of this common principle of matter that material beings can change into one another and form compounds or, in general, undergo essential change. Whether such a change takes place very easily or not, depends on the form of being in which primary matter is, or rather which determines primary matter. So, for instance, in a chemical element primary matter is determined by the form of being of the element in such a way that primary matter is in immediate potency to those compounds into which the element in question enters easily. Its primary matter is, so to speak, ripe for the compound. Hence very little will have to happen to make this primary matter change the form of being of the element for that of the compound. Likewise, we can reason reversely that the element can again be separated from the compound.[1] We said above that primary matter is in potency to become all matter, but that whether primary matter changes easily or not from one form to another depends on the relationship between these forms. To clarify this assertion let us look again at the analogous example of the external form. Just as less is needed to make an ellipse from a circle than from any other form, so also is there less needed to make a compound change into its constituent elements than into others, although the possibility of change into other elements is admitted in principle.

Thus we see that according to Aristotle every material being is composed of *primary matter* and *form of being,* but this again should not be misunderstood. They are not physical components, they cannot be separated in such a way that we can lay hold of them one by one with our hands or in a reaction tube. They are not simple substances in the sense in which chemistry speaks of elements. According to Aristotle even chemical elements fall under this law of "composition," but this composition is not chemical or physical. The composition of primary matter and form of being is one which Aristotle

---

[1]*Metaphysics* XII, 2; 1069b 26-34. We will follow the customary references to Aristotle's works. First the abbreviated title (*Metaphysics*), then the book (XII) and the chapter (2). The numbers after the chapter refer to the pages, columns, and lines in the standard edition of the Greek text published by Im. Bekker, Berlin 1831. Translations are taken from W. D. Ross, The Works of Aristotle (Oxford at the Clarendon Press, 1930).

considers necessary in order to make the reaction of one chemical element upon another possible, because even in this change there must be something that remains and something that changes. Hence Aristotle considers all material beings as non-simple, composed, beings, because a really simple being, i.e. a being which in no respect is "composed," cannot be subject to change. The possibility of change presupposes a certain non-simplicity, for otherwise it is not possible to account for both aspects which are present in change—the aspect of a certain permanence and the aspect of something which is really new. There is a certain inner tension in them in virtue of which they are subject to essential change. For the sake of the reader who is less familiar with Aristotle's thought we will give here a brief recapitulation of his theory.

According to Aristotle we must distinguish in every material thing between substance and accidents. The former gives the material thing its *to be in itself,* a *determinate to be in itself,* such as to be man, horse, iron, copper, etc. This substance is further determined by all kinds of accidents, which cannot be absent, but which to a certain extent can vary without a change in the substance itself. Such a variation is called an accidental change. Examples of accidents are quantity, external shape, color, etc. The material substance itself is composed of *primary matter* and *form of being.* The former makes the thing a *material* thing, the latter makes it a *determinate* kind of material thing. This "inner" composition of the essence of every material thing makes possible so-called substantial change, i.e. a change in the nature of the thing.

For the sake of completeness we mention, without however enlarging upon it, that in Aristotle's theory there is room also for a world of pure forms, pure spirits. However, this world is not the same as Plato's world of ideas, for according to Aristotle the pure spirits are not *the forms or ideas of the material world.* He merely wants to express by it that *not all being* is necessarily of a material nature.

Doctrine of Elements and Compounds. We have already had occasion to make the remark that Aristotle also knew elements in the chemical sense, i.e. chemically simple substances. This chemical simplicity, however, does not imply that as material beings they are not subject to the composition which characterizes all material things, namely, the composition of primary matter and substantial form. Aristotle accepts as chemical elements the same four which we have encountered in Empedocles, fire, air, water, and earth. But he did not consider his duty done by copying them from Empedocles. In the second and third chapters of the second book *On Generation and Corruption* he endeavors to give a comprehensive derivation of these elements.

Aristotle is deeply convinced that this derivation is based upon experience. The problem is to discover the elements, i.e. the substances with the most primary forms which are characterized by the most elementary opposite properties. Since the sense of touch is the primary sense—Aristotle seeks to prove this by a kind of comparative animal psychology[2]—we must seek the primary properties among the qualities which are objects of the sense of touch.

In this search we must pay attention to the pairs of opposite primordial properties which are the foundation of the others. These primordial properties are cold and warm, dry and wet. The possible combinations in pairs of these properties are

Warm — cold	Cold — dry (earth)
Warm — dry (fire)	Cold — wet (water)
Warm — wet (air)	Dry — wet

The first and the last pairs cannot be found in any material being because they are contraries, so that only four pairs remain. Now, observes Aristotle, these four combinations of properties are usually found in material beings which seem to be non-composed and therefore are considered to be so.

Even without any profound analysis we realize that the derivation of this theory of elements is not on the same level as the preceding speculations about change. The latter were concerned with change in general. They appealed to only one fact of observation, namely, that changes do occur in nature, and are of two kinds, changes in which things remain what they are, and changes in which things do not remain what they are. In the derivation of his theory of elements Aristotle appeals to a far more detailed experience which comprises not only a systematic classification of all material properties, but also hypotheses about their mutual dependence, etc. The difference is evident. Whether we consider Aristotle's arguments convincing or not, it is clear that his speculation about change is based upon far more solid data than the derivation of his theory of elements. Later

---

[2]These arguments may be found in the second chapter of the second book *On the Soul*.

on in connection with another problem we will have an opportunity to study the difference more closely.

Aristotle's speculation about chemical compounds is interesting. Now that we are acquainted with his doctrine of change it will not surprise us to hear that for Aristotle chemical composition implies more than a commingling of intrinsically immutable constituents. He rejects explicitly the theory formulated by Democritus. Chemical composition is the *"coming to be one* of the *changed* reagents."* A new substance possessing a new specific form of being comes into existence. The sum total of its properties is not simply the sum total of the properties possessed by its constituent parts. Hence the constituents did not enter the new whole without changing. In entering they underwent an internal change through which they became conditioned for this whole. The nature of the change which the constituents must undergo is, of course, determined by the nature of the whole. This implies that constituents which are able to unite into a given whole have a nature which is intrinsically capable of being united into this whole. Through external influences this *capacity* becomes an *actuality,* i.e. the whole comes to be from the constituents.

Accordingly, there must be some relationship between the properties of the constituents as they are before the union and the properties of the whole. It must be possible to find in the whole something of the properties which the constituents possessed separately. Aristotle explains this by saying that the constituents continue to exist virtually in the compound. Later in the course of history this will give rise to the famous controversy whether elements continue to exist in compounds or not.

Aristotle's theory of chemical composition is really nothing but a development of his theory of change. Primarily it amounts to this: he considers chemical composition as substantial change. The elements, for instance, which enter into composition with each other do not remain what they are, but become a compound. Every part of a compound is compound. The elements can no longer be indicated anywhere, although it is true that the compound remains always potentially the elements of which it is composed. This shows clearly how Aristotle's conception differs from that of Democritus. While Aristotle requires for a chemical composition that the reagents act upon each other and thus undergo an internal change, Democritus is satisfied with an external change in configuration of the atoms, which leaves the atoms unchanged in themselves. From this it should be clear that in Aristotle's theory the smallest particle cannot play the fundamental role it plays in Democritus' system. Of course, we do not mean that in Aristotle's theory of material coming to be there is no room at all for smallest particles. That is an entirely different question, which will have to be answered in the affirmative, although it will not be easy to determine exactly the function which Aristotle attributed to his smallest particles. He mentions then only sporadically. For instance, he observes that the interaction of the reagents in a chemical reaction is easier if the substances are divided into small particles.[3] Reading this we ask ourselves whether this is merely a casual remark based upon some observation or a statement which has a theoretical foundation. Did he think about some definite theory of corpuscles which fits in with his general ideas about philosophy of nature and physics? The reason for this question is certainly not that the concept of smallest particles plays an important part in Aristotle's theories. As we have mentioned already, rather the opposite is true. But it remains a fact that his successors in later ages who developed a detailed theory of smallest particles, continually appeal to Aristotle. This appeal cannot be said to be wholly unwarranted; there are really reasons to justify it.

Aristotle's Theory of Smallest Particles. The principal text in which Aristotle gives us some idea of his own theory of smallest particles is found in the fourth chapter of the first book of *Physics*. He speaks there about Anaxagoras' theory. The better to show the import of Aristotle's thought we shall follow his example and begin with a summary of Anaxagoras' opinion. According to the latter all qualitative differences of material things must be reduced to the qualitative differences of an infinite number of primary substances which are present in all things as kinds of seeds or germs. Every material thing contains the seeds of all other material things, but it is named after the seeds which are most numerous in it. Thus water consists mostly of "seeds of water" although it contains also the seeds of flesh, bone, etc. According to Anaxagoras this is possible because the seeds are infinitely divisible, and therefore they can be infinitely small.

Aristotle's criticism of this last point allows us to determine his own opinion in the matter. After exposing his objections against Anaxagoras' theory that the seeds are divisible, he puts forward the reason why natural parts of a thing cannot be indifferent to size.

---

[3] *On Generation and Corruption* I, 10; 328a 33-34.

Flesh, bone, and the like are the parts of animals. . . . Hence it is obvious that neither flesh, bone, nor any such thing can be of indefinite size in the direction either of the greater or of the less.[4]

He then explains his objections to Anaxagoras' statement that in everything all possible kinds of seeds are found. He chooses as an example water, in which according to his opponent the seeds of flesh must be present.

Let some flesh be extracted from water and again more flesh be produced from the remainder by repeating the process of separation: then, even though the quantity separated out will continually decrease, still it will not fall below a certain magnitude. If, therefore, the process comes to an end, everything will not be in everything else (for there will be no flesh in the remaining water); if on the other hand it does not, and further extraction is always possible, there will be an infinite multitude of *finite equal particles* in a finite quantity—which is impossible.[5]

From both quotations it is clear that Aristotle does not admit the infinite divisibility of matter. However small a removed quantity of flesh may become it will not become smaller than a certain magnitude.[6] Somewhere there must be a limit to divisibility. Another very important point is contained in the second text in the words which we put in italics. Casually, as it were, Aristotle remarks that the minimal particles of flesh are of equal size.

In the sixth book of his *Physics* Aristotle states that there is a limit to the increase and decrease of a thing. He connects these limits with the specific nature of the thing.[7]

What should be our idea of Aristotle's theory of smallest particles? It is certain that in his speculations about smallest particles he thought primarily about living beings and their parts. It is subject to doubt whether or not he had in mind non-living things, although this cannot positively be excluded. For instance, in his arguments against Anaxagoras he does not mention anything which applies specifically only to living things. On the contrary, flesh is living, water is not;

---

[4]*Physics* I, 4; 187b 18-21.

[5]*Physics* I, 4; 187b 28-34.

[6]In a polemic article against our interpretation of this text ("*Is er bij Aristoteles van een minima naturalia leer sprake?*" *Studia Catholica*, vol. 21, page 174) Dr. G. Muskens argues that Aristotle in this text accepts a certain minimal size only hypothetically. This interpretation does not seem tenable because it takes all vigor out of Aristotle's argument, which is based upon the real existence in nature of a limit of divisibility.

[7]*Physics* VI, 10; 241a 32 to b 3.

and both are equally used in his example. Yet it remains true that Aristotle nowhere speaks explicitly about the smallest particles of non-living matter.

Another important point is that for Aristotle the smallest particles are nothing but minima fixed by nature, which would show up only if we tried an infinite division of matter. In modern language we would say that they play a role only in a mental experiment. His argument against Anaxagoras is really such an experiment. The natural minima, therefore, are purely potential parts. Nowhere do we find any indication that Aristotle conceives them as actualized by some process, such as a chemical reaction.

Apart from the passage mentioned above, it would be possible to quote a few other texts of Aristotle which might be interpreted as possible allusions to natural minima. We will not consider them here, because later on in this study we will have an opportunity to refer to them. Certain medieval commentators made the most of them in order to link their own minima speculations to Aristotle's philosophy.

All in all Aristotle's theory of smallest particles appears very primitive. It is still in an embryonic stage, although certain fundamental traits can already be distinguished. To enumerate them once more, according to Aristotle the smallest particles of any given kind of matter are similar, for they are determined by the specific nature of the matter in question. Hence they are different from the smallest particles of other kinds of matter. These differences are abrupt because the differences between the various kinds of matter are abrupt. A remarkable point is also that the smallest particles are not intrinsically immutable. Just as the matter itself of which they are the smallest particles can change wholly into another kind of matter, so likewise its smallest particles. Even without any comment it should be clear how much this conception differs from that of Democritus. However, we will come back to this point later when in the course of history we will encounter an Aristotelian theory of smallest parts which exhibits these same traits more explicitly. As far as Aristotle himself is concerned, we can give only a rough sketch of them by combining a few of his casual but pertinent remarks with his general conception of natural philosophy.

Recapitulation. Our study of Aristotle had to be somewhat extensive because of his great influence on later times. Let us restate it here briefly. The principal characteristic of Aristotle's system is that it shows the twofold trait[7a] which we noticed already in Democritus:

[7a]For the twofold character of Aristotle's system, cf. Andrew G. Van Melsen, *The Philosophy of Nature*, Pittsburgh, 1954, Ch. 2, Sect. 3 and 4.

basically it is a philosophic system, but it contains some scientific considerations. As a philosophic system it endeavors to solve the fundamental problems of being and knowledge. Alongside reason, sense-experience occupies an important place in it, because, according to Aristotle, sense-experience plays an essential role in human knowledge. Because of his acknowledgement of both experience and reason he was obliged to make an intense study of the antinomy arising from the experience of change and its impossibility before reason as formulated by Parmenides. Aristotle thought that he could solve this difficulty by his analysis of the concept *being* and by his theory that matter is intrinsically composed of a material and a formal principle, which composition makes change an essential characteristic of matter. This doctrine of matter and form will provide the key to all other explanations of Aristotle, even in matters belonging to physical science. All explanations of particular phenomena are seen in the light of this fundamental principle of natural philosophy. We will meet it again and again in later times because it forms an important factor in the history of science.

As for a doctrine of smallest parts, it is found in Aristotle's works, but only in a very embryonic state.

8. GRECIAN PHILOSOPHY AFTER ARISTOTLE

Introduction. After Aristotle no new philosophic system arose in Greek philosophy, certainly not in the field of natural philosophy. Most philosophic schools were either continuations and renovations of old systems or attempts to unite elements borrowed from different systems. This, however, does not mean that this period has no interest for the history of science in general and for that of the smallest particles in particular. For as a result of the foundation of the Roman Empire, Grecian science spread throughout large civilized areas. It was taken over by Rome and Alexandria. The latter center especially, showed great interest in the theories of natural philosophy. This will not surprise us if we remember that ancient Egypt had knowledge of highly developed technical arts, such as metallurgy and ceramics. From the combination of the knowledge acquired in these technical sciences and the Grecian philosophy prototypes originated which later developed into pure specialized sciences.[8] Special questions in the

---

[8]See, for example, E. von Lippmann, *Entstehung und Ausbreitung der Alchemie,* Berlin 1919, pages 275ff.

fields of astronomy, physics, and chemistry found devoted students in Alexandria, and thus its scholars developed the philosophy of the Greeks in the direction of specialized sciences. The connection with general philosophy became less strict, but was not lost because general philosophy remained the frame of all specialized sciences.

In Rome, interest was centered on the ethical aspects of Grecian philosophy, witness for instance, Seneca and Cicero. With this difference in interest is connected the difference in preference for one or the other of the Greek philosophic systems. In Alexandria Aristotelianism with an admixture of Platonic elements was prevalent. In Rome Aristotelianism remained insignificant. Apart from some form of neo-Platonism, most systems adopted in Rome were characteristically eclectic, i.e. suitable elements of various systems were united into a whole which was adapted to the Roman philosophy of life.

In the following paragraphs we will survey what happened to the two most important theories of matter and its smallest particles in the East and the West.

Philosophic Atomism. We have already mentioned that the Greek philosophers who came after Democritus did not follow him in his opinions. There is, however, another and more important reason why we do not have to dwell here very long upon philosophic atomism. To a certain extent Democritus' theory was complete, so that little could be added to it. Without doing violence to history we may say that philosophic atomism continued to exist till the seventeenth century, practically without any changes. Rather than adding anything new to it, its relatively few supporters during that period simply took over Democritus' own doctrine.

Epicurus (347-271 B. C.) was one of its best known representatives in the Greek world after Democritus. He made it the foundation of his generally very materialistic philosophy. As a result his system suffered a loss of esteem in subsequent times. Rome became acquainted with the philosophy of Epicurus through the famous didactic poem *De Natura Rerum* of the Roman poet T. Lucretius Carus (96-55 B. C.)

Heraclitus Ponticus (4th cent. B. C.) and Asclepiades of Bithynia (about 100 B. C.) deserve to be mentioned here, although they are not supporters of pure atomism. They differ from it insofar as they conceived atoms as divisible. On other points they exhibit the same conceptions as classic atomism: atoms and their parts differ only in size and shape; they are in ceaseless motion. From the mingling and the separation of atoms result different kinds of matter. An interesting detail is that Asclepiades developed this doctrine into the basis of a medical theory. The body consists of canals, which are formed by the juxtaposition of atoms in a peculiar manner. For good health it is essential that these canals are wide enough to allow passage to the various kinds of smallest particles. This doctrine became the basis of the so-called methodical school among the physicians of later times. It is of interest to us here mainly because it is an effort to explain from a corpuscular point of view certain concrete phenomena. As such it meant an effort in the direction of a physical corpuscular theory.

The Doctrine of Natural Minima in the Greek Commentators of Aristotle. In contrast to Democritus' atomism, Aristotle's theory of smallest particles is found only in an embryonic state in his works. Hence it will be possible to point out its development in the course of history up to the seventeenth century, which saw the birth of the physical atomic theory. The first development took place in the period of the so-called Greek Commentators. This name requires some explanation. The term *commentator* is used here in practically the same sense as it is in ordinary language. It indicates somebody who does not aim primarily at announcing anything new, but at explaining what is already known. Aristotle's work had made a tremendous impression upon posterity. Many believed that once and for all he had discovered the truth. Hence their main occupation was to study his books and to comment upon them in order to explain obscure passages and to assign to new discoveries a suitable place in the framework of Aristotle's philosophy. Such commentators are found not only in the world of Greek civilization, but also, in later ages, in the Arabian world and in the medieval West. Often these commentaries are rather strained. Sometimes they are more like an exposition of the commentator's own ideas, which in deference to tradition are attributed to Aristotle in order to find more support for them. Nevertheless, frequently also they are the fruit of real penetration into Aristotle's thought. When this happens these commentaries are valuable not only insofar as they show the own thoughts of the commentator, but also in order to give us a better knowledge of Aristotle himself.

As regards this last point, the commentaries of the Greek Commentators are obviously very important because their tradition goes more directly back to Aristotle than that of any other commentators. With respect to Aristotle's theory of smallest particles, we are able to discover among these Greeks a marked development of Aristotle's thought, which moreover remains entirely within the limits of Aristotle's theory. The commentators Alexander of Aphrodisias (about 200 A.D.), Themistius (4th cent. A.D.), and Philoponus (6th cent. A.D.) summarize in clear and precise terms the doctrine which we were obliged more or less to assemble from various parts of Aristotle's works. A quantity is, mathematically speaking, infinitely divisible, but not physically. The smallest particles of a body are similar to each other. Apart from thus summarizing Aristotle, they also advance beyond him in certain points, the first of which is the extent to which the theory of natural minima applies. In Aristotle himself it remained doubtful whether the theory applied only to living matter or not. Simplicius resolutely removes this doubt. Besides the examples of flesh and bone, he gives explicitly others of lead and gold.[9] This, however, is not the most important point. The manner in which the Commentators illustrate Aristotle's text gives us an interesting chance to observe their own thoughts. The best opportunity for this is offered by the commentary of Alexander of Aphrodisias, which is preserved by Simplicius. The text refers to Aristotle's refutation of Anaxagoras. Aristotle proceeded from a mental experiment in which he separated steadily decreasing quantities of flesh from water. Alexander comments: "In every separation a certain number of ἐλάχιστα (*elachista*) is separated."[10] What is the meaning of *elachista?* It is the Greek equivalent of minima. Hence it means ordinarily *very small* or *smallest*. Still in reading these Commentators we get the impression that they used the term *elachista* in a special, technical, sense.[10a] Just as for Democritus the term *atomos* does not mean exclusively *indivisible,* but also is a special, technical, term for smallest particles, so also something similar seems to be the case with the word *elachista*. It means the smallest possible part of a certain matter. It is the technical term for some definite idea, just as are our terms *atom* and *molecule*. *Elachista* would thus be the Greek equivalent of the Latin *minima,* which in Latin writings indicates the smallest particles as conceived by Aristotle, just as the term *atomus* is used for the smallest particles as conceived by Democritus. The technical use of the word by itself is already an interesting datum, but more still can be gathered from Alexander's brief sentence: "In every separation a certain number of *elachista* is separated." While Aristotle reasons simply: let us conceive that flesh is repeatedly separated, Alexander changes this

[9]*Commentaria in Aristotelem Graeca edita consilio et auctoritate Academiae regiae Borussicae,* Berlin 1882-1907, vol. IX, 167, 11-18. Edited by H. Diels.
[10]*Commentaria Graeca,* vol. IX, 170, 9.
[10a](See following page for this footnote.)

into: let us conceive that a certain number of *elachista* is separated. The concept has a more concrete meaning for him than for Aristotle. For the latter it means only that by continued division of a body a certain small magnitude will be reached which is no longer divisible. Nothing indicates that he attributed to this smallest quantity a certain measure of independence in the whole of which it is a natural minimum. Alexander, however, sees more than that in the *elachista*. Certainly, for him also they mark the limit of divisibility, but his use of the term indicates at the same time that he attributed to the *elachista* a certain measure of actuality in the whole before the division. A certain quantity of flesh means for him a certain number of *elachista*. It cannot be denied that this is already a development of Aristotle's idea. Its further development will bring us to the second chapter of this book, which is dedicated to the Middle Ages and the Renaissance.

SUPPLEMENTARY NOTE FOR PAGE 17:

A similar pattern reveals itself in any science which makes use of general laws. For the general character of a law, e.g., Newton's law of universal gravitation, implies a fundamental unity and immutability in all kinds of things that at first sight seem to be very different and changeable. Thus Parmenides' demand that being be one and immutable points to something which somehow must lie at the very foundation of the plurality and mutability of the phenomena if these are ever to be susceptible to a rational scientific analysis. No matter, then, how much the conclusions of Parmenides' reasoning seemed to contradict experience, they certainly contained an element of truth.

[10a]A confirmation of the technical use of *elachista* may be found in the work of Michael Psellus (11th cent.) *De omnifaria doctrina. Caput* 93 bears the title: περὶ ἐλαχίστων (*peri elachistōn*). For the history of this work see L. G. Westerink, *Michael Psellus: De omnifaria doctrina. Critical Text and Introduction,* Nijmegen, 1948.

CHAPTER TWO

THE MIDDLE AGES AND THE RENAISSANCE

1. GENERAL OUTLINE

Before we enter into any detailed history of the concept *smallest part* in the periods which are called the Middle Ages and the Renaissance, it will be necessary first to consider briefly the history of philosophy and science in general. The Greek period has taught us sufficiently how closely the conceptions of smallest parts were connected with the whole of philosophic systems and their fundamental problems. We cannot isolate one from the other, neither the theories of corpuscles from the whole, nor always the whole from the theories of corpuscles. For there are periods in history in which the theories of smallest particles contributed to determine the trend of human thought. To a certain extent the fourth century before Christ was such a time, and the seventeenth century will be shown to be so to perhaps even a greater extent. In the intermediate centuries the smallest parts occupy a far less important place. This, however, does not imply that these centuries are without interest to the history of the subject of our investigation. At the end of the previous chapter we saw already that Aristotle's minima theory underwent a valuable development during the Hellenistic period. In order to understand the complicated situation of the seventeenth century, it is not sufficient to examine separately the successive stages of development in the theories of corpuscles. We must perform that examination against the background of the *whole* history. It is really necessary to know more about it *"than that Aristotle dominated science for two thousand years, that the medieval Church protected his authority with her dogmata, and that only in the seventeenth century this situation came to an end with the dethroning of Aristotle and dogma, so that at last true science became possible."*[1]

---

[1] We have hesitated a long time whether this rather sharp description of a certain mentality towards the Middle Ages should be taken over from our book *"Het Wijsgerig Verleden der Atoomtheorie"* (p. 52). One may justly ask whether such a mentality is still frequently encountered in our days. Our hesitation was overcome when we saw that such an authority as Sir James Jeans in a recent work considered himself justified in speaking in the following terms about the Middle Ages: "Then came those darker ages in which the bright light of Greek culture suffered eclipse, and European philosophy with it." *Physics and Philosophy,* Cambridge 1946, p. 18.

Development in the West. Western philosophy, as mentioned, was especially concerned with ethical problems. Then Christianity appeared in this setting. Although in itself not primarily a philosophic system, nevertheless it gave a very positive and trenchant answer to all the fundamental ethical problems of the Roman philosophers. Several Christian writers used the philosophic language of their time for apologetic purposes. They wanted to show that what various philosophic systems vaguely and hesitatingly tried to express, could be found clearly and firmly in Christianity. Reversely, there were also pagan philosophers who on philosophic grounds considered Christianity false or superfluous. This led to philosophical discussions of Christianity so that Christian writers were obliged to become thoroughly acquainted with contemporaneous philosophy. Moreover, apart from these polemics with their pagan opponents, the Fathers of the Church made use of philosophic concepts to lay down the data of Christian Revelation in precise formulas. All this led to something which we may call a Christian philosophy. However, it was not a closed system because from a philosophical point of view its elements were too heterogeneous and its genesis too incidental. It will not surprise us that there was in that time but little interest in problems of natural philosophy. The Roman world was hardly interested in them anyhow, and the nascent Church could not be expected to consider it as one of its first duties to arouse interest in them. Insofar as the Romans had any interest in problems of natural philosophy they were more inclined to physical considerations. It was so, for instance, with Lucretius Carus, who made Democritus' atomism the philosophic basis for his materialistic Epicurian ethics. Violent were the attacks which the Fathers of the Church directed against this atomism. Nobody will be surprised if they did not clearly perceive the difference between atomism as a possible scientific hypothesis and its materialistic background. At any rate its connection with materialism did not promote an increasing respect for atomism.

Among the scholars of this period Augustine above all others acquired a dominating influence upon later times. Philosophically he was close to the Platonic tradition. He explained Christian teaching in the terms of this philosophy. This did not offer him any great difficulties. The Platonic ideas became God's ideas. The contemplation of pure ideas which Plato required for true wisdom and science was reshaped by Augustine into his doctrine of illumination. According to this doctrine illumination by God is the source of human knowledge. However, more important for the history of science than details about his theories is the fact that in Augustine philosophy and Theology are tightly interwoven. In the centuries after him there was no question of any proper, autonomous, philosophy or of any autonomous science in the western world. There was one Christian science, which was based equally upon Revelation and Reason.

This Christian science spread throughout the West especially by means of the monastic schools. Direct acquaintance with, and study of, Greek sources was relatively rare. Yet, slowly, direct contact began to increase so that the West came also in contact with Aristotle, mainly through the works of Boethius (6th cent. A.D.). However, the centuries of destruction which followed the fall of the Roman Empire created in the West a scientific vacuum which continued till the time of the Carolingian Renaissance. From then on intellectual life, drawing nourishment from sparsely preserved sources, began to reach again a higher level. It goes without saying that scientific considerations of nature barely occupy any place at all during this period.

The East. Quite different was the development in the East. During the Hellenistic period natural philosophy had been far more important there than in the West. This implied a preference for Aristotle, whose philosophy, mixed with some elements from other systems, flourished in Alexandria, Antioch, and Byzantium, the great cultural centers of those times. There it was found by the conquering Arabs, who gratefully accepted this inheritance from Greek civilization and cultivated it in their own manner, i.e. they developed it towards the practical trends of the specialized sciences which were traditional in Arabia. Thus medicine and the physical sciences reached a high level among the Arabs.

The Arabian conquest extended not only over the East, but via North Africa it reached Spain and Southern Italy. By this remarkable detour the West regained, in the eleventh and twelfth centuries, contact with Aristotle's philosophy, and through it, contact with a complete system of science in all fields. Moreover, the Arabs did not merely transmit materially the science of the Greeks. They added their own contributions to the specialized sciences and could boast of profound philosophers. We will name only two, Avicenna (980-1037) and Averroes (1126-1198). Typical of their influence is the fact that during the Middle Ages Averroes was called simply "the Commentator", just as Aristotle was called "the Philosopher".

The Development of Philosophy in the Middle Ages.   The acquaintance with Arabian philosophy proved of the greatest importance for Western culture.   Firstly, because it gave a powerful stimlulus to philosophic thought.   On one hand, western thinkers were fascinated by the powerful construction of Aristotle's system, and on the other, they found much in it which militated against Christian dogma and traditional convictions.   This urged them to independent examination and scrutiny of the problems raised by Aristotle so that philosophy soon found itself in a very flourishing condition.   The second reason why the acquaintance with Arabian philosophy became such an important factor is already implied in the first: philosophy really began to be an independent science.   Great medieval thinkers, as Thomas Aquinas and Albert the Great, clearly saw the possibility of a science which is not based upon Christian revelation but only upon sense-experience and its rational interpretation.   This in turn had a direct bearing upon the importance attached to that part of philosophy which treats of matter.   Natural philosophy became one of the most important branches of study.   Enthusiastically many western scholars threw themselves upon the new scientific data.   It is understandable that in doing so they followed Aristotle and the Arabs more or less servilely in matters pertaining to physical science.   This science was something new for them, it meant real progress in their thinking.   Moreover, Aristotle's system was constructed so logically that it could not fail to produce a profound impression upon any one who came in contact with it for the first time.

Of course, for the time being there could be no question of a really *independent physical science* in the modern sense of the word. Everything remained enclosed within the one whole of philosophy and science.   Although even at the very beginning some scholars applied themselves more to some particular detail, and others more to the whole, the general rule remained true that the attention of man in the Middle Ages was centered upon the great questions concerning human existence so that Theology and philosophy remained the core subjects of his study.   The fact that Theology was the central faculty in the structure of medieval universities, which originated during these centuries, shows this clearly.   Other faculties, as Medicine, Law, and Letters, were already known, but philosophy was their common bond.

This development of science was accompanied by the practice of technical arts. In this aspect also the Arabs proved themselves excellent teachers. Within the limits of these technical arts many experiments were made. Hence the amount of experimental data increased steadily, although it did not yet develop into a real independent science. The scientific principles, as incorporated into the whole of Aristotle's philosophy and accepted in those days, were still too faulty to allow such a development.

Characterization of Scholastic Philosophy. Although it can be said that philosophy in the Middle Ages showed more unity than in our days, this does not take away from the fact that even in the Middle Ages there was a great variety of philosophic trends. They are all comprised under the name *Scholastic philosophy.* This name is derived from the Latin "schola." It merely refers to the *method* of teaching, namely the study of science in the frame of a *school.* Hence it does not indicate any uniform philosophic system, although some general characteristics of Scholastic philosophy can be given.

The most important of these characteristics is the close connection between philosophy and Theology. They were *distinct,* but not *separated.* Insofar as they were distinct, Scholastic philosophy differs from pre-medieval philosophic trends. A second characteristic is the high esteem for the Greek philosophers, notably for Aristotle.

While these two characteristics are generally recognized,[2] there is a third which we would like to add to them, namely the view which the Scholastics themselves held of their science. In general they were convinced that their Greek and Arabian masters had dis- covered the truth in all fields of human knowledge, at least in its general outlines. They accepted as certain their fundamental theses in all branches of science. In order to explain this typical attitude of Scholastic thinkers we should not forget that they were already used to such an outlook upon science, for they were primarily theologians. In Theology the fundamental theses were found in Revelation and in the teachings of the Church, and had to be accepted as certain. They formed starting points which were always to be trusted. The same attitude was now extended to other branches of human knowledge. As regards philosophy and mathematics, fundamental theses were available from immediate insights. As regards physical science, they were found firmly anchored in the experience of proven scholars.

---

[2] See F. Ueberweg, *Grundriss der Geschichte der Philosophie,* Berlin[12] 1924, Vol. II p. 143ff.

So for the Scholastics to study science meant to draw consistent conclusions from these fundamental theses and to find the logical connections in the whole of fundamental and derived theses. This is the reason why logic fulfilled such an important function in medieval science. For logic is the art which teaches how to arrange the data in a process of reasoning. While this attitude of medieval man towards the science of his time and especially towards the science of matter may seem rash to us, yet it is understandable. For in many of those points which lent themselves to comparison, the results of Grecian philosophic speculation seem to harmonize egregiously with the unconditionally accepted truth of Faith. The latter functioned as if it were as an external criterion for the purity of a philosophic procedure which nowhere had made an appeal to the data of Revelation. Moreover, we should not forget that the science of the Greeks and the Arabs, which in itself possessed already a notable self-assurance, had meant real scientific progress for medieval man.[3]

The existence of divergent tendencies in Scholastic philosophy does not disprove our assertion. On the contrary, the manner in which the Scholastics argued against each other rather confirms it. Their arguments for and against are to a large extent logical in character, i.e. they tried to convince each other by reasoning.

Trends in the Thirteenth Century. We will now survey succinctly the various trends in Scholastic philosophy. The oldest of them is the Augustinian-Platonic trend. It is the most direct continuation of pre-medieval philosophy. The latter, as known, had the greatest respect for Augustine. In the eleventh and twelfth centuries many Aristotelian and Arabic elements were absorbed, but its foundation remained Platonic in inspiration. Bonaventure (1221-1274) may be considered as its principal representative.

The most important and influential trend of Scholastic philosophy was the so-called Christian Aristotelian trend which arose from the confrontation of the traditional Christian philosophy of the West with the Arabian version of Aristotle. It proceeds from an independent interpretation of Aristotle and does not accept any of the commentaries without criticism. It may best be characterized as an independent Christian philosophy which has great respect for the thinking of the Greeks (especially of Aristotle and Plato) and of the Arabs.

---

[3]Nevertheless there was criticism on details. See, for instance, the commentary of Thomas Aquinas on Aristotle's treatise *On the Heavens*, (*Opera Omnia*, vol. III, Rome 1936, lib. II, lect. 17).

Its principal exponents are Albert the Great and Thomas Aquinas. Another trend is connected with this one. Although Aristotelian, it generally takes over the changes and explanations of the Arabs, notably of Averroes, but relegates to the background whatever is *evidently* contrary to Christian Revelation. This trend is known as Averroism. Its principal defender in the thirteenth century was Siger of Brabant. During the fifteenth century it became very widespread in Italy. Later we will see that mainly this trend of Scholastic philosophy exercised great influence on the development of the Aristotelian theory of smallest particles.

It should be obvious that the above division is rather schematic. There were numerous kinds of intermediate trends. Duns Scotus (about 1270-1308), who represents a Christian Aristotelianism which differs somewhat from Thomism, deserves special mention.

Scholastic philosophy reached its height in the thirteenth century, when it was confronted with Arabic philosophy and obliged to determine its position towards the latter, but even during the subsequent centuries it is not without importance for our study.

Subsequent Centuries. The fourteenth century offers about the same spectacle as the thirteenth, but on a lower level. Yet one remarkable fact may be observed which is generally neglected by historians. While Aristotle's philosophy is not rejected as a whole, it is severely criticized in several *parts,* especially in many of its physical concepts. In this critique the so-called Parisian nominalists were foremost.

The Scholastics who are called nominalists owe their name to the solution which they gave to the problem of universals. This problem, which already for centuries had engaged the attention of Western philosophers, is basically the same as the problem which caused Aristotle to deviate from Plato, namely what is the value of our universal concepts? Plato's solution, as we have seen above, was that our universal concepts correspond to a world in which these concepts lead an independent existence. Aristotle, on the contrary, contended that the universality of our concepts is derived from the human mind. This abstraction is not arbitrary, but based upon the adequate possibility offered by reality. For one and the same essential form in a plurality of individuals corresponds to the universal concept by which these individuals are known and indicated.

Against this conception the nominalists contended that universals do not imply more than a universal name. We give one name to similar things, but this does not mean that in reality there is in these things anything like the same essential form or basic plan.

The principal exponent of this system is the English philosopher William of Occam (first half of 14th cent.). Through his influence nominalism became very powerful in the fourteenth century, especially at the University of Paris. We will omit here the philosophical aspect of their critique on Aristotle, although perhaps it too, was a factor which contributed to the undermining of the faith in Aristotle's physical concepts among the Nominalists. At any rate the Parisian nominalists Buridan (about 1300-about 1358), Albert of Saxony (1316-1390), Nicholas of Oresme (about 1382), and others succeeded in correcting Aristotle's physical concepts in many important points. In this way they prepared the ideas which a century or two later would make Galileo, Copernicus, and Descartes famous.[4]

Nevertheless the Parisian nominalists did not do more that prepare the way. The time was not yet ripe, and the data were not yet sufficient to undermine Aristotle's influence over the entire line. Moreover, although undoubtedly the Renaissance ultimately stimulated the development of physical science, in some aspects it initially retarded this development. For the Renaissance began as a revaluation of the spiritual treasures of classical Antiquity in their original form, independently from the selection and interpretation given by medieval Scholastics. This independence from Scholastic interpretation did not make much difference for physical science, because from the scientific point of view the important thing was not Christian or un-Christian interpretation of Antiquity, but independent research in nature. Therefore, we may say that Scholastic mentality alone is not responsible for the fact that the acquaintance with Aristotle in the eleventh and twelfth century, which formed the beginning of a revival of physical science in the West, did not lead to an ever increasing development of this science. Notwithstanding the characteristic overdose of self-assurance with respect to the newly acquired science, which in my opinion must be assigned to Scholastic philosophy, we must admit that after a time sufficient critical evaluation arose in the ranks of Scholastic philosophers.

The Philosophy of the Renaissance. While Scholastic philosophy was a philosophy of schools and trends which clustered around a single central figure, the philosophy of the Renaissance is one of per-

---

[4]Cf. P. Duhem, *Études sur Leonard de Vinci*, Paris 1906-1913, and E. J. Dijksterhuis, *Die Mechanisierung des Weltbildes*, Berlin, 1954, Ch. II, Sect. 109–116.

sonalities. The typical *school*-element disappeared. Initially it showed itself as an urge to study directly the Greek philosophers, notably Plato and Aristotle, the latter of course independently from the commentaries of the Scholastics and the Arabs. One result of this for physical science we have mentioned already: the new respect for the Greeks did not stimulate the new physical insights which were trying to break through in certain Scholastic circles, especially among the nominalists. Nevertheless there is also a bright side for physical science in the revival of the study of Antiquity, namely the renewed acquaintance with Plato. The latter had considered mathematical proportions as the essence of material phenomena, and thus had been a powerful stimulus for contemporaneous mathematical research. The inspiration provided by Plato's theory must undoubtedly be considered as a contributing factor to the new mathematical methods which were developed in the sixteenth and seventeenth centuries for the purpose of obtaining a better insight into material phenomena.

Nevertheless the greatest positive importance of the Renaissance must be sought in the fact that it relaxed the bonds which kept all sciences within the frame of philosophy. Many new theories originated with or without inspiration from the classics. Although not all of them were important, yet they were very stimulative. From the viewpoint of physical science we may name the German Paracelsus (1493-1541), and the Italians Hieronymus Cardano (1501-1576), Giordano Bruno (1548-1600), and Leonardo da Vinci (1452-1519). To these should be added Copernicus (1473-1543), and Galileo (1564-1642), who were real trailblazers in physical science, although they are unimportant for philosophy in the strict sense. They prepared the way for new and better insights in many physical problems. Systematically they developed what the nominalists before them had proposed hesitatingly. In a short time the plea for the new insights obtained victory.

Especially important is the correct formulation of the laws of falling bodies and of impact by Galileo, because this opened new horizons for mechanics and thereby created the necessary conditions for the development of atomic conceptions along mathematical lines. This fact had a decisive influence upon the development of physical science. Shortly after Galileo, Huygens (1629-1695), and Newton (1642-1727), perfected the insights in mechanics.

Revival of Atomism. Thus we approach the seventeenth century, the century in which Aristotle's authority, against which the philosophers of the Renaissance had struggled with only partial success, was definitely shaken by several factors. This gave another chance to philosophic atomism. For contrary to the critique of the fourteenth century, which was directed against some mechanical and astronomical concepts of Aristotle and did not attack his entire philosophic system, philosophic atomism criticized the very essence of Aristotelian philosophy rather than opposed specific details. However, the events of the seventeenth century belong to another chapter of this book, not only technically on account of the division of this book, but also because from the seventeenth century on this study will assume a different character corresponding to the new aspect of history. The seventeenth century shows a surface-fracture in the history of the concept *atom* because in this century the history of the scientific atomic concept made its beginning. Perhaps the start is somewhat faltering, but unmistakenly it is the start. Again, however, this start is not without connection with the preceding centuries. With this we may conclude our general introduction to the philosophy of the Middle Ages and the Renaissance. We will now see what happened to the concept *atom* during this period.

2. ARISTOTLE'S DOCTRINE OF MINIMA IN HIS COMMENTATORS

Averroes. We may begin our survey of the development of Aristotle's doctrine of smallest parts with the Arabian philosopher Averroes (1126-1198). There is a lapse of five or six centuries between Simplicius, the last Greek commentator who represented this doctrine, and Averroes. It is not known what happened to the theory during the intervening centuries. Likewise not much is known about the fate of philosophic atomism during this period. However, this gap in our knowledge is no great loss because Averroes is closely connected with Simplicius.

The first point of interest in Averroes' works will be his commentary on the well-known passage[1] bk. I, ch. 4 of Aristotle's Physics.[2] He explains Aristotle's argument against Anaxagoras

---

[1] Quoted above on page 42. (Transl.).

[2] We quote from the Latin edition of 1560 (apud Cominum de Trinido, Montesferrati). To give some idea of the enormous dissemination in the West of the works of the Commentator, we may mention that in Venice alone 50 editions of Averroes' works were published. Cf. J. E. Renan, *Averroès et l'Averroisme,* Paris[2] 1861, p. 15.

mainly in the same way as Simplicius; hence there is no reason for us to dwell in it to any extent. Instead of the Greek term *elachista,* he uses the Latin equivalent *minima* in the standing expression *minima naturalia,* natural minima, i.e. minima as determined by the nature of the substance.

However, in reading other parts of Averroes' works we notice immediately that he insists upon the theory of the natural minima far more frequently than Simplicius, and in connection with all kinds of problems. It clearly constitutes a much more essential element of his physical conceptions than in those of Aristotle or the Greek commentators. We shall not enter into details, but simply quote a few texts which may be considered as typical of the stage of development reached by the theory of natural minima when the West became acquainted with it at the beginning of the thirteenth century.

> When we remove a part of fire and repeat this action again and again we finally reach a quantity which is such that by a further division the fire would perish, because there is a certain minimal quantity of fire.[3]

Averroes gives careful attention to the very important distinction between physical and mathematical divisibility, which is the foundation of the theory of natural minima. He speaks about it in several places.

> A line as a line can be divided infinitely. But such a division is impossible if the line is taken as made of earth.[4]

Averroes seeks the cause for the existence of natural minima in the specific action of every kind of substance. Specific action requires a certain quantity.

> It is impossible for something to increase or decrease infinitely, because if the quantity determined by nature is passed, whether by increase or decrease, the being perishes. For the action of every being results from a limited quantity and quality.[5]

Note that in this quotation Averroes names quantity and quality in one breath. He seems to admit not only a quantitative, but also a qualitative, minimum.

---

[3]*Phys.* VIII, comm. **44.**
[4]*Phys.* IV, comm. **72.**
[5]*Phys.* VI, comm. **32.**

Thus far it cannot be said that Averroes' conception surpasses that of his predecessors except for this mention of a qualitative minimum. The whole problem of the smallest particle in these quotations is still seen as a theoretical problem about the possibility of dividing matter. The concept *natural minimum* which occurs in the texts does not yet offer sufficient constructive possibilities for the explanation of really observed physical and chemical phenomena, although it is already much more pregnant in meaning than in Aristotle, as the very use of the term *natural minimum* shows. Yet something like an explanation of phenomena by means of the natural minima may be found in some other texts of Averroes.

> The first thing which becomes or perishes in the generation or corruption of a substance is the smallest particle of this substance, for the minimum of all that becomes is of a limited quantity.[6]

It appears that according to Averroes the minima of a substance are realized as separate units when a reaction takes place between substances. At least the text quoted above seems to indicate that. In connection with this, another remark in *Phys.* I, chapter 4, is important because in it he indicates the minima as actual parts.[7]

Thus it should be clear that for Averroes natural minima mean much more than a theoretical limit of divisibility. They are for him something like physical realities. Later we will find this conception developed by his followers.

Albert the Great and Thomas Aquinas. In our general survey of the Middle Ages we pointed out that the different trends and schools were all under the influence of Averroes, although not all to the same extent. Obviously we had then in mind the essential points only of the doctrine proposed by these different schools. Nevertheless the same holds good for their position as regards the theory of natural minima. Some restricted themselves to a somewhat more systematic treatment of the fundamental concepts which they simply took over from Aristotle, while others followed Averroes towards a theory which showed more development in certain points.

Thus we find in Albert the Great and Thomas Aquinas (13th cent.) clear commentaries on the well-known text of Aristotle, *Physics* I, 4. However, except for the fact that they explicitly apply the

---

[6]*Phys.* VI, comm. 32.
[7]*Phys.* IV, comm. 34.

doctrine of natural minima to inorganic substances, they do not really proceed beyond the speculations of Aristotle.[8]

This does not surprise us as far as Thomas Aquinas is concerned because, although in keeping with the customs of his time his works embrace physics also, it is clear that he is primarily interested in theological and general philosophic problems. I rather expected to find more in his master Albert the Great, because the latter shows a pronounced interest in physical problems and occupies an honorable place in the history of the technical arts, but a search of his works did not reveal anything. The theory of natural minima is a part of his general conception of matter, but he does not mention it in his theory of chemical composition. There is, however, one point in his theory of natural minima which is of interest with respect to a later stage in the development of that theory, but it will be better to reserve that till we reach that stage.

Among the disciples of Albert the Great and Thomas Aquinas we find the same conceptions, for instance in Aegidius the Roman (1247-1316). It was in the works of this medieval philosopher that the French physicist and historian P. Duhem encountered for the first time in his research the theory of natural minima. This led him to the erroneous assumption that Aegidius had introduced a subtle form of philosophic atomism. As a matter of fact, however, Aegidius had done nothing else than explain a theory which was traditional among the Aristotelians of his circle and trend.[9]

Neither in Aegidius nor in any other follower of Thomas Aquinas in this and in the subsequent centuries can we find an application of the minima theory to chemical reactions. They limit themselves to the well-known theoretical explanations. What we do find, however, especially in later times, are extensive polemics against followers of philosophic trends who held divergent views about the minima. We

---

[8]Albertus Magnus, *Opera Omnia,* vol. III, Paris 1890, *Phys.* I, tractus II, cap. XIII, comm. 38.
Thomas Aquinas, *Opera Omnia,* Vol. II, Rome 1934, *Phys.* I, lectio IX, 9 and 10.

[9]P. Duhem, *Études sur Leonard de Vinci,* 2e série, p. 11ff. For an extensive treatment of the point see A.G.M. van Melsen, *Het Wijsgerig Verleden der Atoomtheorie,* p. 73ff. Duhem's mistake is understandable, because in the beginning of the twentieth century this theory of minima was practically unknown. P. Hoenen is mainly responsible for drawing attention to it. We have been able to base ourselves upon his publications. See the following works of P. Hoenen: *Prof. Jaeger over Aristoteles en de Scholastiek,* in *Studien* 94 (1920), p. 36; *Annotationes Cosmologicae,* Rome 1930; *Cosmologia,* Rome[3] 1945, p. 519ff. (first edition in 1931) ; *Filosofia della natura inorganica,* Brescia, 1949, Ch. 2, Sect. 2.

will speak about these polemics in the chapter which is concerned with
the seventeenth century.

The Scotists. In Scotistic circles the minima were accepted, but
only for heterogeneous matter. So, for instance, writes Walther
Burleigh (14th cent.), an immediate disciple of Scotus:

> We must, therefore, say that in homogeneous things maximum and
> minimum are impossible, but this does not hold for heterogeneous
> things, such as living beings.[10]

It is clear that this conception or minima closely adheres to the
literal interpretation of Aristotle's texts which refer to this problem.
For "the Philosopher" named as examples of natural minima only
flesh and bone. The Scotists defended their opinion by pointing out
that the requirement of a minimal magnitude flows from the organic
structure of the living body. The latter requires a certain size for the
exercise of its specific functions.

With this explanation in mind we will not be surprised when we
fail to encounter among the Scotists any development of the theory of
natural minima in the direction indicated by Averroes. For such a
development would require that the theory be applied to all substances.

The Nominalists. Interesting is the modification of the minima
theory among the nominalists. Already in the first half of the fourteenth century we find in the works of Buridan a formulation of the
concept which is slightly different from those we have thus far
encountered:

> One could have such a small quantity of a substance that it does
> not continue to exist for a noticeable time. This small quantity
> will continually tend towards its own destruction.[11]

Thus for Buridan the main point in the theory is that a substance
is not stable below the magnitude of its natural minimum. This is a
new point of view, for in the doctrines of Aristotle and Averroes the
question is not whether a substance remains *stable* below a certain
minimal size or not. The concept of natural minima as developed
by them indicates that a certain substance *cannot exist at all,* i.e. cannot
be realized in any way, with a quantity smaller than that of the natural
minimum.

---

[10]Gualt. Burlaei *de Physica Auscultatione Commentaria,* Venetiis 1589,
p. 70A.
[11]*Magistri Johannis Buridani Questiones totius libri Physicorum,* lib. I,
q. XIII, *Utrum omnia entia sint determinata ad minimum.* Cf. P. Duhem,
Études, II, 384.

Clearer still than Buridan does Albert of Saxony (1316-1390) express this new view on the problem:

> It is true that in a given environment and in given conditions a substance can exist only above a certain minimum. However, this minimum depends on environment and conditions, so that a certain quantity of a substance which is too small to exist in one environment could very well be stable in another. Therefore it is not correct to speak in an absolute sense, and without any indication of environment and conditions, about a minimum below which a substance cannot exist.[12]

The text does not need any comment, it speaks for itself. Of course we are very interested to know whether the nominalists made any attempts to obtain more precise knowledge about the influence of environment and conditions upon the size of the particles. An explanation such as that of Albert of Saxony looks like an invitation to it. Moreover, we know how intensely interested the nominalists were in physical problems—the reader will recall how fertile their ideas have proved to be for mechanics and astronomy—but we are disappointed. I have not been able to find among the nominalists any physical development of their minima theory. This does not mean that there has not been any at all, for numerous unedited manuscripts of those days are still preserved in our libraries. It is possible, therefore, that eventually something will come to light, although I do not consider it very likely because in the polemical writings of their opponents there is no mention either about such a development of the theory by the nominalists.

As an additional remark we may mention that this nominalistic conception dates from before the fourteenth century.[13] It is mentioned in the thirteenth century, for instance, by the well-known Averroist Siger of Brabant, who opposes it.[14] He also mentions another opinion, namely that a natural minimum can exist below a certain limit but cannot exercise its action.

The Averroists. Siger of Brabant's own opinion closely follows the interpretation of Averroes. The same holds for most of the

---

[12]*Acutissimae Questiones super libros de physica auscultatione ab Alberto Saxoniae editae;* in lib. I, q. X. Cf. Duhem, *Études,* II, p. 15.

[13]In a previous work, *Het Wijsgerig Verleden der Atoomtheorie,* p. 80, we mentioned already that we suspected this on account of the fact that Burleigh refers to the nominalistic conception.

[14]*Questiones super libros I, II, III, IV et VIII Physicorum,* I, 26. *Les Philosophes Belges. Textes et Études,* Tome XII. *Siger de Brabant,* par F. van Steenberghen, vol. I, *Les Oeuvres Inédites,* Louvain 1931, p. 183.

Averroists whom we had opportunity to consult. Among them especially may be found the outspoken tendency to elaborate on the problem of minimal and maximal size. We have already pointed out that Averroes himself shows clearly the tendency to transfer the speculations to the physical plane. The same is true of his followers, although they do it differently. So, for instance, John de Jandun (died 1328), who states that the volume of water can be increased so much that the maximum size is passed, and water becomes air. Reversely, air becomes water when air is condensed.[15] We may say that John de Jandun in his speculations on the minima thinks about division,[16] but not only about division, for he connects these speculations with the expansion and shrinking of substances. To avoid misunderstanding we must point out that Aristotle considered expansion and condensation respectively as continuous dilation and shrinking, and John de Jandun took this idea over from him. Among later Averroists we will find other opinions on this question which will be closer to our modern conception. It is, of course, of special interest to us whether John de Jandun speaks about the minima as more or less actual parts. From what we have seen of him above, this is not to be expected. A search of his works did not produce any result: his speculations remain wholly within the frame of the problem *"Whether natural substances have a maximal and a minimal limit"* (*An naturalia ad maximum et minimum terminata sint*).

However, in the brief annotations of a certain Helias which are added to the edition of John de Jandun's works which I consulted, the above-mentioned opinion of Averroes can be found. "The natural minima are actual parts, i.e. parts which can exist when actually divided."[17] This is the conception which the Averroists of the subsequent centuries will continue to develop.

A good idea of the manner in which the theory of natural minima was taught among the Averroists of the sixteenth century can be obtained from the works of Augustine Nifo (1473-1546).

His commentary on Aristotle's *Physics* follows that of Averroes closely, but he develops it on many points and adds numerous appli-

---

[15]Joan. de Janduno, *Super octo libros Aristotelis de Physico auditu subtilissimae quaestiones:* Venice 1551, in lib. I q. XVI.

[16]*"A natural substance, as fire, can be divided infinitely insofar as it is a quantity, i.e. insofar as it has a certain volume, but not insofar as it is a natural substance. If division is continued to a certain degree the form of being is destroyed and fire will change into air or water."*

[17]*Heliae Cretensi Philosophi et Medici in dictis Averrois super libros Physicorum clarissimae adnotationes,* Venice 1551, p. 145.

cations. We will omit his remarks on the well-known text of
Aristotle, upon which he comments in the usual way, although more
extensively. Obviously the minima theory is dear to his heart and
occupies the central place in the sphere of his interest. Continually
he tries to give the reasons for his conception of it. For instance,

> Every specific action requires a determinate quantity. Now since
> no thing is without a specific action, no thing will be without its
> own definite quantity. Therefore no natural substance can be
> divided infinitely.[18]

This is a beautiful argument, adds Nifo. It is striking that Nifo introduces the subject of the minima wherever there is the slightest opportunity for it. A typical example may be found in the eighth book
of the *Physics*. Aristotle speaks there about the excavation of a stone
through the steady drip of water:

> There cannot be a continuous process either of increase or of
> decrease . . . The theory [that all things are always in motion]
> resembles that about the stone being worn away by the drop of
> water . . .: if so much has been extruded or removed by the drop,
> it does not follow that half the amount has previously been ex-
> truded or removed in half the time . . . The amount removed is,
> it is true, divisible into a number of parts, but no one of these was
> set in motion separately: They were all set in motion together. It
> is evident, then, that from the fact that the decrease is divisible
> into an infinite number of parts it does not follow that some part
> must always be passing away: it all passes away at a particular
> moment.[19]

One can feel in this text of Aristotle the difference between mathematical and physical divisibility as well as the admission of natural
minima, which is at the basis of this reasoning; but they remain un-
named. Before reproducing Averroes' commentary on this text Nifo
remarks: *"Aristotle does not give the reason* [why the process of increase and decrease takes place in a discontinuous way], *but Averroes
does,"* and giving full approval to the latter he continues:

> Averroes proceeds from the supposition that every increase or
> decrease consists in the adding or the subtracting of a certain num-
> ber of natural minima. Therefore the process of excavation is dis-
> continuous.[20]

[18]Augustinus Niphus, *Expositio super octo Aristotelis Stagiritae libros de
Physico auditu*, Venice 1569, p. 519.
[19]*Phys.* VIII, 3: 253 b. 13-23.
[20]Niphus, *Expositio,* p. 576 col. B.

The fact that Nifo in imitation of Averroes enters more frequently than Aristotle or any other Aristotelian into the theory of natural minima is an indication that this theory holds a more important position in their system.   Yet it is no proof that the Averroistic minima theory contains elements which make it more important than the theory of Aristotle, its original founder.   As a matter of fact, however, it is more important, especially from the viewpoint of physical science.

The Difference between Aristotle and the Averroists.   Repeatedly already we have mentioned that Aristotle speaks about the natural minima only in connection with the theoretical division of some substance.   He applies it only in a mental experiment, such as his argumentation against Anaxagoras.   For many of his medieval commentators the minima did not acquire much more reality.   Some of them explicitly limit the minima to living beings so that they signify the smallest biological structural units rather than what we nowadays would call atoms or molecules.   Even for the others who do not accept this limitation, the concept *minimum* does not imply more than the concept *maximum,* i.e. the extremes between which all intervening sizes are possibles, as we saw clearly in the early Averroist John de Jandun.

However, in Averroes himself and in Nifo we get an entirely different picture.   In a substance the natural minima are present as *parts,* they are certain physical entities which actually appear in certain physical and chemical processes.   This conception was not entirely unknown to the Greek Commentators.   We have only to point to Alexander of Aphrodisias, for whom a certain quantity of flesh represented a certain number of minima (*elachista*).   Nevertheless, generally speaking, we may say that before Averroes and the Averroists the conception of minima with a more independent existence was not fully developed.   But the Averroists do not leave us in doubt.   They attributed to the minima not only a more independent existence, but also a certain function in several physical and chemical reactions, as we have seen in the example of the excavation of a stone.   In their opinion the increase or decrease in quantity of a substance amounts to the addition or subtraction of a certain number of minima.   The fundamental importance of this view for physical science will soon become clear.   Because the minima had acquired more physical reality, it became necessary to examine how the properties of minima could be reconciled with the sensible properties of the substance.   This necessity produced a certain mentality which was not so much concerned with possible divisibility as with concretely observable properties; in other words, the very mentality of the physicist in the modern sense of the word. However, let us not anticipate the events of the seventeenth century, for we have reached now only the beginning of the sixteenth.

One of the most interesting views of Averroes is without doubt the application of the concept *minima* to quality. Alongside discontinuous changes in quantity he admits also discontinuous changes in quality. He indicates it only summarily, but the point is broadly developed by Nifo. His development of the point in question contains a surprise for the modern student of physical science.

Nifo distinguishes between the *"minimum on the part of the subject"* (*minimum ex parte subjecti*) and the *"minimum on the part of the form"* (*minimum ex parte formae*). The former is the quantitative minimum or the natural minimum in the sense in which we have used the term thus far, the latter is that part of a quality which is produced at once by the natural agent. Hence just as quantitative increase takes place discontinuously, so also qualitative change occurs discontinuously, in leaps, because increase means the addition of minima. The difference between a powerful agent and a less powerful one consists in this, that the former produces more minima in the same lapse of time.[21] We may ask: how does Nifo conceive the action of an agent? He answers as follows:

> The agent starts by producing in the substance the quantitative minimum which corresponds to a qualitative minimum. Next it produces a similar change in a second quantitative minimum. Meanwhile the first minimum undergoes a second change of quality which corresponds to the qualitative minimum. When it is the turn for the third quantitative minimum to change, the second gets its second change of quality, and the first its third, etc.[22]

Who would not be reminded of Planck's problem of energy in reading about the discontinuous structure of quality which is proposed in these qualitative minima? However, it would not be correct to consider Averroes or Nifo as medieval forerunners of Planck, as will be clear after we have considered Planck's theory. On the other hand, the enunciation of the concept *qualitative minimum* remains something remarkable and deserves to be mentioned, especially when we consider that in the twentieth century Planck's idea was held to be very revolutionary and attacked precisely on philosophic grounds.

---

[21]Niphus, *Expositio,* p. 475a.
[22]Niphus, *Expositio,* p. 476b.

We are of course very much interested in Nifo's treatment of chemical composition and we may expect that he will attribute an essential role to the natural minima. Our expectation will not be disappointed. Let us have a look at his commentary on Aristotle's work *On Generation and Corruption,* in which the latter explains his theory of chemical reaction. In the first chapter of this book we analyzed his theory, mainly in order to give a clear picture of the essential difference between Aristotle and Democritus. Let us review that analysis briefly.

For Democritus the generation of a new substance means nothing but the association of essentially immutable atoms into a certain configuration. This conception implies that ultimately every change is a change of location, i.e. a purely extrinsic change.

Aristotle, however, requires above all an intrinsic change of the components. According to him the association of immutable atoms would lead only to a mixture and not to a chemical compound. The difference between mixture and compound is that in the former the forms of the various components continue to exist alongside each other, while in the latter a new form comes into existence. A new unit arises in which the forms of the components continue to exist, but only potentially.

Two questions arise from this. Firstly, what exactly is meant by *"continue to exist potentially"*? The answers of the commentators vary considerably, as we will see. Secondly, granted that chemical composition is more than the association of smallest particles, does this imply that the latter do not exercise any function in effecting the composition? Has their association and separation no importance at all in producing the composition? Let us begin with the second question. Some texts of Aristotle can be quoted which show that in his opinion the division of the components into small parts promotes the chemical composition. For instance,

> 'Dissociation' and 'association' affect the thing's susceptibility to passing-away. For if water has first been 'dissociated' into smallish drops, air comes-to-be out of it more quickly: while, if drops of water have first been associated, air comes-to-be more slowly.[23]

Upon reading this and other similar texts of Aristotle we spontaneously ask ourselves: what does he mean? Are they casual remarks which convey the general experience that finely divided substances

---

[23]*On Gen. and Corr.* I, 2; 317 a 27-30.

react more easily, or did Aristotle think about a special kind of small particles, and more specifically, about the smallest possible particles of every substance, the natural minima which he himself mentions in his *Physics* I, ch. 4? For two reasons the first supposition is more probable. In the first place, the Greek text never has ἐλάχιστα, the smallest, but always ἐλάττω or μικρά, i.e. smaller or small. Secondly, and this is more important, the whole sphere of Aristotle's concept of minima is such that we cannot expect him to give any concrete application of the minima theory to chemical problems. In the course of centuries, however, this sphere underwent a change. Aristotle's conception was perfected, and gradually the concept *minima* acquired a more direct physical meaning. Hence Nifo did not hesitate at all to connect the minima with his consideration of chemical composition. The manner in which he did this is very remarkable. In his commentary on Aristotle he gives two translations of his text. One is literal, and the other according to Nifo is more in keeping with Aristotle's intentions. In the literal translation he uses the accurate Latin equivalent of *smaller* and *small,* but in the free translation he methodically replaces these words by *smallest*[24] and adds *"According to Aristotle and Averroes it must be said that when elements react upon each other they are divided into minima."*[25] Shortly after, he asks: What divides the elements into minima? His answer shows that generally a certain influence is attributed to local motion.[26]

All this shows what a development the theory of natural minima had undergone in certain circles during the course of time. The importance which it holds in Nifo's system is not based upon personal preference, but corresponds to a widespread conception, as can be confirmed from a passage in the commentary of Toletus (1532-1596), one of the best-known sixteenth century commentators of Aristotle:

> Concerning the manner of chemical composition, the opinions of authors vary, but they all agree in this: the reagent substances are divided into natural minima. In this division the separated minima of one substance come alongside the minima of the other and act upon each other till a third substance, having the substantial form of the compound, is generated.[27]

---

[24]Niphus, *In libros de generatione et corruptione commentaria*, p. 17b.

[25]Niphus, *In libros de gen. et corr. commentaria*, p. 68c.

[26]*Ibid.*

[27]Toletus, *In libros de generatione et corruptione commentaria;* lib. I, cap. 10, q 19.

The remark must be added that it was principally in the Averroistic circles that in the emphasis on the minima theory the shift occurred from mere limits of a theoretical division to components with physical import. Toletus recognizes this explicitly, as also other well-known commentators of the sixteenth century; for instance Pererius,[28] and Soto.[29]

The second question which we asked when speaking of Aristotle's treatise on chemical composition was concerned with the manner in which the components continue to exist in the compound. The answer to this question constitutes one of the most violently disputed problems of the Middle Ages. We will have to examine it somewhat more extensively.

The Problem of the Permanence of Elements. Upon seeing how Nifo and others speak about natural minima and conceive them as actual parts, as real physical components, we may ask ourselves whether this is still an Aristotelian theory or rather an atomistic conception inspired by Democritus, or even by Empedocles. Does not chemical composition for these Averroists amount to the-becoming-adjacent of immutable minima? Does it not really amount to a kind of atomism, based upon Empedocles rather than on Democritus, if the minima of different substances are held to be qualitatively different? For the former and not the latter admitted qualitatively different minima. The question really amounts to asking whether or not the development of Aristotle's minima theory from Alexander of Aphrodisias, Simplicius, and Averroes to the Averroists of the fifteenth and sixteenth century is not fundamentally a return to pre-Aristotelian atomic conceptions. Before we answer the question it will not be out of place to indicate briefly the various manners in which the Aristotelians have interpreted Aristotle's conception of the so-called potential permanence of the element in compounds. The reader will remember Aristotle's conception: in order to form a real compound and not a mixture the forms of the components may not be actually present in the compound; hence these forms disappear. After the reaction there is one form, the form of the compound, in which, however, the forms of the elements remain potentially. In later times the term *virtual* came also into use to express this type of potentiality. It means that the matter of the compound

---

[28]*De communibus omnium rerum naturalium principiis et affectibus*, lib. X, cap. 23.

[29]*In octo libros Physicorum Quaestiones; Phys.* I, q 4.

remains through its form in direct potency to the forms of the elements. In many different ways efforts were made to get a clearer picture of what exactly takes place in a chemical composition. The term a *clearer picture* is not meant as a figure of speech, but literally. Several medieval philosophers tried to render the abstract concept more concrete and to visualize it physically. They asked themselves: What exactly remains of these forms? In what does their potentiality show? The Arabs had given them the example in this. Avicenna had proposed the opinion that the forms of the elements remain undiminished and integral, but that their properties change through the interaction of the elements. Averroes, on the contrary, thought that the forms did not remain integrally, but in a diminished degree, in a debilitated 'to be.' In the West some, as Thomas Aquinas, limited themselves to the general explanation that the forms remain not as forms but virtually, while others, as Albert the Great, followed the opinion of Avicenna. We will not elaborate on the many distinctions which were introduced in this matter, but restrict ourselves to the manner in which the later Averroists tried to solve the problem. Essentially all the different answers are variations of the same fundamental thought: The form of the compound is new, indeed, but it is the resultant of the forms of the components.

Achillinus (died 1518) explains this as follows. The components are divided into minima which react upon each other. This produces a new form, which is shared by all particles in such a manner that the new form is found in every particle together with the forms of the components. The latter must be considered as parts of the form of the compound. Hence they should really no longer be called forms of the elements, because they have been received into the new whole.[30]

Nifo, however, has a slightly different explanation. The minima act upon each other in such a way that all receive something of the forms of the other particles while retaining their own form. From this "equalization" of all material particles results the *forma mixti,* the form of the compound.[31] Zarabella (1532-1589) gave another formulation to this opinion, which seems to have made the biggest impression upon posterity. He states explicitly: 1) There is but one specific form in the compound, namely the form of the compound. 2) This form is composed of the changed forms of the elements, which he calls

---

[30]Achillinus, *Liber de elementis,* art. 3, quoted in *Philosophiae naturalis Joan. Duns Scoti, auctore Faventino,* Venice 1616, theorema LX.

[31]Niphus, *In lib. de gen. et corr. commentaria,* Venice 1577, p. 68.

subordinated forms.[32] Zarabella's view, however, was nothing new. It agrees entirely with that of Aureolus (died 1321), who compared the specific form of the compound to the harmony of tones.

Some points in these opinions demand our special attention. In the first place, we notice that all these opinions try to express more concretely the relation between the forms of the elements and that of the compound. They are efforts to express, without abandoning the Aristotelian unity of form in the compound, something which we may call a structural concept, the construction of a compound from its components. Although obviously this will put the minima in the foreground, nevertheless there is no question of an atomistic conception, especially not in the sense of Democritus, because the smallest particles are qualitatively determined. They are particles of elements or compounds and exhibit their specific characteristics. Neither is there question of atomism in the sense of Empedocles, because Empedocles' particles were intrinsically immutable, while the minima of the authors named above are *subject to change*. They do not enter unchanged into composition. Moreover, the unity of the compound is explicitly maintained through the unity of the form in the compound. Hence we must give a negative answer to the question whether Nifo's variation of the minima theory shows a tendency which can easily lead to a compromise with atomistic conceptions. As a matter of fact this is exactly what happened in the seventeenth century when in both theories the philosophic aspect was pushed into the background, while the more physical aspect which was common to both systems came to the foreground. Meanwhile we must emphasize that already at this time the minima theory of the Averroists showed a definite physical aspect. This is clear also from their opinion about the permanence of the components in the compound. While certain Aristotelian circles, as those of the Thomists and Scotists, limited themselves to the consideration of the minima and of chemical composition within the framework of general philosophic categories, such as actual, potential, form, etc., the Averroists unmistakably proceed in the direction of physical considerations. They want to form a concrete view of the relation between the constituents and the compound formed by them. They also visualize the minima, which play an important role in this relation, more and more concretely, and ask themselves how certain properties of a substance are connected with the minima that compose it.

---

[32]Zarabella, *Liber de mixtione,* cap. 7, quoted in the work referred to in footnote 30.

For the time being the result was not very spectacular, but on the other hand it was neither so little that it can be passed over unobserved. This is clear especially in a man such as Scaliger.

3. SCALIGER

Julius Caesar Scaliger (1484-1558) was a universal scholar whose fame had spread all over Europe. A physician by profession he published, apart from some poems, several works on philology and a study in natural philosophy entitled *Exercitationes,*[1] which has exercised a great influence upon later ages, and for which he deserves to be studied in this book.

In his interpretation of Aristotle Scaliger follows Averroes, as is clear especially from his theory of natural minima. It exhibits all the characteristics of the trend in which Averroes and the Latin Averroists developed the minima theory. Even if Scaliger did not have any importance in the history of physical science, it would still be worth while to speak of him at length. No other author speaks more extensively about the minima theory, or—and this is more important—applies it so frequently to physical and chemical problems. Although Scaliger's applications remain wholly within the framework of Aristotle's erroneous chemical conceptions, such as the theory of the four elements, nevertheless we find in him numerous ideas which half a century or a century later became commonplace among the supporters of new and better conceptions in physical science.

Typical of his time is the fact that Scaliger's works are no longer a regular commentary on Aristotle, but a kind of encyclopedia. All kinds of physical, philosophical, chemical, geographical, technical, and medical problems are treated promiscuously. Moreover, the whole work is one long polemic answer to the treatise *De Subtilitate Libri XXI* which a few years before had been published by Cardano, a philosopher of the Renaissance (Basel 1554).

Scaliger's Theory of Natural Minima. His minima theory is scattered all through his work. Only one short chapter is entitled *The Natural Minimum,*[2] but in other places Scaliger makes statements

---

[1]The full title is *Julii Caesaris Scaligeri Exotericarum Exercitationum Libri XV de subtilitate ad Hieronymum Cardanum.* The first edition was published in 1557. We quote under the abbreviation *Ex.* the edition of 1607 published at Frankfurt.

[2]*Ex.* XVI, ch. 4.

which are just as important for the understanding of his view of the problem. His entire work is full of applications of the minima theory. The fact that it is easy to unite these fragments into an harmonious whole shows that Scaliger had some definite concept of it in his mind. We will limit our exposition of his conception to those points in which it surpasses, or at least deviates from, that of the Averroists, notably of Nifo, whose ideas we have already reviewed.

Concerning the gradual excavation of a stone by drops of water Scaliger remarks:

> That small piece of stone [which is removed every time at once] will be the smallest particle of stone and the "first particle of the compound."[3]

This quotation is important insofar as it shows that Scaliger considers the natural minima not only as the limits of division but also as the first building blocks of a whole. Although in this text he does not go farther than Nifo, in whose work we noticed the same shift in meaning of the term *minima,* his formula is far more explicit. But this is not all. With the aid of the conception that the natural minima are the first building blocks he tries to explain several physical and chemical properties of matter, for instance, density. The cause of density is homogeneity. If there is no air between the natural minima of a substance, they are very compact so that the substance has a high density. If there is air between them, the substance has a low density. High and low density, says Scaliger, should not be confused with the fineness and coarseness of a substance, as was done by Cardano. For fineness and coarseness are properties of the minima themselves:

> A substance whose minima are very small is fine. Just as small minima can be very compact, so also bigger minima of coarser substances can be very close together. Therefore neither fineness nor coarseness is the cause of density, but homogeneity.[4]

A few points in this text are very important. In the first place, the minima of different substances differ in size. Elsewhere Scaliger even ventures to make some suppositions about the proportional size of different minima, as we will see presently. First, however, we must draw attention to another point. Some properties of matter, such as fineness and coarseness, depend on the minima themselves, while

---

[3]*Ex.* p. 83.
[4]*Ex.* p. 852.

others depend on the manner in which they are joined. He gives an interesting example:

> Hail is as coarse as rain, but of greater density. Snow is as coarse as rain, but of a lesser density. Yet the matter of all three is the same.[5]

We see here how, thanks to the speculation on the minima, a good concept of the states of aggregation begins to break through: rain, snow and hail are all of the same *coarseness* because they are composed of the same minima, but their density is different because the minima of these three substances are at a smaller or a greater distance from one another. In still other places Scaliger shows that a true insight into the states of aggregation, which was of such fundamental importance for the development of physical science, begins to break through. The conception did not reach full maturity in him, but nevertheless it was the beginning of a better insight into the true nature of the states of aggregation.

Let us return now to the question of the proportional sizes of different minima. Scaliger's definite opinions on the matter were not arbitrarily chosen, but based upon various physical data. Obviously everything remains within the frame of the four elements so that his speculations are primarily concerned with the proportional size of these supposed elements. In his opinion the minima of earth are biggest, the others follow in this order—water, air, fire. He explains the smallness of the fire minima by the properties of fire. Heat makes a substance less dense. Now this can be explained only if the minima of fire are very fine, so that it becomes possible for them to penetrate between the minima of a substance and thus to cause its expansion.[6] The minima of air cannot be very different from those of fire, for air very easily becomes fire.[7] Concerning earth he states:

> Why does an earthy or earthlike particle receive the form of fire but slowly? Would it not be because an earthly natural minimum is about a hundred times as big as a minimum of fire?[8]

Obviously from a modern point of view one would be justified to a certain extent in considering these speculations about the proportional size of minima as of little importance. Factually they are not very exact. However, they can also be viewed from a different angle, namely insofar as we can discern in them an outspoken tendency to account

[5]*Ex.* p. 852.
[6]*Ex.* p. 96.
[7]*Ex.* p. 70.
[8]*Ex.* p. 80.

for the physical character of the minima and for the relation of this character to the sensible properties of matter. Sooner or later this tendency was bound to lead to the realization of the deficiences in the conception of matter, and this is a very important result. Or, to express it in a different way, Scaliger transferred the speculation about the smallest particles to the sphere of what nowadays is called experimental verification.

Scaliger knew not only minima of elements, but also of compounds, although he does not mention the latter as systematically as the former. We will not press this point, but rather turn our attention to his speculation about the nature of chemical composition. He offers some fairly profound considerations on this matter.

Aristotle's definition of chemical composition as *"the union of the reagents" (mistio est miscibilium unio)* does not satisfy him. He proposes another one: *"Chemical composition is the motion of the minima towards mutual contact so that union is effected."*[9] Here we see in Scaliger the same idea we noticed already in Nifo and Toletus: the minima play a role in effecting the composition. This view, therefore, is not unusual.[10] For Scaliger the main point in this definition is that a real unity is effected:

> Our particles are not only lying close together as the atoms of Epicurus, but they do this in such a manner that a continuous body which forms a unit results. It becomes 'one' through the continuity of its limits and is common to all that has entered into the composition.[11]

For a true composition he further requires a single new form. All this characterizes the Aristotelian. Typical of Scaliger also is that he realizes the difficulty of determining whether there is really a new form or not, in other words, whether a true compound has been produced. Even in this hesitation he shows a somewhat more pronounced physical orientation. For his hesitation arises from the fact that he does not restrict himself to a general division of substances into mixtures and compounds, but searches for practical criteria to determine whether or not something is a mixture or a compound. In this search he is faced with difficulties. Here again the primarily

---

[9]*Ex.* p. 345: *"Mistio est motus corporum minimorum ad mutuum contactum ut fiat unio.*

[10]Cf. also R. Hooykaas, *Het Begrip Element*, Utrecht 1933, p. 138, who mentions that the same definition is given by Mennens and Pantheus, two chemists of the sixteenth century.

[11]*Ex.* p. 346.

important thing is not the proffered solution or the lack of any solution, but the fact that theory and practice are confronted.

Scaliger's Importance for Physical Science. Scaliger's ideas about density and the decrease of density through heating undoubtedly have influenced the development of physical science. They revealed a new insight into the nature of states of aggregation. In Scaliger himself this insight was certainly not yet firm but still faltering, yet he contributed very much to make minds ripe for a better insight. Witness, for instance, that fifty years later the Dutch atomist Van Goorle categorically denied that the evaporation of water is a transformation of the element water into the element air. Van Goorle, who knew Scaliger's *Exercitationes,* uses approximately the same expressions as Scaliger, but is more radical on certain points. Even if we make abstraction from the problem of the states of aggregation, we may still say of Scaliger's minima theory that in general it offered opportunities for the explanation of phenomena which were but little inferior to those which the atomic theory offered its supporters fifty years later. Numerous explanations and suppositions of the first atomists in the seventeenth century, which are considered very important by the historians of physical science, can already be found more or less clearly expressed by Scaliger, as we will see in the following chapter.

4. ATOMISM

Our sketch of the minima theory in the Middle Ages and the Renaissance had to be long, but we can be brief about atomism because the atomistic form of the corpuscular theory led only a lingering existence during that period. True, it was not unknown, for one of the principal sources from which we know the conceptions of Empedocles, Anaxagoras, and Democritus are the writings of Aristotle, which were assiduously studied during the Middle Ages and the Renaissance. However, the atomistic theory did not find any important supporters, and there was certainly no question of any steady traditional atomism. Historians mention only a few adherents of atomism in the eleventh and twelfth centuries, namely William of Conches and Constantine the African in the eleventh century, and Hugo of St. Victor and Adelard of Bath in the twelfth century. However, the proofs by which historians intend to show that these men held atomistic views have not been able to convince us fully that they really were atomists. The few texts which are usually quoted show only that *smallest particles* play a role in the speculations of these thinkers.[1] Too little is really known about them to determine the tradition to which they belong. True, it is certain that they were partially inspired by the Arabs, but this implies only that we may not neglect the possibility that their smallest particles must be interpreted as minima. For the time being we can only confess our ignorance in the matter.

At any rate the supporters of true atomism in the Middle Ages were very few. Best known of all is Nicolas of Autrecourt (fourteenth century). In our opinion, there are two reasons why atomism did not obtain more influence. In the first place, Democritus' system suffered from an hereditary infection of anti-Christian materialism. As a result it was studied, but not defended in the university curriculum. Secondly, and this is more important, as far as there was need for physical explanation in the Middle Ages, the Aristotelian minima theory offered at least as many possibilities as atomism. From a physical view point there was practically no reason for medieval thinkers to prefer atomism to the minima theory. Hence the causes of the revival of atomism in the seventeenth century must not be sought in the desire to utilize corpuscular theories, as we will see in the next chapter.

At the end of the sixteenth century we encounter some scholars who, although they cannot be considered as representatives of a pure atomistic system, contributed nevertheless to its revival; for instance, the philosopher of the Renaissance, Giordano Bruno (1548-1600), who in connection with his own new philosophic system developed also his own minima theory. However new his theory may have been, we can find many points in it which are borrowed from the Aristotelian minima theory, and others which remind us strongly of Democritus. In our opinion Giordano Bruno's importance lies in that he aided in breaking through the framework of Aristotelian thought. His own speculations are relatively unimportant and have not left any traces in history. Another thinker who prepared the way for the revival was Eilard Lubin (1565-1631), a philologer, whose works are mainly a refutation of peripatetic arguments against philosophic atomism. A few others could be named, but they really belong to the seventeenth century. We will reserve them for the next chapter.

---

[1] It should not be forgotten that most historians neglect the minima theory. Hence when they encounter corpuscular conceptions somewhere, the latter are immediately classified as atomistic. As the reader understands now, such a classification should not be made, without close scrutiny.

5. THE DEVELOPMENT OF PRACTICAL CHEMISTRY

While in the sixteenth century the theory of smallest particles was still clearly dominated to a large extent by Aristotelians, nevertheless several factors were already at work in that century and even in the preceding ones which cannot be neglected if we are to get an accurate idea of the events of the seventeenth century. We mean the development of practical chemistry. Although this development consisted mainly in an increase of experimental data, yet various theoretical aspects can be seen coming to the fore. In itself this is nothing strange, for experimental data had always been dressed up in theoretical garments anyhow. However—to continue our metaphor—up to that time the cloth for these garments had practically always been supplied by philosophic speculations which were mainly Aristotelian in origin, although mixed with some neo-Platonistic elements. According to modern conceptions these philosophic theories were more or less detached from the data of experience. They had more the character of philosophic perspectives in the light of which the data of experience were seen, rather than that of truly general theories which arose from the data of experience and from which these data could have been derived as particular instances. However, alongside these philosophic theories gradually there grew up something like a theory which, without losing its general philosophic garments and foundation, began to show a more specifically chemical character. Such a theory is, for instance, the so-called doctrine of two principles or the sulphur-quicksilver theory. It taught that there are two particularly solid compounds of the four elements and named them sulphur and quicksilver. Obviously these compounds are not the same as our elements sulphur and mercury. They are a kind of relative elements, called principles. The term *relative* should be understood as implying that according to this theory chemical reactions are concerned only with these relative elements, because in a chemical reaction the principles are not dissolved into the four absolute elements. Quicksilver represents the metallic character, sulphur the combustibility of a substance. The more quicksilver a substance contains, the nobler it is and the more metallic; for instance, it will be more easily plated and smelted. If the sulphur contents rises, the combustibility increases, and the substance is less noble.

Thus we see that the theory is concerned with a relationship between data that are subject to experience. It was useful to a certain extent in practice because it really harmonized with two independent series of data, one series based upon the supposed properties of the principle "sulphur" and the other upon those of the principle "quick-silver." When an alchemist drew from one series of data some con-clusion about the predominance of sulphur, he could use this also as a basis for some assertion about the properties for which quicksilver was responsible. So, for instance, gold which is incombustible does not contain any sulphur, which corrupts the properties of metal. There-fore gold contains much quicksilver. The properties of gold confirm this: for instance, it can easily be plated. Another confirmation is that gold easily forms amalgam, i.e. reacts with *"argentum vivum,"* which contains a large amount of quicksilver. The principle that only related substances can act upon each other was accepted as a dogma by all.[1] While the theory of two principles still remained within the framework of Aristotle's doctrine of elements, the same no longer holds for the theory of three principles proposed by Paracelsus (1493-1541). Al-though neither theory is purely chemical, nevertheless the latter is con-nected directly with the fairly general chemical datum of experience that by distillation of most substances three components are obtained, one solid (salt), one liquid (quicksilver) and one volatile (sulphur). The theory of the three principles was not made subservient to that of the four elements, but proposed as a rival theory. Moreover, its philosophic perspective is rather neo-Platonic than Aristotelian. How-ever, it would lead us too far afield to examine this more closely. We refer the reader who is interested in the history of chemistry to the works mentioned in the bibliography at the end of this book.

The importance of these chemical theories lies in that they can continue to exist independently from their philosophic background be-cause they are connected directly with the experiments of the alchem-ists. They contain the possibility of developing into an independent science whose philosophic perspective recedes more and more. The above mentioned theories themselves are not yet suitable for this be-cause they do not yet sufficiently harmonize with the whole of the data that require explanation. But they are an *effort* towards an inde-pendent chemical theory, and as such they are important. As to the question whether a scientific theory can be *entirely* independent from a philosophic perspective or not, this is a point which we shall not at-tempt to answer before the last chapter of this book. Meanwhile this much is certain: the bonds which connected Greek and medieval science to philosophy were too tight.

---

[1]For the theory of two principles, see R. Hooykaas, *Het Begrip Element,* Utrecht 1933, p. 43ff. Our explanation is based upon his paraphrase and analysis of the medieval alchemist Geber.

CHAPTER THREE

THE SEVENTEENTH CENTURY

1. THE SPECIAL IMPORTANCE OF THIS CENTURY

Among the many centuries which are covered by the history of the concept *atom,* the seventeenth century occupies a very special place for two reasons. In the first place, it is the century which saw the revival of philosophic atomism in the sense of Democritus and the rise of an original corpuscular theory which, however, in many aspects is related to that of Democritus, namely the corpuscular theory of Descartes. The picture presented by the preceding centuries, in which Aristotelian philosophy dominated, undergoes a radical change. Nevertheless this is not the main reason why the seventeenth century occupies a special place. It owes its outstanding importance to the fact that a *scientific* atomic theory came into existence. Although physical science did not yet reach full emancipation in this century, certain signs presaged its imminence. The road towards full emancipation was clearly laid out.

In the following pages we will endeavor to trace this road through the most prominent representatives of the corpuscular idea in this century, Daniel Sennert, Sebastian Basso, David van Goorle, Peter Gassendi, René Descartes, and Robert Boyle.

2. SENNERT

Daniel Sennert (1572-1657), was born in Breslau. After studying philosophy and medicine he became a professor of the Faculty of Medicine in Wittenberg. In this capacity he attached great importance to chemistry in the practice of medicine. These details are not mentioned without reason, for Sennert is primarily a chemist and a physician and only secondarily a philosopher. In philosophy his orientation is Aristotelian, but he shows a pronounced eclectic tendency. He does not hesitate to use data of very diverse origins in the formation of his own chemical and physical theories, notably in his corpuscular considerations. Basically his theories are derived from the doctrine of natural minima, especially as developed by Scaliger, but they also contain, notably in his later works, typically atomistic ideas. The most striking idea of Sennert is his effort to reconcile the minima

81

theory with Democritus' atomism. The two theories really amount to the same, he finds, and from a chemical point of view something can be said for his opinion, as we will see later.

Summary of Physical Science. Sennert's principal work, which is also the first work in which he reveals his ideas about the minima, is his *Summary of Physical Science (Epitome Scientiae Naturalis).* In it he unfolds his general philosophic conceptions. The work appeared in 1618 and was still of an outspoken philosophic and Aristotelian nature. We can find in it, for instance, a deduction of the minima theory which could without any change be inserted in the commentary on Aristotle of some medieval commentator.

In this work the minima are limits of division rather than anything else. It contains hardly any trace of Scaliger's conception of the minima. This is all the more remarkable, because in another work which he published exactly one year later Sennert showed that he was very well acquainted with the conception of Scaliger and kindred philosophers. In the *Summary* of 1618 he only mentioned his name, and then not even in connection with the minima theory.

Meanwhile it should not surprise us than an Aristotelian of the seventeenth century preaches a minima theory which adheres to the literal interpretation of Aristotle. It was a traditional procedure to repeat only and to put into logical order what had been taught by Aristotle and his commentators. Later in this chapter we will allow another seventeenth century representative of this tradition to explain his views.

In connection with the development which can be observed in the later works of Sennert we may mention that in the *Summary* he follows Zarabella with respect to the problem of the permanence of elements in compounds. The form of the compound is "one," but it is constructed from the forms of the elements.

Points of Agreement and Disagreement Between the Chemists and the Followers of Aristotle and Galen. As mentioned, Sennert's second work was published in 1619. Its title is *De chymicorum cum Aristotelicis et Galenicis consensu et dissensu, (Points of Agreement and Disagreement Between the Chemists and the Followers of Aristotle and Galen).* The exposition of his theory of smallest particles in this work is far more detailed than in the previous treatise. The smallest particles are no longer mere limits in a theoretical division, but are also introduced in the discussion of chemical problems; for instance, in the explanation of chemical composition (*mistio*). Sennert accepts

Scaliger's definition: *"Chemical composition is the motion of the minima towards mutual contact so that union is effected."* Moreover, there cannot be any question of a compound in the proper sense, unless this union implies not only continuity but also unity of form.

> Concerning the question however, how this union of minima takes place, *whether the forms of the reagents remain intact in the union* or are commingled, broken, or totally destroyed,[1] it is so difficult to see the answer in the total darkness of this problem that even great scholars as Scaliger cannot easily decide which opinion should be preferred.[1a]

Sennert himself considers it as most probable that in the composition the reagents are divided into their smallest parts, which subsequently unite through their minima and then act upon each other through opposite properties. In this process they do not entirely lose their forms. Otherwise there would be no union of changed reagents, but of annihilated reagents. Nevertheless the forms fuse into a unity, or rather they are made "one" by a form of a higher order. Here again he appeals to Scaliger. He leaves it to others to decide whether the forms of the elements remain intact or are diminished, but at least it is certain for him that they are not annihilated because the compound can always be decomposed into its elements.[2]

> The opinion about chemical composition which we have related above is without doubt the opinion of very ancient philosophers and also of Democritus himself. For the latter stated that all things are composed of atoms and that generation is nothing but commingling and separation. It is not very likely that this outstanding knower of nature and the world, as Hippocrates calls him, who according to Pliny consulted on his travels the wise men of Persia, Arabia, Ethiopia, and Egypt, would have made such stupid assertions about atoms as are usually attributed to him.[3]

This is rather surprising, for what Sennert proposed as his own opinion deviates considerably from Democritus. Yet he does not believe everything that is told about the latter. In his opinion Democritus only wanted to explain that generation, the coming to be of a new substance, results from the commingling of corpuscles which do not necessarily have to be elementary. Hence new compounds can

---

[1]The traditional dispute between the followers of Averroes and of Avicenna.
[1a]D. Sennert, *Opera Omnia* I, Paris 1641, p. 999. We will refer to these works as *Opera.*
[2]*Ibid.*
[3]*Opera* I, p. 999.

be formed from the corpuscles of compounds. And that is exactly what Scaliger meant by his definition, says Sennert.

For a good understanding of this, it is necessary to anticipate an important point in Sennert's theory of corpuscles which we will consider later. For chemical reasons Sennert is convinced that non-elementary substances also can form compounds so that the minima of these compound substances are the reagents. In explanations which are based upon Aristotle's traditional definition of chemical composition, which does not mention the minima, there is question only of compounds formed by the four elements. Therefore the concept *chemical composition* was tied to that of the four elements. These explanations failed to give Sennert any possibility to speak about the *"compositions of a higher order"* which he knew so well from chemistry. But he thinks that this possibility is safeguarded if the ancient idea of *commingling* and *separation* of corpuscles is drawn into the definition of chemical composition, as was done by Scaliger. And according to Sennert, that is the only thing which Democritus wanted to emphasize. From the fact that Sennert takes this one point of Democritus' theory out of its connection with the whole, it is clear that his main preoccupation is to find a satisfactory chemical theory which is applicable to practical data. He does not worry very much about its philosophic background. He realizes that his corpuscles are not exactly what is generally understood by Democritus' atoms, but he does not admit that Democritus himself taught all the things which are attributed to him. It does not follow, says Sennert, that because Democritus did not deny the mathematical properties of atoms he did not attribute any physical properties to them. We know how much Sennert is mistaken, for the exclusively mathematical character of atoms is an essential point in Democritus' atomism. Neither is Sennert convinced that Democritus really taught that natural things originate from the casual meeting of atoms:

> Nevertheless natural things do not come into existence through a casual cooperation of atoms—even if perhaps Democritus thinks so—but through a dominating superior form.[4]

Meanwhile he only half believes that Democritus really did think so.

From the foregoing, Sennert's own position should be clear. He started from the Aristotelian tradition, but is not satisfied with the traditional interpretation of the minima theory, and feels far more

---

[4] *Opera* I, p. 1000.

attracted by the Averroistic interpretation because in the latter the minima play an essential role in the theory of chemical reaction. He sees in Democritus the great champion of the idea of smallest particles and interprets him entirely in the spirit of the Averroistic minima theory. After all this is natural, for what Sennert, as a chemist, needed for the explanation of chemical phenomena were *"corpuscula sui generis"*, corpuscles with their own chemical nature, and not Democritus' atoms without any qualities. In order to get a better idea of Sennert's corpuscular conception we must now consult the third chapter of his book *Notes on Physics (Hypomnemata Physica)*.

The Corpuscular Theory in His Notes on Physics. The *Notes on Physics* date from 1636. Hence they are posterior to the public defense of philosophic atomism in Paris which led to a bitter struggle between its defenders and its opponents. Sennert appears well acquainted with this struggle and tries to insinuate that the whole struggle is really senseless because the viewpoints are not so very divergent.

He begins his book with the warning not to cling too literally to Aristotle, nor to dispute about the pro and con of opinions. Many of them are attributed inaccurately to Aristotle anyhow. He quotes and approves Zarabella's warning that we must search nature and not limit ourselves to commenting upon Aristotle and adapting nature to his oracles.

Sennert's explanation of atoms and chemical composition begins with a eulogy of Democritus. Although Democritus' doctrine of atoms and indivisible corpuscles is generally considered repulsive, yet it is not absurd provided it be correctly explained.

> Now it appears that the atomic theory must be explained as follows. Since natural things are subject to a perpetual change of generation and corruption, it is necessary that there are certain simple corpuscles of a very special nature out of which compound bodies are generated and into which the latter in turn decompose.[5]

> [These smallest particles] are called minima of nature, atoms, and indivisible corpuscles of bodies. They owe their names to the fact that they cannot be further divided through natural processes, and reversely form the building blocks of all natural bodies. They are, however, so small that they escape detection by sense experience.[6]

----

[5] *Opera* I, p. 150.
[6] *Opera* I, p. 151.

> Very many learned philosophers know the atoms, not to men-
> tion Empedocles, Democritus, and Epicurus, whose doctrine is
> suspected because, perhaps, it is not properly understood.[6a]

Sennert is surprised that the atomic theory is considered a novelty.

> Everywhere among philosophers and physicians, in ancient times
> as well as in later ages, there is question either of smallest cor-
> puscles or of atoms.[6b]

He abstains from mentioning them all *"because perhaps they would
be suspected because of their scorn for the old* [i.e. Aristotelian]
philosophy or their zeal for novelties." Therefore he restricts himself
to one witness above suspicion, Francis of Aquilo, a supporter of the
theory of natural minima. It is clear that Sennert is concerned
primarily with the idea of corpuscles which play a role in chemical
processes. Hence he turns against Aristotle, in whom he does not
find this idea, and joins all those who attribute an important role to
the minima. Among them there are supporters of atomism as well
as of the minima theory, i.e. that minima theory in which the minima
are more than mere limits of a theoretical division. Meanwhile his
own theory of smallest particles deviates very much from that of
Democritus.

> Atoms are not all of one kind, but there are several kinds in
> accordance with the diversity of natural bodies. Therefore we
> ought to consider separately the atoms of simple bodies, which
> are called elements, and those of compound bodies.[7]

Sennert then examines in turn the atoms of fire, water, air, and
earth. His speculations on the respective natures of these atoms
closely follow those of Scaliger, whom he quotes several times. As
a matter of fact, *Sennert's atoms are nothing but Scaliger's minima.*

Another passage deserves special attention. In it he speaks about
the second kind of atoms, namely the atoms of compounds. In
modern terminology they would be called the molecules of the
compound.

> Apart from the atoms of elements there is still another kind
> of atoms which eventually can be called *"prima mista"* [first
> compound principles]. They are the atoms into which other
> compound bodies can be dissolved as into homogeneous things.[8]

[6a] *Ibid.*
[6b] *Ibid.*
[7] *Opera I*, p. 151.
[8] *Opera I*, p. 154.

In this text Sennert states something of extraordinary importance, namely that a compound can be divided into atoms of the compound, just as an element can be divided into atoms of the element. These atoms have the same form of being as the whole. This is the same problem as the one touched in his previous work—namely it is not necessary that in every reaction a substance shall disintegrate into elements.

Sennert sees the best proof for his assertions in the working methods of chemistry which *"prove the existence of atoms."* We will cite only one example. When vapor rises from water this does not mean that water changes into air, but that water is divided into its smallest atoms. The latter again become water when they are re-united.[9] Thus Sennert draws all the consequences from Scaliger's theory.

The last paragraph of the chapter on atoms gives Sennert an opportunity to say something about the nature of his smallest particles. The size of the atoms depends on the substantial form of the substance. Thus Sennert's atoms express the same idea as Scaliger's minima.

The next chapter is concerned with chemical composition. It too, contains some important statements. In this later work Sennert still agrees with Scaliger's definition of chemical composition, but now he experiences some difficulties.

These explanations [of Scaliger] do not clear up all difficulties because they do not sufficiently explain the nature of chemical composition. There remain two problems, whose solution will throw much light on physics and chemistry. For although we admit that a true chemical compound is only that which really is formally "one," nevertheless we ask two questions. The first is whether it is necessary for the reagents which through the action of one form are united and joined into one compound to lose their own forms, or whether they can retain their own forms under a single form in the compound. Secondly, I wonder whether only elements can form a compound, i.e. whether every division into minima which occurs in a reaction always continues till the elements themselves are reached, or whether it can also be said that other substances of a higher order than elements enter into composition.[10]

The first question concerns the old problem whether the forms of the elements remain in the compound. While Sennert initially had ac-

[9]*Opera I*, p. 154.
[10]*Opera I*, p. 156.

cepted the viewpoint of Zarabella in this matter, now he is no longer
satisfied with it, but sides with Albert the Great and Avicenna and
thinks that the forms of the elements remain integral in the compound.

> Although a new unity arises from a plurality of components,
> it is not necessary that the simple components perish. This
> however, does not mean that only an aggregate is formed, for
> the simple components are united through the higher form of the
> compound. This doctrine of the Ancients that elements and
> simple substances integrally retain their own nature in com-
> pounds is the key to the whole of physical science.[11]

To a certain extent this viewpoint of Sennert is very remarkable,
as is clearly seen when we compare it to that of Zarabella. Sennert
deviates from Zarabella in two more or less opposite directions. On
one hand, he is a resolute follower of those Aristotelians who admit
the permanence of the forms. He clearly realizes that this is a
deviation from Aristotle which tends towards the atomistic view.
His love for Democritus appears to be not merely Platonic! On the
other hand, however, he is more Aristotelian than Aristotle himself.
In his theory the superior form of the compound hangs in the air.
It has become a kind of dominating entity which holds sovereignty
over the forms of the elements. Thus this form becomes something
independent, a substance, and acquires a significance which far surpasses the role it ever played in Aristotle. The form exists already
before the compound and causes the latter by drawing the elements
under its domain.[12] In Zarabella the form was merely the resultant of
the changed elementary forms.

The second question which Sennert asked himself in reading
Scaliger's treatise was whether or not it is possible for other corpuscles
than elementary atoms to form a compound. We have already seen his
answer. Sennert not only replies in the affirmative, but even thinks
that only very rarely a substance disintegrates into elements. Generally a substance will disintegrate into particles which, although they
are called minima, are not minima in the strict sense. They are only
minima in their own kind, so that other substances can again be formed
from them.

Importance of Sennert's Corpuscular Theory. The importance of
Sennert's theory lies in his clear distinction between elementary
atoms and *"prima mista,"* atoms of the second kind. This distinction

---

[11]*Opera I,* p. 157.
[12]*Opera I,* p. 159.

forced itself upon him through his chemical experience, but fitted wholly and naturally into the theory of natural minima, which from its very beginning had known minima with their own chemical nature. Nothwithstanding the regular use of the term *atom*—which, moreover, was used as an alternative for natural minima—it is clear that Sennert's theory does not fit in with Democritus' system of atoms without qualities, because the latter leave no room for minima with a specific nature nor for the form of a compound.[13] For this reason we considered him as a representative of the minima theory and in a certain sense as the last one, at least of those who are important for the development of the concept *smallest particle*. For from the seventeenth century on our attention must be primarily directed towards scientific theories of smallest parts. Philosophic conceptions fall into the background.

In Sennert himself the beginning of this process can already clearly be discerned. He shows a strong tendency to devise a theory which primarily endeavors to explain certain phenomena by means of corpuscles without worrying much about the philosophic consequences. This tendency will continue to increase and finally even become dominating in a figure such as Robert Boyle.

3. BASSO AND VAN GOORLE

At the end of the sixteenth and the beginning of the seventeenth century there were many philosophers who prepared the way for a revival of philosophic atomism. We have already mentioned one, but the most outstanding two of them, the Frenchman, Sebastian Basso, and the Dutchman, David van Goorle, received only passing mention. Although the atomistic conception did not yet reach full maturity in David van Goorle, he opens the series of true atomists. His posthumous work *Exercitationes* (1620) is a queer mixture of Aristotelian, nominalistic, and atomistic concepts. It is, moreover, literally a juvenile work, for van Goorle wrote it at the age of twenty when he was a student at the University of Leyden. Above, in our study of Scaliger, we have expressed the opinion that van Goorle came

---

[13]Concerning Sennert's position in tradition see the discussion between R. Hooykaas and the author. R. Hooykaas, *"Het ontstaan der chemische atoomleer,"* in *Tijdschrift voor Philosophie*, vol. 9 (1947) p. 63-135; A. G. M. van Melsen, *"De betekenis der wijsgerige corpuscula-theorieen voor het ontstaan der chemische atoomleer,"* in *Tijdschrift voor Philosophie*, vol. 10 (1948) p. 673-716.

under the influence of Scaliger. As a matter of fact his ideas are not very different from those of Scaliger.

> In the atoms the cause of evaporation and condensation is given. For substances evaporate when the atoms become disconnected and air penetrates between them. Thus in the vapor of water the water-particles have separated, and the intervening space is filled with air. In condensation the air is driven out and the particles come again closer together. Hence those who think that air also can be made thinner are mistaken. Only of earth and water and of the substances which are formed of them may it be said that they can be rare or less rare, as is clear from the foregoing.[1]

Philosophically van Goorle pronounces himself in favor of atomism. He explicitly rejects the concept of form which played such an important role in Sennert. But this does not prevent his explanations from being factually the same as those of Scaliger. For two closely connected reasons we consider it necessary to stress this point. The first is that it is not correct to attribute ideas such as those of van Goorle, which were indubitably extremely fruitful, exclusively to his atomism, for these ideas can already be found in earlier supporters of the minima theory. Hence it follows, and this is our second reason, that the better physical insights which we encounter in the seventeenth century did not result from some *philosophic* conception, but from the fact that scholars made a more intensive study of physical phenomena. They flowed from the more physical elaboration of originally purely philosophic conceptions. The corpuscles began to figure in physical and chemical theories of explanation. In this manner it came to pass that van Goorle took over Scaliger's elaboration of the minima theory without its philosophic background. He replaced the latter by another one, but practically this did not make much difference. Later we will have an opportunity to come back to this.

About Basso little is known except that he wrote a *Natural Philosophy (Philosophia Naturalis)*, which was published in 1621. The sub-title shows its purpose sufficiently: *"In which the rejected philosophy of the Ancients is restored to honor and the errors of Aristotle are rejected for solid reasons."* As far as its foundation is concerned Basso's atomism is no more a reproduction of Democritus than that of van Goorle. His atomism also contains elements which are borrowed from Anaxagoras. We will not analyze it in detail, but only stress

---

[1] *Exercitationes Philosophiae*, ex. 13, p. 248-249.

one point. Basso particularly emphasizes the possibility that from the original atoms so-called secondary particles *(particulae secundae)* are formed, and from the secondary particles tertiary ones. Such particles have a certain stability, although the possibility remains that by a change of composition they are transformed into each other.

The idea of particles of a higher order which we found in Sennert is more or less common to all corpuscular theories of the seventeenth century. We will examine its import later.

Like van Goorle, Basso had a good insight into the transition of water into vapor. He realized, however, that this was nothing new and explicitly mentions that he follows Scaliger, to whom he is opposed in other questions.

4. GASSENDI

Contrary to the above mentioned systems the atomism of Peter Gassendi (1592-1665) faithfully copies Epicurus, and therefore also Democritus. Gassendi explains his doctrine in a series of annotations to his critical edition of the tenth book of Diogenes Laertius. The latter was a biographer who lived in the times of the Roman Empire and is one of the oldest sources of Greek philosophers. The tenth book is an exposition of Epicurus' doctrine. Gassendi rendered a real service to his contemporaries by making them acquainted with the oldest complete source of philosophic atomism. His *Observations on the Tenth Book of Diogenes Laertius (Animadversiones in decimum librum Diogenis Laertii)*, which was published in 1649, contains the Greek text with a Latin translation and numerous annotations.[1] The primary purpose of these annotations was to divest Epicurus' system of the naturalistic interpretation with which it was hereditarily infected. We have seen above that although there were other reasons also, this close connection between philosophic atomism and a materialistic view of life was exactly the reason why the system was viewed unfavorably by the Greeks, the Fathers of the Church, and the medieval philosophers alike.

Gassendi, who was a Catholic priest, had great success with his work. As Lasswitz expresses it, atomism soon became fashionable. Although the differences between the atomistic systems of Epicurus

---

[1]Although the complete work was not published before 1649, Gassendi's ideas were already widely known before that time. See Lasswitz, *Geschichte der Atomistik*, II, Leipzig[2], 1926, p. 126ff.

and Gassendi arise principally from the latter's expurgation of materialistic ideas, some of these expurgations implied certain consequences
for the system itself. Thus in Gassendi's interpretation the atoms are
not eternal, but created by God. Neither is their motion eternal; it is
a force with which God has endowed them for the purpose of motion
and mutual connection. Gassendi also rejects Epicurus' opinion that
the atoms are infinite in number.[2] Generally speaking, however, his
theses are the same as those of Democritus. The atoms are qualitatively equal and differ only in size, shape, and weight. All change
is based upon the motion of atoms in the void. There is one point in
Gassendi's explanation of Epicurus' system which demands special
attention. Lactantius had reproached Epicurus that no seeds are
needed for any natural things since everything is composed of atoms
anyhow. Gassendi replies:

> From the atoms certain molecules are formed first, which differ
> from each other and are the seeds of different things.[3]

And elsewhere concerning the same question he states:

> As letters are the elements of writing and from letters are formed
> first syllables, and then successively words, phrases, and speeches,
> so also atoms are the elements of all things. From the atoms the
> smallest molecules are joined together first, and then successively
> somewhat bigger ones, still bigger ones, the finest and the coarsest
> bodies, and finally the biggest bodies.[4]

Gassendi's emphasis on molecules should not surprise us. For a
long time corpuscles had played an important role in the speculations of chemists and philosophers. Certain definite physical and
chemical properties were attributed to these corpuscles; they were
corpuscles possessing a definite nature and not atoms without any
qualities. These ideas had been developed principally in the circles
of Averroists and chemists, as has been mentioned. Since the idea
atom all by itself was not very illuminating, Gassendi had to 'adapt'
his atomic theory to the science of his time. Yet he did not escape
the reproach that his atomic theory was after all entirely superfluous.
For instance, Morinus, an Aristotelian of the seventeenth century,
argues against Gassendi as follows:

---

[2] *Animadversiones*, p. 127.
[3] *Animadversiones*, p. 108.
[4] *Animadversiones*, p. 123.

If it is supposed that nature resolves a compound into its smallest particles, undoubtedly these particles will be the smallest particles of the elements. Why then should it be necessary to accept apart from these minima, also the atoms of Epicurus?[5]

To a certain extent this reproach is justified, but not entirely. For even if a system factually does not offer much new, nevertheless it may be very stimulating, and that is exactly what happened to Gassendi's atomic theory, albeit in a lesser degree than the corpuscular theory of his contemporary Descartes. We will come back to this later when we have seen in what form the ideas of Gassendi and Descartes were taken over by posterity. For the purpose of our investigation this means that we must now first study Descartes and then Robert Boyle. Far more than any of the figures thus far mentioned in the seventeenth century, these two scholars have left their seal upon the science of their time, Descartes as a philosopher, and Boyle as chemist and a physicist.

5. DESCARTES

While Gassendi's system is practically without any trace of originality, the corpuscular theory of Descartes (1596-1650), is original in outline and execution, as is the rest of his work. Not without reason does every historian of philosophy begin a new period with Descartes. This should, of course, be understood *cum grano salis,* for historical periods never begin or end abruptly with one person. However, for the purpose of facilitating a survey of history there may be sufficient reasons to begin a historical period with one person. The characteristics of the new period, which previously were present only in a concealed and scattered form, become clearly outlined in him and reach full development. Descartes was such a person in many fields, primarily in pure philosophy, but also in physical science.

Philosophic Principles of Descartes' Physical Science. Although this study does not directly intend to determine Descartes' place in the history of philosophy, from our study we know how closely in the past general philosophic ideas were connected with scientific ideas. However original Descartes may have been, even in his case the same is still true to a large extent. In this respect Descartes does not differ

---

[5]Jeannes Baptista Morinus: *Dissertatio de atomis et vacuo contra Petri Gassendi Philosophiam Epicuream,* Paris 1650, p. 9.

from his predecessors. But his approach is different. The ancient systems did not satisfy him.

> Because I could not find anybody whose views seemed worthy of my support and preference above others I was constrained, as it were, to construct my view of life by consulting only my own reason.[1]

> I resolved no longer to seek any other science but that which I could find in myself or in the great book of nature.[2]

Only that which is clear and perspicuous is declared worthy of a place in Descartes' system. By his methodic doubt he decides what is clear and perspicuous, that namely which it is impossible to doubt. These fundamental traits which dominate his entire philosophy had also a decisive influence upon his philosophy of nature. The only thing which is perspicuous in matter are mathematical proportions. Therefore the only thing which is real in matter is extension. Matter and extension are the same. Consequently mathematics, the science of extension, is the only science which can teach us something about matter and its properties. Descartes' doctrine of smallest particles also bears the marks of the fundamental principles outlined above. It was utterly impossible for him to think along the atomistic lines of Democritus, Epicurus, and Gassendi. For if matter and extension are identical, indivisible atoms do not make sense. The same holds for the 'void' which is the second basis of Democritus' system. As far as Descartes is concerned, the concept 'void' is a contradiction in terms. Where there is space, there is by definition extension and therefore matter.

The differences between these two contemporaries, Gassendi and Descartes, are far from trivial, yet they stand fraternally united in history as the renovators of atomistic thought in the seventeenth century. A closer study of Descartes' doctrine of smallest particles will show us how this is possible. For, however strange it may seem in view of his identification of matter with extension, Descartes offered a fully developed theory of smallest particles. To the questions which arise immediately as to how these particles are separated and distinct from each other, Descartes answers: *"By a body or a part of matter I understand all that which moves together."* [3] When a quantity of matter moves together that quantity forms a unit, a certain body, dis-

---

[1] *Discours de la Méthode, Oeuvres,* VI, p. 16 (Edition Ch. Adam et P. Tannery, Paris, 1897-1910).

[2] *Discours de la Méthode, Oeuvres,* VI, p. 9.

[3] *Principia Philosophiae,* II, 25; *Oeuvres,* VIII, p. 53.

tinct from other bodies which perform different motions. In such a body parts can be distinguished insofar as these parts have their own motion within the general motion of the body. With surprising ingenuity he works this out in detail, not only for celestial bodies, but also for terrestrial elements. He could have done it in various manners, but being well versed in contemporaneous science he knew the importance attached to smallest particles. Many physical phenomena were explained by means of the smallest particles. The reader will recall Scaliger, Sennert, van Goorle, Basso, and others who all gave about the same explanation notwithstanding the different philosophic backgrounds of their theories. If Descartes wanted to embody this fairly generally accepted explanation in his universal explanatory science, he had to devise a corpuscular theory. His thesis that matter initially was entirely uniform offered an opportunity to do this. His corpuscular theory may be found in the third part of his principal work, the *Principia Philosophiae*.

Descartes' Corpuscular Theory. According to Descartes, at the beginning of the world all matter was divided into particles of equal size. These particles were in constant motion and filled all space. Now this is possible only if the motion is circular, and the original form of the material particles is not spheric, because spherical objects naturally leave some 'empty' space. As a result of the original motion some particles were gradually ground into a spherical form, but this does not cause any difficulty because the resulting intermediary space became filled with these 'grindings.'

This hypothesis supplies Descartes already with two kinds of matter, very finely ground matter ('splinter-matter'), which forms the 'finest' matter and possesses according to him the greatest velocity, and the remaining spherical particles which are less fine than 'splinter-matter' and have a smaller velocity. In addition there is a third kind of coarser particles which originated from those original particles which were not subject to grinding and became united into bigger parts.[4] This third kind of matter has the smallest velocity.

Though Descartes' distinction in kinds of matter has little direct bearing upon the development of physical science, indirectly it gave him an opportunity to introduce some important concepts which really exercised an enormous influence upon physical science. One of these is the concept *mass*. Since this concept played an important role in Descartes' mechanics, it was imperative for him to explain how it could

---

[4]*Principia* III, 48-52; *Oeuvres*, VIII, p. 103-105.

be possible for one body to have a bigger mass than another. His distinction of matter into three kinds offered a welcome answer. The third kind (the coarsest) accounts for the mass. Hence the mass of a body depends on that part of its volume which is occupied by matter of the third kind.[5] However this does not solve all difficulties, because the question may be asked: Whence does matter of the third kind get this quality of inertia? Descartes gives an explantion, but his speculations on this point have no direct bearing on the object of our study:

A second important concept is that of *vacuum*. As seen above, Descartes could not accept an absolute vacuum, but he endeavors to make a relative vacuum acceptable. All space is filled with continuous matter, but space containing only matter of the first and second kind may be considered as 'vacuum' with respect to bodies which contain matter of the third kind.

Thus Descartes arrived at a corpuscular theory which could offer a plausible explanation for many physical properties. For instance,

By heat and cold nothing else is to be understood but respectively the acceleration and deceleration of material particles.[6]

The motion of the particles is called heat when it is greater than normal and affects our sense of touch, for the concept *heat* is derived from sense experience.[7]

When bodies are moved by heat more than usually, they cannot remain in as narrow a space as they usually occupy when in rest or less in motion. For they have irregular shapes which being close together in a certain manner when they are at rest, occupy less space then when they are separated by continuous motion. Hence it is that heat causes nearly all bodies to expand.[8]

Bodies which are divided into many small particles which constantly move in different directions are fluid but bodies of which all the particles are resting alongside each other are solid.[9]

Evaluation of Descartes' Corpuscular Theory. Descartes' conceptions considered in themselves were already fruitful in many aspects, but more important still was the general tendency which was implied in his explanations. His corpuscles are characterized by differences in mass, in amount of motion, etc., properties, therefore, which can

---

[5]*Princ.* III, 121; *Oeuvres,* VIII, p. 170
[6]*Princ.* IV, 46; *Oeuvres,* VIII, p. 231.
[7]*Princ.* IV, 29; *Oeuvres,* VIII, p. 218.
[8]*Princ.* IV, 31; *Oeuvres,* VIII, p. 218.
[9]*Princ.* II, 54; *Oeuvres,* VIII, p. 71.

be expressed in definite measurements and treated mathematically. The seventeenth century knew how useful these concepts were for the mathematical consideration of many physical phenomena. However arbitrarily Descartes may have proceeded in the derivation of his different kinds of corpuscles, he finally arrived at corpuscles endowed with exactly the properties which could be used by contemporaneous mechanics. Hence Descartes could make an attempt to express mathematically the laws which govern the motions and the collisions of particles. In this manner it became possible to say that the result of the behavior of the smallest particles represented a certain physical property which could be experimentally verified. Most important of all, the relation between the properties of the particles which constitute matter and the properties of matter itself were governed by accurately formulated mathematical laws. Of course, Descrates' use of mathematical methods was not something incidental, but flowed from his fundamental conceptions about the essence of matter. Because matter was identical with extension it was up to the science of extension, mathematics, to bring light in problems of matter.

Although Descartes himself made a not unimportant contribution to the development of new mathematical methods, as for instance analytical mathematics, nevertheless the results which he achieved in formulating the laws of impact and motion were not very spectacular. His insights were far inferior to those of Galileo. *"Of the mechanical truths which are easily attainable in the beginning of the seventeenth century Galileo took hold of as many and Descartes of as few as was well possible for a man of genius"* says Whewell.[10] However, Galileo did not apply his mechanical insights to the smallest particles, at least not to any large extent.[11] It is Descartes' great merit that he did make this application. True, everything was not exactly as it should be, but the start was made. The corpuscular theory became embodied in the fast-growing 'new' mechanics. Descartes was fully aware of the importance of his corpuscular theory. He knew what he was doing when he connected his corpuscular speculations with mechanics, as is clear from a passage in which he compares his own doctrine to that of Democritus. The passage is interesting also for another reason.

Never has anyone rejected Democritus' atomic theory because it admitted particles which are so small that they escape sense-

---

[10] W. Whewell, *History of the Inductive Sciences,* II London[2] 1847, p. 52.
[11] For Galileo's corpuscular speculations see p. 111.

experience. Neither because it attributed to these particles different sizes, shapes, and motions, for no one can doubt the existence of these particles, as we have just demonstrated. But it was rejected first, because it supposed the atoms to be indivisible . . . secondly, because it imagined them surrounded by a vacuum . . . thirdly, because it attributed weight to them [as an absolute property]. . . . Finally it was rejected because Democritus did not show how individual things come to be solely as the result of the concourse of corpuscles, or if it be admitted that he showed it for some things, his reasons did not have internal harmony, at least insofar as can be judged from what has been preserved of his doctrine.[12]

Of course, Descartes' reproach at the address of the historical Democritus is unjust. Twenty centuries after Democritus it was easy to criticize him. However, if we keep in mind that in Descartes' time the doctrine of Democritus was again being propagated in its original form, his reproach makes sense. At any rate, it shows what Descartes expected from a corpuscular theory. He was not satisfied with the mere assertion of the general idea of corpuscles, as so many did in his days, but he wanted something which we nowadays would call a physical corpuscular theory. Physical properties had to be ascribed to the corpuscles. At this stage of our study Descartes' demand will not surprise us. For since its origin from a Greek philosophic setting of problems, the theory of smallest particles had evolved in the course of centuries towards a theory which could be used in more specifically physical problems, as is exemplified by the various phases of the minima theory.

From the foregoing one may be inclined to conclude that, after all, a scholar like Gassendi does not really have any great importance. We do not consider this conclusion to be correct. True, in itself the proposal of a corpuscular theory was no novelty in the seventeenth century, for the preceding centuries had already witnessed other corpuscular theories. Moreover, the renewal of the acquaintance with the atomism of Democritus and Epicurus, which was the result of Gassendi's labors, offered factually very few new viewpoints. Yet all this does not imply that Gassendi's work did not have any importance. For, as we remarked in our evaluation of Democritus' atomism, his system contained very fertile physical initiatives. Unfortunately they were entirely concealed by the philosophic tendency of his theory and could not be evaluated properly by the Greeks, whose attention

---

[12]*Princ.* IV, 202; *Oeuvres,* VIII, p. 325.

was centered upon the philosophic setting of the problems. But in the seventeenth century this state of affairs had changed, and slowly something like a proper physical setting of problems had developed. Precisely in connection with this the re-introduction of Democritus was important, for the latter's atomism because of its quantitative character was far more suitable for an application of mathematics and mechanics that the minima theory. Although Gassendi himself, the promoter of atomism, did not make use of this opportunity, the renewal of atomism gave the required stimulus for the application of mathematics and mechanics. But there is still another reason. The minima theory was wholly immured in the classical doctrine of the four elements, which was one of the pillars of Aristotelian physical science. Neither for Gassendi nor for Descartes did this limitation exist. Hence their corpuscular theories could be handled with far more liberty. As a matter of fact this is exactly what was done soon after by the English physicist, Robert Boyle.

6. ROBERT BOYLE   *93619*

We just called Boyle a *physicist*. This is really the qualification which distinguishes him from most of the others thus far mentioned. The latter were almost all primarily philosophers whose general philosophic theories come first. Frequently their knowledge of physical science embraced hardly any details, and even when they possessed a detailed knowledge, it was always closely connected with their general philosophic ideas. In Robert Boyle (1626-1691), however, we encounter a scholar who primarily, and more or less methodically, aimed at an independent physical science, just as Galileo and Newton had aimed at independence in the fields of mechanics and astronomy. But a science does not suddenly become autonomous. We will find striking examples to show that even Boyle's corpuscular theory preserved many ties with philosophic traditions. Nevertheless at the end of our study of Boyle's corpuscular theory we will have to conclude that his theory more than any other thus far mentioned tends to be purely scientific.

Boyle's ideas of smallest particles are found scattered through his entire voluminous works, but are explained most systematically in his two main works *The Sceptical Chemist* (1661), and *Origin of Forms and Qualities* (1666).[1]

---

[1]We quote the edition prepared by Thomas Birch and published at London in 1774 under the title *"Works of the Honourable Robert Boyle"* (five volumes).

Influence of Descartes and Gassendi. By matter, Boyle understands extended substance which is divisible and impenetrable. *"Because this matter being in its own nature but one, the diversity which
we see in bodies must necessarily arise from somewhat else than the
matter they consist of."*[2] This *"somewhat else"* is motion. Through
motion, which effects the division of general matter, *size* and *figure*
obtain meaning. Although the last two properties are not as primary
as motion, yet the three together may be considered as the most essential properties of divided matter, i.e. of the smallest particles of general
matter.

The importance which Boyle attaches to motion as a property of
matter clearly shows that he was influenced by Descartes and also by
Gassendi. After motion, size, and figure, he considers order and situation as important properties of matter. They are, however, not
properties of particles in an absolute sense, but only relatively to other
particles, because only in respect of other particles can there be any
question of a certain situation and order. Following the example of
Democritus and Aristotle, Boyle illustrates the various properties
with alphabetic symbols. A and N differ in figure, AN and NA in
order, Z and N in situation. Order and situation may be indicated by
the term *"texture."* Ordinary sensible qualities find their explanation
in the figure, motion, and texture of the particles.[3] All this does not
contain much news; it is but a variation of the fundamental tenets of
atomism with some Cartesian additions.

Connection of Corpuscular Theory and Chemistry. Just as Descartes is important for the scientific atomic theory, because he sought
a direct connection between his corpuscles and the data of mechanics,
so also is Boyle because he tried to connect his corpuscles to chemistry.
Chemistry could not use the atoms of Democritus or Descartes because they did not have any qualities. Chemistry wanted smallest
particles endowed with specific properties. Moreover it needed large
numbers of smallest particles belonging to exactly the same kind. It
had no use for Democritus' atoms which were all slightly different.
The reader will recall that Democritus in principle banned every concept of species from his atomic world and replaced it by an infinite
variety of sizes and shapes. However, the reader will recall also
that the atomists of the seventeenth century, such as Basso and Gassendi, introduced atomic compounds in order to have corpuscles of

---

[2]*Origin of Forms and Qualities, Works* II, p. 461.
[3]*Origin of Forms and Qualities, Works* II, p. 465.

a certain kind. For a long time the chemists had been working with such corpuscles. They had found them ready for use in the traditional Aristotelian minima theory, according to which minima were essentially of a specific nature.

Boyle was too much a chemist to be satisfied with the general idea of corpuscles as proposed by Descartes or Gassendi. Their atoms were not chemical enough for him and did not offer a theoretical foundation for the experimental data of chemistry. However, since this is not the place to discuss Boyle's merits for the improvement of chemical methods and the increase in experimental data, we will mention only one general aspect which is closely connected with his doctrine of smallest particles. Boyle clearly saw that neither Aristotle's traditional theory of elements nor the three principle theory of Paracelsus was capable of giving a satisfactory explanation of the empirical data of his time. The *Sceptical Chemist* with its suggestive title is a sharp and mostly accurate critique of both systems. To any unprejudiced mind it must have shown conclusively that neither the three principles (quicksilver, sulphur, and salt), nor the four elements (earth, water, fire, air), are the true products of analysis. Boyle points out continually that the products of analysis are compounds, just as is the original matter which is subjected to analysis. *"Though they seem homogeneous bodies, yet have they not the purity and simplicity which is requisite to elements."*[4] The so-called 'salt' which results from the analysis of one body is quite different from the 'salt' which is obtained by the analysis of a different body, although they should be the identical element. The same holds for sulphur and all other principles and elements.[5]

The conditions which Boyle requires for an element are the following: 1) It must be possible to obtain it through analysis from other bodies; 2) The substances obtained through analysis from different bodies as belonging to the same element must be identical with each other. Without any doubt these conditions are empirical in nature, for Boyle does not speculate on the concept *"element,"* but tries to indicate the empirical characteristics of an element. Nevertheless he also knows a speculative definition of elements.

> I now mean by elements, as those chymists that speak plainest do by their principles, certain primitive and simple, or perfectly unmingled bodies; which not being made of any other bodies, or

---

[4]*Sceptical Chemist, Works* I, p. 329.
[5]*Sceptical Chemist, Works* I, p. 336.

of one another, are the ingredients of which all those called
perfectly mixt bodies are immediately compounded, and into which
they are ultimately resolved.[6]

Hence the empirical conditions mentioned above are not sufficient to
characterize an element. In addition an element must *not be subject
to chemical analysis.* Writers of chemical history frequently argue
whether or not Boyle was in possession of the same concept of elements as Lavoisier. With Hooykaas[7] and others we think that the
answer should be in the negative. For Boyle an element is a body
which is *not subject to analysis,* whereas for Lavoisier it is a body
which as a matter of fact *has not been analyzed* by chemical methods.
In other words, Lavoisier's definition is wholly empirical. Nevertheless, in our opinion, mention should be made of the fact that Boyle prepared the way for Lavoisier, at least insofar as he made clear that
nothing should be called an element unless it fulfills certain empirical
conditions.

Boyle himself did not dare to name any substances as elements.
Although he saw clearly that the traditional elements did certainly
not deserve that name, he did not see any satisfactory method to
determine which substances are true elements.

I have not yet, either in Aristotle or any other writer, met
any genuine and sufficient diagnostic for the discriminating and
limiting the species of things.[8]

Although he does not dare to name any elements, nevertheless he
maintains theoretically the difference between elements and compounds. This difference is felt also in his corpuscular theory. As
mentioned before, chemistry had no use for Democritus' atoms, but
wanted corpuscles of the same nature as ordinary substances, because
otherwise phenomena such as distillation could not be explained. In
distillation the vapor had to consist of corpuscles identical in nature
with the liquid. If a liquid could be dissolved into atoms that are
specifically distinct from the liquid, it would not be possible to explain
why the vapor continues to exhibit the same properties as the liquid
itself. These properties, therefore, were specifically proper to the
smallest particles and could not be the result of a configuration. Such
must have been Boyle's line of thought when he wrote that the

---

[6]*Sceptical Chemist, Works* I, p. 356.

[7]R. Hooykaas, *Het Begrip Element,* p. 203ff.

[8]*Origin of Forms and Qualities, Works* II, p. 484.

smallest particles of general matter (the atoms of Gassendi) were associated into so-called *"primary concretions as were not easily dissipable into such particles as composed them."*[9]

Thus the primary concretions are corpuscles with definite qualities. In Boyle's eyes they are the true building blocks of the chemist. Their composition has no practical importance for him, because he cannot dissolve them by any physical or chemical means.

> Though not absolutely indivisible by nature into the prima naturalia, that composed it, or perhaps into other little fragments, yet, for the reason freshly intimated, they very rarily happen to be actually dissolved or broken, but remain intire in great variety of sensible bodies, and under various forms or disguises.[10]

They may have a permanent texture.[11]

Practically, Boyle's primary concretions correspond to the smallest particles of elements, and consequently he treats them as such.[12] As elements of things, the primary concretions can combine to form compounds of a higher order which may be compared to Sennert's first compound principles *(prima mista)*. Although Sennert's corpuscular theory was based on the minima theory, and Boyle's theory on the ideas of Gassendi and Descartes, practically their theories are not very different. Both theories know compound principles, which in both theories are composed of elementary particles. For Sennert, these particles are elementary, both theoretically and practically. For Boyle, theoretically they are not elements, but practically they are, because in chemical and physical processes primary concretions are not dissolved. This agreement of the English chemist with the German physician is not accidental. Boyle was very well acquainted with Sennert and, notwithstanding his aversion of Aristotelians, he spoke very highly of him. But this acquaintance of the English chemist with his German predecessor is not the only reason for their agreement. The time was past that speculations about smallest particles found favor only in philosophic problems. They had already become part of a physical and chemical theory which urgently needed and demanded a difference between elementary and compound corpuscles. However, before we can consider this matter in detail, we must first finish with Boyle's explanations.

[9]*Sceptical Chemist, Works* I, p. 300.

[10]*Origin of Forms and Qualities, Works* II, p. 471.

[11]*Ibid.*

[12]*Introductio ad Historiam Qualitatum Particularium*, p. 9.

The first compound principles, in turn, can form combinations of the second order, etc. Instead of the term *texture,* which he uses to indicate the structure of primary concretions, Boyle prefers to use the term *mixture* in speaking about combinations. Hence a mixture differs from a texture insofar as a mixture is always a combination of heterogeneous particles. Sometimes, however, the terms are used indiscriminately. Both mixture and texture are called *structures.* Boyle does not even object to the use of the Aristotelian term *form,* provided it be not taken in the sense of substantial form.[13] Substantial forms were his big nightmare, which shows the utter incapacity of the contemporary Aristotelians, who, in order to explain any unknown phenomenon, simply resorted to some unknown form.

Boyle's Critique of the Concept Form. Boyle's critique of the concept *form* as proposed by his Aristotelian contemporaries, is largely justified. We may recall how, for instance, in Sennert the concept *form* had acquired far more meaning than it ever had for Aristotle. It had become an independent being which by its presence dominated supremely the reaction of the elements. Meanwhile Boyle was fully aware of the fact that his critique was not directed primarily against Aristotle himself. He mentions, for instance, that neither Aristotle nor the Greek Commentators had taught such a concept of form.[14] Notwithstanding his vehement anti-Aristotelianism it is therefore no surprise to find in Boyle a text which describes the concept *form* in such a way that it could have come straight from the pen of Aristotle himself. In that text Boyle indicates in which sense the term *structure* may be replaced by the term *form.*

> [What is] called its form which is consequently but a certain character or a peculiar state of matter, or, if I may so name it, an essential modification: a modification, because it is indeed but a determinate manner of existence of matter, and yet an essential modification, because that though the concurrent qualities be but accidental to matter, yet they are essentially necessary to the particular body.[15]

At closer inspection, however, it becomes clear that Boyle's concept of form differs considerably from that of Aristotle. The following quotation shows this clearly.

---

[13] *Sceptical Chemist, Works* I, p. 361.
[14] *Origin of Forms and Qualities, Works* II, p. 476. It is not true that all Latin Commentators admitted the criticized concept of form.
[15] *Origin of Forms and Qualities, Works* II, p. 475.

Since an aggregate or convention of qualities is enough to make the portion of matter it is found in what it is, and denominate it of this or that determinate sort of bodies; and since those qualities, as we have seen already, do themselves proceed from those more primary and catholic affections of matter, bulk, shape, motion or rest, and the texture thence resulting, why may we not say, that the form of a body being made up of those qualities united in one subject, doth likewise consist in such a convention of those newly named mechanical affections of matter, as is necessary to constitute a body of that determinated kind. And so, though I shall for brevity's sake retain the word *form,* yet I would be understood to mean by it not a real substance distinct from matter, but only the matter itself of a natural body, considered with its peculiar manner of existence; which I think may not inconveniently be called either its specifical or its denominating state, or its essential modification, or if you would have me express it in one word, its stamp. For such a convention of accidents is sufficient to perform the offices, that are necessarily required in what men call form, since it make the body such as it is, making it appertain to this or that determinate species of bodies, and discriminating it from all other species of bodies whatsoever.[16]

This quotation clearly shows how strongly Boyle was influenced by atomism, although he fully realized its weakness and therefore also the difficulties inherent to his own concept of form. For a thing which is but the sum total of its components has no true unity, but is only an aggregate, an accidental being *(ens per accidens).*[17] However, Boyle does not think that this objection is conclusive.

In the notion that divers learned men have of an *ens per accidens,* namely, that it is that which consists of those things *quae non ordinantur ad unum,* [which are not joined together into a unity], it may be said, that though we do not admit substantial forms, yet we need not admit natural bodies to be *entia per acci-*

---

[16]*Ibid.* p. 470.

[17]In philosophy the term *ens per accidens* indicates something which as the result of adventitious circumstances appears to be 'one,' while in reality it is 'many.' For instance, a heap of stones is an *ens per accidens.* Every stone is a complete and separate being so that there are *many* beings in one heap of stones. As, however, they happen to lie side by side and one upon another, they may be considered, to a certain extent, as 'one.' Mechanisms, as watches, engines etc., are also accidental beings, although their parts are certainly not arranged in a certain order 'by accident.' Nevertheless they are called accidental beings because their various parts fit into the whole on account of their accidental qualities, as shape, hardness, etc. They can without difficulty be removed temporarily and be put again into position or be replaced by another part of similar shape and qualities. The term *accident* should be taken in the Aristotelian sense. An animal is not an accidental being, because its various parts, such as limbs and organs, are *essentially* parts of the whole. If a part of a living body is separated, it instantly ceases to be what it is.

dens; because in them the several things that concur to constitute the body, as matter, shape, situation, and motion *ordinantur per se et intrinsece* [tend immediately and intrinsically] to constitute one natural body. But if this answer satisfy not, I shall add, that for my part that which I am solicitous about is, that what nature hath made things to be in themselves, not what, logician or methaphysician will call them in the terms of his art; it being much fitter in my judgment to alter words than to affix a wrong nature to things, that they may be accommodated to forms of words that were probably devised, when the things themselves were not known or well understood, if at all thought on.[18]

To appreciate this splendid answer properly, one must understand the circumstances. Aristotle had introduced his concept of form as a philosophic concept in a fundamental philosophic problem in order to explain the possibility of change. But it had become a concept which was used in season and out of season, especially to explain all kinds of details in physical phenomena. Of course, this was nonsense. As an answer to the question how change in matter is possible, the appeal to a fundamental composition made sense, as did the answers given by Empedocles and Democritus. But it was nonsense to answer a question like "Why is a body hard?" with the formula "because of its form." For in asking this question we want to find out why *this* body is hard while *that* one is soft, in other words, we want to find certain structural characteristics which can cause hardness, as for example a certain configuration of atoms. An appeal to the form does not make sense, because the concept *form* is applied to *every* body to characterize the body as a body and to explain the mutability to which *every* body is subjected. Hence the concept *form* was useless to explain the differences in behavior of bodies which interest the physicist. Now since the questions raised by Boyle belonged primarily to the physical order, the philosophic concept of form could hardly be of any use. The answer to his questions had to be in terms which have reference to sensible and measurable properties.

As to this affair I observe that if (for instance) you ask a man what gold is; if he cannot shew you a piece of gold, and tell you this is gold, he will describe it to you as a body that is extremely ponderous, very malleable and ductile, fusible and yet fixed in the fire, and of a yellowish color; and if you offer to put off to him a piece of brass for a piece of gold, he will presently refuse it, and (if he understand metals) tell you, that though your brass be coloured like it, it is not so heavy nor so malleable, neither will it

---

[18]*Origin of Forms and Qualities, Works* II, p. 487.

like gold resist the utmost brunt of the fire, or resist aqua fortis. And if you ask men, what they mean by a ruby, or nitre, or a pearl, they will still make you such answers, that you may clearly perceive, that whatever men talk in theory of substantial forms, yet that, upon whose account they really distinguish any one body from others, and refer it to this or that species of bodies, is nothing but an aggregate or convention of such accidents as most men do by a kind of agreement.[19]

In his eagerness to get rid of the hated concept *substantial form,* Boyle unfortunately uses the expression *"convention of accidents."* This amounts to expelling the devil through Beelzebub, because the concept *accident* is also borrowed from a philosophic problem. Hence Boyle's repeated declaration that a convention of accidents is sufficient to constitute a body without a proper form, provoked immediately the reproach that therefore every compound body is an accidental being. That, however, is not Boyle's intention. He assures us that in his opinion these compound bodies are *entia per se,* beings with an essential unity. The reasons which he puts forward are not without weight. He realizes that everybody will not be satisfied with his answer, but he does not want to enter into any discussions about all those terms. As far as he is concerned two things are certain: in the first place, the properties of bodies must be explained by their composition, and secondly, the compound body is nevertheless truly 'one.'

Theory of Subordinated Forms. While searching for a connection in contemporaneous terminology for the formulation of his twofold conception concerning the unity of the compound and the explanation of the whole by its parts, Boyle came across Sennert's and Zarabella's theory of a superior and subordinated forms. The idea appealed to him, though he had certain objections which we will consider shortly. Because the theory of subordinated forms had grown out of the same desire which animated Boyle, namely to connect the properties of compounds with those of elements, it was only natural that this theory found favor in his view. The classical objection against it is that no new unity arises if the forms remain. This objection is justified if the concept *form* is taken in its original philosophic meaning. Hence, in order to escape from this difficulty, Zarabella and his followers invented the superior form. In their view, the superior form is the only form, and the other forms are merely components or parts of it, so that there is true unity.

---

[19]*Origin of Forms and Qualities, Works* II, p. 469. 9.

Boyle's objections against Sennert's idea of a superior form are easy to see. They flow from the substantialization of the form.

> Those actions which Sennertus and others attribute to the conspiring of subordinate forms to assist the specifick and presiding form, we take to be but the resultant actions of several bodies, which being associated together, are thereby reduced in many cases to act jointly, and mutually modify each other's actions; and that which he ascribes to the dominion of the specifick form, I attribute to the structure, and especially to the connexio of the parts of the compounded body.[20]

Nevertheless Boyle again confirms explicitly that the compound body is not an accidental thing but a being with essential unity *(ens per se)*. As a physicist Boyle felt strongly attracted to a viewpoint which works with the simple concept of structure instead of form and its hereditary sequel of endless disputes. But since he did not dare to accept the consequences of atomism, he turned to the theory of a superior and subordinated forms, because this theory is somewhat similar to the concept of structure, and explicitly asserts the unity of the compound.

Epilogue. At the outset we called Boyle a physicist. This qualification applies to him also with respect to his corpuscular theory, although it would not be correct to consider his theory as purely physical. It is too clearly connected with philosophic atomism, and Boyle enters too explicitly into all kinds of philosophic problems. Nevertheless there is an unmistakable tendency towards a pure physical theory. He tries to find empirical, strictly determinate, characteristics, and uses concepts borrowed from atomism without connecting them with the consequences of this philosophic system. Hence it is difficult to place him in any of the corpuscular traditions which we have reviewed above. On one hand, he is very close to Gassendi and Descartes and declares his indebtedness to them, but on the other hand he continues in many respects the tradition of Sennert. We may therefore say that, to a certain extent, the various currents meet in Boyle. His corpuscular theory reminds us of both traditional doctrines, of corpuscles with a specific nature, as well as of particles without qualities which compose these corpuscles. He rejects the concept of form, but accepts a concept of structure which safeguards the unity of the compound. The explanation is clear—Boyle's theory is the outcome of the practical need for a reasonable explanation of contemporaneous physical and chemical problems. Naturally he profited

---

[20]*Origin of Forms and Qualities, Works* II, p. 532.

from the achievements of his predecessors by borrowing their formulas and terms, but his predominant interest is not in the original philosophic meaning but in their usefulness for his physical theory. This usefulness is his only criterion.

With Boyle we have reached a new phase in the history of the atomic theory. The foundation of a pure physical theory, which the Averroists had prepared and which Sennert had started, was brought to perfection by Boyle. Provisionally it could not be more than a foundation, because too many data were still missing; for instance, to use Boyle's terminology, a *"diagnostic"* to determine which things are elements and which compounds. From now on we will be primarily interested in the development of physical science and the gradual increase in physical meaning of the concepts used. This will be the work of physicists and not of philosophers. Nevertheless the physicists remain closely connected with philosophy. Their concepts still show all the marks of their origin, and in the background the philosophic setting of the problems continues to exert influence.

We must now leave Boyle, but in the final section of this chapter we will endeavor to give a comprehensive view of the seventeenth century which will reveal still better his position in this century.

7. THE MECHANICS OF THE SEVENTEENTH CENTURY

The Physical Character of the Seventeenth Century Corpuscular Theories. When speaking about Descartes, Sennert, and Boyle we pointed out that their corpuscular theories, notwithstanding their connection with the traditional problems of philosophy, clearly exhibit physical characteristics, i.e. their corpuscles have properties of physical importance. Descartes' corpuscles have mass and a certain amount of motion. Sennert's corpuscles, say of water and gold, have certain chemical properties; hence certain properties of gold remain when it is alloyed with silver, certain properties of water remain when water is distilled, etc. Chemically these ideas had been prepared in the preceding centuries, not only by the experimental data of the alchemists, but also by the speculations of the minima theory, which was the 'scientific' theory of the Middle Ages. Physically, especially from a viewpoint of mechanics, the theory of natural minima, had not achieved very much. Its close ties with Aristotle's faulty mechanics had prevented this. Moreover, before there could be any question of applying mechanics, the minima theory had first to undergo considerable development, because the particles had to obtain a relative autonomy. This autonomy was not acquired before the fifteenth century. As long as the minima remained theoretical limits of division, they could hardly become a subject of mechanical speculations. To this we may add that the emphasis which the Aristotelian theories laid upon the qualitative aspect of the minima did not stimulate quantitative considerations. The traditional range of Aristotelian concepts was not adapted to them, and tradition occupied a very prominent place in the esteem of Aristotelian systems. Hence although the Averroistic minima theory was capable of supplying the services demanded by *chemistry,* the *physical* aspects suffered neglect.

The Relation Between the Revival of Atomism and Mechanics. In our opinion it may be said that the major value of atomism in the seventeenth century lies herein that it emphasizes that aspect of the corpuscles which the minima theory had neglected, namely that the corpuscles could be drawn into a process which is governed by the laws of mechanics. Obviously, the question can be raised whether the revival of philosophic atomism preceded the desire to apply mechanics or vice versa. For mechanics also passed through a period of renewed vigor. We do not think that the question can be answered with a choice between the alternatives, because the disjunction is too simplified. For what is to be understood by philosophic atomism? It can be understood precisely as the system devised by Democritus and his followers as an answer to a problem raised by a certain Greek philosopher of the fifth century B.C., Parmenides, who declared all change to be impossible because it is unintelligible. As will be recalled, Democritus answered that no change is intelligible except local change. But this historical problem and its answer do not constitute the whole of philosophic atomism. For, in a certain sense, every thinker is a Parmenides, every thinker is a Democritus. In other words, under the more or less fortuitous form which the problem assumed for Parmenides and Democritus some permanent problem is hidden. This is true not only with respect to Parmenides and Democritus, but applies also to Socrates, Aristotle, and Plato, to the Greek sceptics and sophists. It may happen that in a certain period some currents of thought of which these thinkers are the prototypes fall somewhat into the background, but they continue to exist. Hence they should be taken into consideration in every period of time, as was done by the medieval thinkers with respect to atomism, if only for the purpose of rejecting it after due consideration.

All this must be kept in mind when the question is asked whether the revival of atomism was prior or the new mechanics. If this is done, the question loses much of its alternative character. The urge for a mechanical explanation of phenomena came as much from the Democritus who is in every thinker as from the historical Democritus, though it may be admitted that the influence of the latter strengthened the former. Reversely, the solution of many mechanical problems gave new food to atomistic thought. In many thinkers the slumbering Democritus woke up, as always happens in similar situations, even in our days. By our days we mean the time in which various autonomous sciences are known. Even nowadays a new viewpoint in a specialized science will usually entail the revival of an old philosophic dispute, as will become abundantly clear in the last chapter. The seventeenth century, with which we are presently concerned, was different insofar as there was not yet question of any autonomous physical science. Problems of details were drawn immediately into the sphere of a general vision, and these general visions were traditionally expressed in the systems of the great philosophers. Hence the fall of Aristotle did not mean that henceforth scientific problems were going to be considered independently from a philosophic system. Provisionally the fall of Aristotle meant only that his place was taken by philosophic mechanism, either in the classical form of Democritus or in that of Descartes.[1] Thus, on one hand, the renewal of mechanism and its victories in the explanation of phenomena implied a revival of Democritus' atomism, and on the other hand, this atomism stimulated the study of mechanics. Hence our answer to the alternative question concerning the relative priority of mechanics and atomism will have to be that, in this period, the philosophy of Democritus was closely allied to mechanics, and vice versa, so that the two theories exerted a reciprocal influence.

The Development of Mechanics—Galileo and Huygens. Our survey of the renovators of atomic thought needs to be completed with a sketch of the development of mechanics in the seventeenth century. However, it will not be more than a sketch, so that we must limit ourselves to an indication of the various phases in its development, especially of those phases which have a bearing on the atomic theory.

Galileo opens the ranks of outstanding scholars in the science of mechanics. The mechanical achievements of the Ancients, such as

---

[1] By mechanism we mean the philosophic system which holds that all change must be explained as local motion.

Archimedes, are mostly limited to the field of statics, the science of equilibrium. Dynamics, the science of motion, could not be developed because it is founded on the Principle of Inertia, of which the Ancients had no correct notion. We owe our knowledge of this principle to Galileo, who stated that a body upon which no forces are working remains in the same state of motion. Rest, for the purpose of this law, may be considered as a state of motion. Galileo had also a correct idea of fall: if the resistance of air is excluded, all bodies fall with the same velocity, and this velocity continues to increase.

Obviously, Galileo also had corpuscular explanations. They are, however, relatively unimportant because his concept of smallest particles is too confused.[2] Moreover, Galileo was not yet able to grasp mathematically a system with a plurality of bodies. His dynamical considerations are correct, but limited to mechanical problems concerning the motion of a single body. The mechanical problems of a system composed of several bodies were solved by Christian Huygens (1629-1695), and Isaac Newton (1642-1727).

These two thinkers are generally known as adversaries in the problem of light. The wave theory of the one is opposed to the corpuscular theory of the other. Less generally known is that to a certain extent they were also opponents in the mechanics of solid bodies, especially in the problem of gravitation. While Newton tackled this problem with the concept of forces acting from a distance, Huygens tried to solve it with the laws of impact. Huygens accepted Newton's mathematical description as correct, but objected to the idea of a **force acting** from a distance. Such a force could only be some occult quality, for which there is no room in a mechanical system that admits only bodies-without-qualities and motions. Inspired by Descartes' ideas, Huygens therefore constructed a theory which asserts that the earth and celestial bodies are surrounded by a very subtle fluid, the ether, whose state of motion is such that it drives coarser bodies towards the earth. There is no reason for us to dwell long upon this theory. Its chief value lies in the fact that Huygens clearly shows that he realizes the physical character of his hypotheses, for he makes use only of the mechanical laws known in his time. That he did not succeed in solving all connected problems is less important than that he seriously endeavored to explain the phenomenon of attraction exclusively through the phenomena of pressure and impact, for this endeavor had a most beneficial influence upon the theory of these phenomena.

---

[2]See K. Lasswitz, *Geschichte der Atomistik,* II p. 37ff.

Huygens succeeded in his efforts to give a precise formula to the laws of impact. Henceforth a correct mathematical treatment of the impact phenomena was possible, and thus the corpuscular theory got a firm footing. From certain hypotheses concerning mass, size, and velocity of the corpuscles, conclusions could now be drawn about observable phenomena, which is a *necessary* condition for a physical theory which has any real value. In itself, however, this condition does not suffice, because a good theory presupposes also true physical and chemical data about the nature of the smallest particles. Provisionally few of these data were available, so that the corpuscular theories of the seventeenth century could do little else but formulate relatively arbitrary hypotheses about the physical properties of smallest particles. This arbitrary procedure could come to an end only when the foundation of the distinction between elementary and compound particles in physical and chemical processes was clearly understood. Neither the four elements of Aristotle nor the three principles of Paracelsus and other chemists were true elements. That much was certain, but which things, then, were the true elements? As long as this problem was not solved, the atomic theory could not make any progress. Mechanics and its auxiliary sciences could develop all right, but sufficient certainty about the nature of the corpuscles concerned was lacking. Thus physics, in the stricter sense of the word, had to wait for chemistry, while chemistry in turn had to wait for the physics, not of smallest particles, but of the properties of matter in general. In the knowledge of these properties physics was capable of making considerable strides without chemistry. This will not surprise us if we keep in mind that the classical object of mechanics, the solid body, is visible to the naked eye. Bodies can be observed to fall, to collide, etc. Chemistry, however, penetrates more profoundly into the interior of matter. Its classifications alone presuppose a high degree of development in the various physical methods of determining, say, density, boiling point, melting point, and many other data which characterize a material substance. For this reason the entire evolution of chemistry and physics in the seventeenth and eighteenth centuries, even when not concerned with smallest particles, is more important for the atomic theory than corpuscular theories themselves. After a long period of evolution as a part of philosophic theories, corpuscular speculations in the seventeenth century had reached a stage in which the corpuscles needed to be determined exactly by means of their physical and chemical properties. They had allied themselves to the physical and chemical theories of their time, and the waiting was now for further development of these physical and chemical theories. Before, however, we can trace this development in the next chapter, we must first turn our attention to two thinkers of the seventeenth century who exercised a powerful influence upon this development.

Newton and Leibnitz. The first of these thinkers is Isaac Newton (1642-1726). His contribution to mechanics is so well known that there is no need to dwell long upon it. By means of his law of gravitation Newton succeeded in explaining at the same time the phenomena of fall and astronomy. He posited his law of attraction as a universal law which applies to all bodies. All bodies, even the smallest particles, attract one another with a force proportioned to their mass and inversely proportional to the square of their distance. This law was very important for the corpuscular theories.[3]

We will omit the question as to how far Newton himself conceived the force of attraction as a mathematical description of the phenomenon of motion or as a definite physical quality which is the cause of motion. For us the important point is that as a result of Newton's law the corpuscular theories entered into a new phase, because generally Newton and not Huygens was followed. How urgently something such as Newton's general attraction was needed becomes clear from a study of Boyle's corpuscular theory. On one hand, the atomists wanted to retain atoms without qualities, and on the other, there was need for corpuscles with definite chemical properties. According to the atomistic creed these properties could result only from the manner in which the particles were connected. Hence Boyle's primary concretions. But the question was: How are these complex particles connected? Before Newton, recourse was had to hooks or jig-saw patterns of a surprising variety.[4] All this now became superfluous. True, the idea itself of a force acting from a distance had something mysterious, but at any rate it was a concept that had proved its value in mechanics and astronomy. It was not an hypothesis invented for the sake of convenience. Everything pointed towards gravitation as a universal property of matter, so there was no reason to avoid using it.

Newton must also be mentioned together with Leibnitz as the creator of the mathematical method of differential and integral calculus. This method offers a possibility of obtaining a mathematical grasp of the processes of continuous change. Practically, this meant

---

[3]See Isaac Newton, *Optics*, p. 31.
[4]See H. Metzger, *Les doctrines chimiques en France du debut du XVIIe à la fin du XVIIIe siecle,* I, p. 272ff.

that another condition was fulfilled for the truly general application of mechanics, because most processes of change are continuous. There is no need to explain the corpuscular theory of Leibnitz (1646-1716), because it is too special and too closely linked to his personal philosophic ideas[5], which did not give rise to any new school of thought. Moreover, from the second half of the seventeenth century on we are less interested in philosophic atomic theories. After the seventeenth century, i.e. after the rise of physical science as a more or less autonomous science, the physical atomic theories are far more important for the history of the atom. Philosophically we are still interested in the philosophic background which these physical theories possess, but that question can be touched only when the scientific atomic theory has been fully explained. For the time being our attention will be concentrated upon the scientific atomic theory. Hence the aforementioned mathematical achievement of Leibnitz is more important for the problems which concern us than his corpuscular theory, although the latter is very remarkable from a philosophic point of view.

Apart from his contributions to infinitesimal calculus, Leibnitz took also a very lively part in the discussions about the fundamental principles of dynamics. He introduced the concept of the "living force" mv^2, which later on was developed into the well-known formula of kinetic energy

$$E_{kin} = \tfrac{1}{2} mv^2$$

Thus the theoretical foundations of the future kinetic gas theory also were laid in the seventeenth century.

8. REVIEW OF THE SEVENTEENTH CENTURY

The seventeenth century produced a rich harvest of corpuscular theories. Rich not only because of the number of theories, but also and especially because of the progress which became so clearly manifest. Hence spontaneously the question arises: to what do we have to attribute this progress? In the preceding pages we have already touched on this question in a passing way. Now that we have reached the end of the chapter and possess a clear idea of the whole period, it may be useful to face this question more explicitly.

---

[5]A brief summary of Leibnitz' theory may be found in the first volume of the *Dutch Scientific and Philosophic Library,* C. H. van Os, *Getal en Kosmos,* Amsterdam, 1947, p. 51.

An Historical Misconception. The investigation of the cause of
the progress made in the seventeenth century will give us also an
opportunity to point out a misconception which is fairly common
among the historians of the atomic theory. These authors justly stress
the importance of the revival of philosophic atomism, but—and herein
lies their misconception—they seek its importance primarily in the
fact that it proposed the idea of smallest particles, and in the possibilities which this entailed for the explanation of physical and chemical
phenomena. This misconception is the result of their almost complete
ignorance of the minima theory which existed in the preceding centuries. It was thought that medieval thinkers did not know any
smallest particles and that the very idea itself was squarely opposed
to the Aristotelian concept of matter. Lasswitz, for instance, who
without any doubt is a man of the highest authority on the history
of the atomic theory, wrote as follows about Sennert:

> The connection of the Aristotelian concept of matter and form
> with the finite divisibility of matter characterizes Sennert's theory
> as a purely physical atomic theory with entirely practical purposes.[1]

Hence according to Lasswitz the Aristotelian concepts of matter and
form are opposed to the finite divisibility of matter. This is a rather
remarkable opinion, since practically all Aristotelians and Aristotle
himself have defended the finite divisibility of matter. Whatever
differences may have existed among them concerning details of the
minima theory, all of them accepted minima for living bodies and most
of them for all bodies. Lasswitz, however, did not know anything of
the minima theory, or rather he did not know anything about its
existence before the seventeenth century.

Hence he interpreted it as an endeavor to reconcile Democritus
and Aristotle in a last effort to save the dying scholastic philosophy.[2]
This interpretation does not cause any immediate difficulties to a
historian who limits himself to the second half of the seventeenth
century. But difficulties arise when the study is extended to authors
who wrote before the publications of the first atomists. Jaeger,[3] for
instance, does not know what to do with the Aristotelian Anselm de
Boodt (1550-1632), a Flemish physician and student of natural
science, who already in 1604 spoke about corpuscular concepts and

---

[1]K. Lasswitz, *Geschichte der Atomistik*, I, p. 448.
[2]K. Lasswitz, II, p. 486ff.
[3]F. M. Jaeger, *Historische Studien*, p. 118.

mentioned minima. For anyone who knows the minima theory this is nothing extraordinary, but for the others it constitutes an intriguing problem.

This neglect of the minima theory was bound to lead to misrepresentations of history. Lasswitz, for instance, writes:

> [It was Giordano Bruno's special merit] that he determined the concept *atom* in a clear and unassailable manner. As long as the atom is considered merely as the terminus of division, it remains doubtful whether such an atom has eventually to be admitted or not. The insight, however, that clear understanding requires a *primary [building block] of composition* makes the concept *atom* a necessary concept. Hence Bruno taught that there must be a primitive whole which is at the beginning of our speculation, and this whole is the atom. Moreover, he acknowledges the relativity of the concept *atom*.[4]

Some of Lasswitz's remarks, we think, are to the point. The transition from terminus of division to first building block is, indeed, of the greatest importance for physical science, as we have already pointed out on several occasions. But this transition had been made already by Averroes in the twelfth century. From that time on, his view had become traditional among the Averroists. We may remind the reader that, shortly before Bruno, Scaliger explicitly had called the minima the first building blocks of the compound *(prima ad compositionem)*.

Neither is the view that the minimum is a relative minimum characteristic of Bruno. It was the common view of those who admitted minima. In connection with this we may point to the fact that the correct notion of states of aggregation is exclusively attributed to atomists such as van Goorle (1611), and Basso (1621), but it can already be found in Scaliger (1557). The reason for this misconception is the following. When in the nineteenth century extensive studies were made about the history of physical science, practically nothing was known about the Middle Ages. Moreover, the philosophic orientation of nineteenth century physical science was entirely mechanistic, and only this system was deemed worthy of attention. Whatever it may be, it is certain that long before the forerunners and renovators of atomism, there existed in Averroistic circles ideas which have borne fruit in the future evolution of the atomic theory.

---

[4] K. Lasswitz, I, p. 381.

Through years of study the author is thoroughly acquainted with these Averroists, about whom others speak so little. Yet personal preference was not the reason why this section has been developed so broadly. Neither was it done because of a desire to do justice to history. What the reason was we will see presently in the following section.

The Cause of the Physical Character of Atomism in the Seventeenth Century. The question must be asked why seventeenth century atomism almost immediately appeared as a theory with a pronounced physical character. For Democritus, atomism was a theory with a much wider goal, and in his successors it represented almost as much an ethical as a physical theory. What is the reason that while there is almost no mention of Democritus' atoms in the seventeenth century, there were discussions about complex bodies composed of these atoms, bodies to which certain physical and chemical properties were attributed? The answer to this question is difficult if one believes that before the seventeenth century the concept *smallest particles* did not form a part of the scientific stock of ideas. If this were true, how could the concept have so suddenly emerged in the seventeenth century, not only as a general idea, but also as a concept which was adapted to, and closely allied with the level of contemporaneous science? If, however, one knows that in certain circles the concept lived already before the seventeenth century, the matter is not surprising at all. Sennert, van Goorle, Bruno, Basso, and de Boodt could build upon ideas which their predecessors had already developed.

Undoubtedly, it is true that a simple reference to Aristotle's minima theory does not suffice as a proof that the Middle Ages and the Renaissance knew the concept of smallest particles, for the minima theory existed in several very different variations. The manner, for example, in which the Scotists and the Thomists treated the minima problem offered few points of connection for the speculations of Sennert and the like. A glance at some famous sixteenth and seventeenth century manuals of philosophy will be sufficient to show this. Thus the commentary of the professors of Coimbra broadly develops the question of the minima as limits of division, and whether minima are found in non-living bodies or not[5], but rejects explicitly the definition of chemical composition as *"the motion of minima towards mutual contact so that union is effected."* Likewise, they reject the possibility

---

[5]*Commentaria Collegii Conimbricensis S.J. in octo libros Physicorum Aristotelis Stagiritae, Coloniae* 1596, in lib. I, cap. IV, q 1.

of a composition between other than elementary components.[6] It may be recalled how vigorously Sennert attacked this opinion. Of course, neither did the interpretation of form proposed by Averroes and Avicenna find favor with them, although they admitted that many texts of Aristotle can be interpreted in this manner.[7] Speculations about the relative sizes of the elements, such as Sennert proposed, are likewise rejected.[8] This may suffice as an example, but many others could be added. It shows clearly again that not every Aristotelian trend developed the theory of natural minima in a physical direction. As we have mentioned before, this development must be sought principally in the Averroistic tradition. The latter proved itself fruitful for later scientific speculations. The content which the concept *minimum* acquired among the Averroists was such that the smallest particle was seen as a reality capable of physical and chemical determinations.

To a certain extent we may therefore say that the very fact that in the preceding centuries there existed a corpuscular theory with a somewhat physical character forced atomism to show at once a pronounced physical character at its revival in the seventeenth century. People were already used to the fact that the smallest particle occupied a place in scientific speculations. In order to prove its right of existence philosophic atomism had to offer a concept of smallest particle with at least the same usefulness in the explanation of phenomena as the extant concept of minimum. Hence atomism pushed its atoms-without-qualities into the background, and its complex particles-with-qualities into the foreground.

The Merits of Philosophic Atomism. From the simple historical fact that this Averroistic minima tradition existed, we may therefore conclude that it is not correct to attribute the introduction of the concept *smallest particles* to the revival of philosophic atomism, for smallest particles were known in the preceding centuries. The merits of atomism lie in its strong emphasis on the *quantitative* aspect of the problem. This emphasis was not accidental but intentional. We touch here again the question whether the search for mechanical explanations through mathematics was prior to the return to Democritus' philosophic views, or whether the return to Democritus was prior to

---

[6]*Commentarium Collegii Conimbricensis S.J. in libros de Generatione et Corruptione Aristotelis Stagiritae,* Moguntiae 1606 (2nd ed.), in lib. I, cap. X, q II, art. 2.

[7]*In librum I de Generatione et Corruptione,* cap. V, q III, art. I.

[8]*In librum II de Generatione et Corruptione,* cap. VI, *explanatio.*

the quest for mechanical explanations.   The reader will recall the answer given above on page 111 : there was reciprocal influence insofar as the return to Democritus promoted the application of mathematics to mechanics, and reversely, the possibility of this application favored the return to Democritus' system.   No autonomous physical science existed as yet, so that explanations by means of mechanics were seen as particular applications of a general philosophic view, as had always been the case up to that time.   Scientific explanations borrowed their concepts largely from philosophic problems.   The concept *minimum* was tied to the concept *form* in the Aristotelian sense, and the concept *atom* was connected with the concept of *intrinsically immutable being without qualities.*

The Importance of the Seventeenth Century.   The importance of the seventeenth century lies in the fact that a *start* was made with the construction of an independent system of scientific concepts. Sennert intentionally made an indiscriminate use of the terms *atom* and *minimum* in order to get a philosophically neutral concept of smallest particle.   He states that this smallest particle is practically immutable, because in this way it could be most useful in his chemical speculations.   To this extent he follows Democritus.   On the other hand, his atoms are minima possessing a proper nature *(minima sui generis)* which is specifically different in different substances. This is borrowed from Aristotelian philosophy, but again primarily for scientific reasons.   The list could be continued.   Sennert uses the concept *form,* because chemical processes do not follow a fortuitous course, but show tendencies and determinations.   This is another Aristotelian idea.   Sennert, however, does not endeavor to harmonize the philosophic background of all these concepts—he was philosophically too well trained to foster any illusions in this matter—but he wants to find expressions for the various stages of chemical happenings, and in order to describe them accurately, provisionally he is compelled to have recourse to philosophic terms.

The same is true of Boyle, with this difference: whereas Boyle sought connection with the atomistic tradition, Sennert was more closely allied to the Aristotelian tradition.   But in Boyle also there are clear deviations from the purely atomistic trend of thought.   We may recall his strong emphasis on the essential unity of the compound, whose component parts intrinsically tend to form a unity. Boyle expresses himself here in Aristotelian terminology.   This could not be avoided, for he had to make use of the available stock of ideas.

Hence in him also we find data which are borrowed from philosophic theories. Of course, it is open to discussion whether Boyle took a middle course between Aristotle and the atomists, as we have defended in our work *The Philosophic Past of the Atomic Theory* [9], or arrived at his viewpoint by means of purely experimental chemistry without being influenced to any great extent by philosophic theories, as Hooy- kaas [10] asserts. We think that both opinions are correct. Boyle was led primarily by chemical considerations, but this did not prevent his *concepts* from being greatly influenced by the manner in which his predecessors had expressed the data of chemical experience. Now these data had to be expressed in terms borrowed from philosophic traditions, because physical science did not yet have its own termi- nology. Hence Boyle was obliged to make use of Aristotelian, and still more of atomistic, concepts in order to express the insights which chemical experience forced upon him.

On account of this use of philosophic terms and concepts, Boyle's corpuscular theory is closely connected with philosophy. If Boyle's corpuscular theory had already progressed so far as to be entirely independent from philosophic thought, Boyle and others in the seven- teenth century would not have attached themselves so strongly to philosophic atomism. But they still sought a philosophic foundation for their ideas, although the connection with philosophy was already less strict than in the preceding centuries. Partially this was a result of the fact that they had borrowed elements from very different philo- sophic sources, for thus the philosophic setting automatically fell into the background.

There is another point which deserves our attention. We have seen how in the course of centuries a theory of smallest particles with a more pronounced physical character began to develop. Initially it was closely connected with Averroism, but from the beginning of the seventeenth century it sought contact with atomism. Most sup- porters of the corpuscular theory launched vehement attacks on Aris- totle. Whence came this sharp change of course? For as a matter of fact the ideas of, say Scaliger on one hand, and those of Basso and van Goorle on the other, did not differ very much, just as Boyle's concept of structure was not essentially different from the Aver- roistic concept of composite form. Perhaps one would be inclined

---

[9] See *Het wijsgeerig verleden der atoomtheorie,* p. 164.
[10] R. Hooykaas, *Tijdschrift voor Philosophie,* vol. 9, p. 63-135. See also A. G. M. van Melsen, *Tijdschrift voor Philosophie,* vol. 10, p. 673-716.

to see in this change of philosophic background nothing but a change of fashion. Every period has its own philosophic fashion, and when Aristotelianism went out of fashion, atomism got the preference. However, there is more than a change of fashion behind this preference, for the philosophic background of atomism will continue to accompany the scientific atomic theory till the twentieth century, as we shall see in the second part of this study.

The Break With Aristotle. Since a complete analysis of the radical break with Aristotle would be beyond the scope of this book, we will indicate only a few points.[10a] The first, and in our opinion the most important point is that although philosophic atomism was proposed as a metaphysical theory, as the ultimate necessary explanation of all change, nevertheless it exhibited also an unmistakable physical character which corresponds to some general trait of every physical theory. It will be recalled that in order to save change Democritus reduced everything to change of position or local motion, which according to him was something intelligible. With Aristotle we may object that such a view is too narrow, but this does not prevent Democritus' idea from being very attractive, for it is simple and easy to visualize. As long as the emphasis in scientific thought fell on general philosophic problems, as was the case in ancient Greece and the Middle Ages, the deficiencies of philosophic atomism as a universal explanation of the world were so glaring that its very simplicity seemed to be a disadvantage. It was too simple. When, however, the steadily increasing data of physics and chemistry began to need special theories which were meant to embrace only these data, the simplicity of atomism became an advantage. Scant attention was paid to the original purpose of philosophic atomism, so that elements which are incompatible with atomism could easily be introduced into it, as for instance, the concept of beings with an essential unity, fixed structures, etc.

Certainly, we do not want to claim that nothing remained of Democritus' original intention. As stated before, to a certain extent every man is a Democritus. The idea of immutable particles is easy to handle and simplifies visualization, because we have to deal only with local motions, which are easily comprehended. Hence the idea is attractive, and we try to see how far we can get with it, even though we do not want to claim with Democritus that *all* change and *all* phenomena must be explained through it. It is the most obvious working method; hence our previous remark that the physical char-

---

[10a] Cf. the author's *The Philosophy of Nature*, Pittsburgh, 1954, Ch. 4, Sects. 4 and 5.

acter of atomism corresponds to a general trait of every physical theory.

In the seventeenth century the tendency to explain physical phenomena by means of local motion got special support from two factors. In the first place, the development of mechanics supported the atomistic theory, because by means of mechanics the atomic theory could be worked out concretely along mathematical lines, and just at that time the mechanical method of explantion had many great successes to its credit. Of equal importance is the second factor, which consists in the position occupied by Aristotelianism in the seventeenth century. The strength of Aristotle can be summed up in the following three points.

1) The imposing character of his philosophic thought which accounts for the general structures of reality. His solution of the fundamental problems shows a calm balance between the requirements of sense experience on one hand, and the intellectual interpretation of this experience on the other.

2) His enormous empirical knowledge. His system embraced practically everything which fell within the limits of ordinary experience.

3) The rigorous logical connection of the system in which he compressed all this knowledge. Aristotle is the founder of scientific logic. Only in the last hundred years did man succeed in developing logic beyond Aristotle. Even so, the outstanding modern logician Scholz,[11] who is not only thoroughly acquainted with modern symbolic logic but also with the history of logic, states: *"Even nowadays Aristotle's Organon* [works on logic] *is still the most beautiful and instructive introduction into logic of all."* No wonder that for a long time everybody remained under his spell, especially because he had become more or less the official philosopher of the theologians at a time when Theology was the central science in the medieval universities.

As we have mentioned before, in the late Middle Ages it was thought that science had reached its perfection with Aristotle. Hence study of science meant the study of the logical connection between universally accepted fundamental theses and their deductions in terms of Aristotelian philosophy.

---

[11]H. Scholz, *Geschichte der Logik,* Berlin 1931, p. 27.

When, however, the Middle Ages became acquainted with Arabian and Greek science, physical science began to flourish and slowly it became clear that there was something wrong with Aristotle's physical science. Efforts were made to remedy this by diverse modifications and interpretations of the original terms. Scholars tried to express new data in the trusted old Aristotelian terms which fitted in with the whole system. This procedure was bound to end in failure for the simple reason that many of the new data were in flagrant contradiction to Aristotle's views. A real break, however, could not take place before there were sufficient data to formulate an entirely new system. Thinkers were accustomed to see everything in one great whole, because for centuries the school of Aristotle had trained them in this frame of mind.

This explains also the remarkable tenacity with which thinkers held on to Aristotle's system for centuries. It was not opposed by any new whole which could either take over the entire function of Aristotelianism or treat the problems of a particular field in an independent way, for up to that time every part had always been seen in its connection with the whole. As long as the particular data of a branch of science were too sparse to allow an autonomous development, the integration of all sciences worked in Aristotle's favor, because it led the attention to the general philosophic problems in which Aristotelianism found its greatest strength. When, however, the particular data became more numerous and varied, the reference to the general setting of problems no longer gave satisfaction. Thinkers wanted an explanation of this or that particular phenomenon. Then not only Aristotle's physical explanations fell short, but also his concepts, which owed their existence and value to the philosophic setting of problems. They were unsuitable for the clear and exact expression of many physical data. The concept *form* is an instructive example. Aristotle was convinced that a chemical compound is a new substance. Although generated from the components and capable of being resolved into them, nevertheless the compound was something new and distinct. Borrowing his terms from the problem of change, he expressed this by saying that the compound had a new form. It was *one* substance, and therefore had to have *one* form. Consequently it followed that every quantitative part of the compound, of the new substance, was determined by this form. Every part of the compound is compound, says Aristotle. In other words, the compound is homogeneous. But what is meant by this homogeneity? Nothing except that every part is the compound in question. All this is wholly

acceptable as a part of the Aristotelian philosophic setting of problems. However, does it imply that such a homogeneous compound
has everywhere in its parts the same properties? This question is
concerned with a new type of homogeneity. It is the homogeneity
in which physicists and chemists are interested. Aristotle himself
probably thought that non-living things possessed also this second
type of homogeneity, so that all their parts would have exactly the
same properties. For living beings he did not admit it. Although
every part of a dog is "dog," the different parts of a dog have different properties. In Aristotelian circles, however, there was a steady
tendency to relax somewhat the homogeneity of inorganic things, as
appears from the manner in which Aristotelians spoke about the permanence of the forms of elements in the compound. The original
forms of the elements were said to remain. This impaired the unity
of the compound in virtue of the rule: one substance means one
form, and a plurality of forms means a plurality of substances. As
far as living beings were concerned, this did not offer any difficulty,
because Aristotle himself spoke of organs, bones, flesh, etc. Concepts
derived from sense experience were available which could signify the
different parts in such a manner that their heterogeneity could be
expressed, while philosophic concepts assured a correct consideration
of the homogeneity of the animal. It was a being with unity, every
part of an animal was animal.

For Aristotle, then, inorganic beings were homogeneous in both
senses. This opinion was not correct, but in view of the limited possibilities for experiments in those days, we can understand Aristotle's
mistake. When, however, the increase in chemical knowledge raised
all kinds of doubt about this homogeneity, the question could no longer
be treated within the framework of Aristotelian concepts. Concepts
such as form were forced into the straitjacket of problems for which
they were not suited. This led to all kinds of contradictions. As a
result some Aristotelians held on to the original meaning of the terms
and thus retained a logical system, which however was not in agreement with experience. They were mostly the theorists, the philosophers, the theologians, and the logicians. For them Aristotle's philosophy remained the center of gravity. The result was not immediately
a complete separation of philosophy and physical science, but the germ
of division was laid.

The others, especially the students of the empirical *arts,* tried to
compromise between a more or less consequent system and the

demands of experience. Scaliger and Sennert belong to this group.
The situation may be summed up as follows: slowly an empirical
knowledge had grown, which, on one hand, flatly contradicted Aristotle's teaching, and on the other was so new that it could not be
suitably expressed in the terms of Aristotle's philosophy, at least not
if it had to fit in with the whole. This was felt to be an unbearable
burden. They wanted to get rid of it, because it caused all kinds of
disputes which were not to the point. Every deviation from the Aristotelian inheritance which was expressed in terms of philosophy was
logically analyzed and refuted without mercy by means of sacrosanct
axioms. Let us illustrate with an example. If one admitted that
some body was a compound, the logical conclusion had to be drawn
that it possessed only one form. Whoever insisted that the properties
of the constituents remained in the compound got into logical difficulties. Endless logical solutions were sought and definitions proposed
which would both do justice to the components and express also the
unity of the compound. It may have been excellent training in logic,
but it did not answer the question that was scientifically far more
important: What are the physical, sensible criteria to determine
whether a thing is a compound or not? That was exactly the question
asked by Boyle. From this question a new science was bound to arise.
It would use a new set of ideas, which would aim directly at the physical, experimental, aspects of material reality. Thus the new mechanics
was born with its concepts of mass, quantity of motion, living force,
etc. This new mechanics was connected with a corpuscular theory
which possessed a concept of particles that was subordinated to the
concepts of the new mechanics, although it remained in close contact
with the concepts of chemistry. A suitable climate for these new
concepts was offered by a revised atomism which placed its physical
aspects in the foreground and relegated its philosophical foundations
to the background. Many, however, continued to prefer Aristotelianism as their more general philosophic outlook, so that the fall of
Aristotle was not very abrupt. Factually, this equivocal attitude
amounted to the separation of the scientific and philosophic settings of
problems. Various fields of knowledge, each with its own theoretical
concepts, began to be distinguished. Boyle too, took part in this. For
instance, in the preface to *Origins of Forms and Qualities*,[12] after a
violent tirade against the Aristotelians, he declares:

---

[12]*Works* II, p. 456.

Nevertheless I would not be understood to censure or decry the whole Peripatetick philosophy, much less to despise Aristotle himself, whose own writings give me sometimes cause a little to wonder, to find some absurdities so confidently fathered upon him by his scholastic interpreters. For I look upon Aristotle as one of those famed ancients, whose learning about Alexander's time ennobled Greece; and I readily allow him most of the praises due to great wits, excepting those which belong to clear-headed naturalists. And I here declare once and for all, that, where in the following tract, or in any other of my writings, I do definitely depreciate Aristotle's doctrine, I would be understood to speak of his physicks, or rather of the speculative part of them nor do I say that even these may not have their use among scholars, and even in the universities, if they be retained and studied with due cautions and limitations.

The quotation is typical of the period. It was difficult to cut loose from centuries of tradition, but it had to be done. Even if abstraction is made of Aristotle's numerous erroneous explanations, the fusion of different fields of knowledge in Aristotelianism was a serious handicap for the progress of science. The violent reaction against Aristotle was caused not only by his erroneous explanations, but also and perhaps more so by the fact that justice could not be done to specifically scientific problems, because through philosophic concepts everything was drawn into the sphere of philosophy. We may add that the endeavor to solve physical problems by means of concepts borrowed from philosophy did violence to these concepts themselves and therefore also to the philosophic viewpoint itself.

This brings us to the end of our survey of the seventeenth century. It is a very important period in the history of physical science, not only because many new discoveries were made, but also because the foundation was laid for the autonomy of physical science. A system of physical theories arose which primarily intended to embrace the physical data of experience, without connecting them with the most fundamental problems of philosophy. Of course, all this took place in a gradual way. In the seventeenth century the connection between philosophy and physical science continued to exist, but it was no longer as strict as during the preceding centuries. In this matter there is one misconception to be avoided. The new physical science did not arise suddenly, but developed from what the preceding centuries had thought when the framework of an autonomous physical science did not yet exist. It is precisely this autonomous frame of mind with respect to physical science which began to grow in the seventeenth century and took definite shape in the eighteenth, especially as regards the atomic theory. In the seventeenth century there could not yet be question of a fully independent physical atomic theory. Such a theory did not arise before the eighteenth century began to change into the nineteenth, as we shall see in the next chapter.

PART TWO

THE CONCEPT *ATOM* IN PHYSICAL SCIENCE

CHAPTER FOUR

THE ORIGIN OF THE PHYSICAL ATOMIC THEORY

1. THE DEVELOPMENT BEFORE DALTON

The Relative Value of Historical Divisions. Science faces the necessity of making divisions. The historian less than anyone else can escape the subsequent superficiality. Thus Dalton's publication of *A New System of Chemical Philosophy* (1808), is proclaimed the birthday of the modern atomic theory. No one can dispute the right to make such an assertion provided that sufficient attention be paid to the events which occurred before Dalton. For Dalton is not only the beginning of a new era, but also the end of another. Our study has made it clear that Dalton's proposal of the concept *atom* was nothing original. In the course of this chapter it will become clear that even his further development of the general concept *atom* shows but little originality. Dalton's importance lies in the fact that his atomic speculations were directly connected with the new views about elements and compounds which were coming to the fore. In other words, Dalton and Lavoisier are inseparable.

More than anything else, the atomic theory after the seventeenth century was in need of better chemical insights. The eighteenth century is important insofar as it supplied these insights. By the eighteenth century we mean the whole eighteenth century, for these insights were not the work of Lavoisier alone. It cannot be stressed too much that historical reality is not the divided whole which rigorous schematic divisions tend to make it. It is customary to think according to sharp lines of divisions. Physics, for instance, begins with Galileo, chemistry with Lavoisier and Dalton. Whatever went before may still have some value, but is not physics or chemistry in the modern sense of the words. The historian who shows that certain conceptions already existed before that period is considered a nuisance, because he spoils the beautiful schemes. He cannot be ignored completely; therefore, he and his historical corrections are relegated to footnotes. The schemes remain, and the footnotes mention a few exceptions. For instance, physics still starts with Galileo, and the Parisian nominalists are mentioned in a footnote; corpuscular theories originated in the West in the seventeenth century, and previous supporters of the minima theory stay in the footnote.

131

In this study we have endeavored to stress the continuity of growth in the physical atomic theory, even in its pre-physical phase. But by speaking of the physical and the pre-physical phases we underscore again the idea of division into periods. As a matter of fact, both views can be defended. Whoever prefers sharp divisions finds support in the facts, provided he be willing to soften the abruptness of his divisions by a sufficient number of footnotes. Whoever wants to emphasize the continuity of the development is bound to point also to the fairly abrupt accelerations of development. We have met already one of these accelerations in the seventeenth century, when the concept *atom* suddenly began to develop more swiftly. We will encounter another at the turn of the eighteenth century. In this short period the process went so fast we may have the impression of meeting something entirely new. For instance, Lavoisier's view is so remote from the theory of four elements and that of the three principles that one would take it to be something wholly original. In fact, however, his view was prepared step by step. To follow this process of preparation in detail would require a very extensive study. We will, therefore, illustrate our assertion by one example only and examine the preparatory role of the phlogiston theory in the eighteenth century. True, the idea *smallest particle* did not play an important role in the phlogiston theory, so that this theory would not seem to have any direct bearing on the development of the atomic theory. Nevertheless indirectly the phlogiston theory did exercise a great influence insofar as it prepared the way for Lavoisier (1743-1794). For, as will be remembered, the atomic theory stood in need of a true understanding of the distinction between elementary and compound substances.

The Phlogiston Theory and the Law of Lavoisier. George Ernest Stahl (1660-1734) was the chief exponent of the phlogiston theory which taught that all metals are composed of calces—our metal oxides —and a combustible material, called phlogiston. The process of combustion of metals was conceived as the expulsion of phlogiston. The less calx remained after the combustion of a metal, the more phlogiston it contained. Carbon consisted almost entirely of phlogiston. If carbon was added to a metallic calx—in modern terminology we would speak of the reduction of oxide by carbon—the calx would absorb phlogiston and become again a metal. The value of this theory is that it made possible the systematization of the phenomèna of oxidation and reduction, which are so important from the chemical point of view.[1]

---

[1] See E. J. E. Huffer, *Chemie,* Roermond-Maaseik 1948, p. 22ff.

As we will see presently, the theory did not correspond to *all* the facts, but the main argument usually advanced against it, especially in college textbooks—that bodies do not become lighter but heavier by combustion—is not conclusive, unless weight be considered as an immutable property of matter. However, chemists before Lavoisier did not admit this. Their attention was directed towards the qualitative properties of matter so that quantitative aspects remained in the background. Hence the increase in weight was no reason to reject the phlogiston theory. Lavoisier's well-known experiments have conclusive value only for those who attribute an essential role to constant weight in the systematization of the phenomena of combustion. But there was no *a priori* reason for attributing such a role to weight. Only the success of the systematization based on the assumption of constant weight could and did prove in later times the correctness of this viewpoint.

Hence it will not surprise us that the reasons why the phlogiston theory was gradually abandoned were primarily of an internal nature.

There were difficulties in the theory itself; for instance, the difficulties which resulted from the discovery, or rather the better insight, into oxygen and hydrogen through the experiments of Cavendish, Scheele, and Priestley. Hydrogen showed all the characteristics needed to identify it with phlogiston. Oxygen was considered as air which was deprived of phlogiston and therefore suported combustion. It deprived metals of their phlogiston. The new data, however, showed that the reaction of hydrogen with oxygen does not produce *air* but *water*. Thus the phlogiston theory led to such difficulties that it became necessary to start an entirely new line of speculation. The most obvious thing to do was to take the Law of Conservation of Weight as the starting point. This law was intimately connected with the current theory that matter was something indestructible. True, the same law was likewise the ultimate basis of the phlogiston theory, which explained chemical processes as the absorption or privation of an immutable substance endowed with certain properties, called phlogiston; but the phlogiston theory did not postulate the conservation of *weight*. Lavoisier, however, postulated the conservation of weight, as a primary condition, because weight was a property which offered an excellent basis for accurate experiments and fitted in with the quantitative methods which had been so successful in physical science. Lomonosov (1711-1765) and others had preceded him in the use of this working method, but its value could not be fully realized before the discovery of new data which undermined the old conceptions.

Concerning the question whether the so-called Laws of Conservation are purely experimental laws or views which precede specific experience, Meyerson remarks that the laws are experimental but inspired by a general fundamental idea which holds the attention of the mind. Man's mind, therefore, is willing to accept as plausible every law which states such a conservation in general, but experience must determine what exactly is conserved.[2]

We will not try to determine to what extent Meyerson's view is correct in its generality, but it is certain that the general idea "certain essential things remain" dominated all thinking even before Lavoisier, and that the latter's application of this general idea was supported by specific experimental data. We can find in Lavoisier both elements to which Meyerson attributes importance in respect of the origin of the so-called Laws of Conservation. In his experiments Lavoisier discovered that bodies after combustion are heavier instead of lighter, as should have been the case according to the phlogiston theory combined with the Law of the Conservation of Weight. He, therefore, concluded that metals are not compound but simple, at least as far as the phenomena of combustion are concerned.

What is special in Lavoisier is that he called the metals *elements*. Since metals could not be resolved by any of the known chemical processes with the means at his disposal, he considered them as elements. Hence the concept *element* had an empirical content for Lavoisier: it indicated a substance which *in fact* is not resolved. Whether resolution takes place or not is something which was decided according to the chemical norms supplied by the methods of analysis.

In every manual of chemistry Lavoisier's law is inseparable from Proust's law (1807), that every chemical compound has a constant composition. This law expresses a second important phase in the evolution of the chemical ideas of those days. No more than the law of Lavoisier did it arise suddenly—but the purpose of our study does not allow us to enter into details. We may be satisfied with the remark that Proust's battle against Berthollet, who denied the constancy of chemical composition, was decided in favor of Proust by means of very accurate analyses. Thus Proust's law, as well as that of Lavoisier, was supported by many experiments.

---

[2]E. Meyerson, *Identité et Réalité,* Paris[3] 1926, p. 162.

2. DALTON'S ATOMIC THEORY

Its Physical Character. The outstanding achievement of John Dalton (1766-1844) was that he connected the chemical data mentioned above with his atomic theory. Basing himself to a large extent upon scientifically well-founded data, he gave a new shape to the general idea that physical and chemical phenomena ought to be explained by means of smallest particles. His atoms were no longer smallest particles with some vague properties, but atoms endowed with those properties which the advance of chemistry demanded. We said that Dalton based himself "to a large extent" upon scientific data. For the time being we must be satisfied with this vague expression, but later we will be able to indicate exactly to what extent Dalton's atomic theory cannot be said to have been based upon scientific data.

Dalton's work shows signs not only of the influence of Lavoisier and Proust, but also of Newton, as is clear from a reading of the famous passage with which Dalton introduced his *A New System of Chemical Philosophy*.

There are three distinctions in the kinds of bodies, or three states, which have more especially claimed the attention of philosophical chemists, namely, those which are marked by the terms *elastic fluids, liquids, and solids*. A very familiar instance is exhibited to us in water, of a body, which, in certain circumstances, is capable of assuming all the three states. In steam we recognize a perfectly elastic fluid, in water a perfect liquid, and in ice, a complete solid.

These observations have tacitly led to the conclusion which seems universally adopted, that all bodies of sensible magnitude, whether liquid or solid, are constituted of a vast number of extremely small particles, or atoms of matter, bound together by a force of attraction, which is more or less powerful according to circumstances, and which, as it endeavours to prevent their separation, is very properly called in that view, *attraction of cohesion;* but as it collects them from a dispersed state (as from steam into water) it is called *attraction of aggregation,* or more simply, affinity. Whatever names it may go by, they still signify one and the same power. It is not my design to call in question this conclusion, which appears completely satisfactory, but to show that we have hitherto made no use of it, and that the consequence of the neglect has been a very obscure view of chemical agency, which is daily growing more so in proportion to the new lights attempted to be thrown upon it.

The opinions I more particularly allude to, are those of Berthollet on the Laws of Chemical Affinity; such as that chemical agency is proportional to the mass, and that in all chemical unions there exist insensible gradations in the proportions of the constituent principles. The inconsistence of these opinions, both with reason and observation, cannot, I think, fail to strike every one who takes a proper view of the phenomena.[3]

The last paragraph shows that Dalton, in keeping with his atomic theory, definitely sided with Proust against Berthollet. The remainder of the passage shows the extent of Newton's influence on Dalton.

Whether the ultimate particles of a body, such as water, are all alike, that is, of the same figure, weight, etc. is a question of some importance. From what is known, we have no reason to apprehend a diversity in these particulars: if it does exist in water, it must equally exist in the elements constituting water, namely, hydrogen and oxygen. Now it is scarcely possible to conceive how the aggregates of dissimilar particles should be so uniformly the same. If some of the particles of water were heavier than others—if a parcel of the liquid on any occasion were constituted principally of these heavier particles, it must be supposed to affect the specific gravity of the mass, a circumstance not known. Similar observations may be made on other substances; therefore we may conclude that *the ultimate particles of all homogeneous bodies are perfectly alike in weight, figure, etc.* In other words, every particle of water; every particle of hydrogen is like every other particle of hydrogen, etc.[4]

Obviously, we are especially interested in what Dalton himself calls a "question of some importance." In it he clearly follows along the traditional line of the seventeenth century corpuscular theory and its forerunner, the Aristotelian minima theory, which both admitted specifically different particles for every kind of matter. Dalton specifically appealed to the *determination* of density to support his thesis that the smallest particles of a substance are alike. Meanwhile he realized that his thesis itself was not new, but only his rules for the determination of relative atomic weights and the like.

It is one great object of this work to show the importance and the advantage of *ascertaining the relative weights of the ultimate particles, both of simple and compound bodies, the number of simple elementary particles which constitute one compound particle, and the number of less compound particles which enter into the formation of one more compound particle.*[5]

---

[3] *A New System of Chemical Philosophy*, London[2] 1842, chapter II, p. 141.
[4] *A New System*, p. 142.
[5] *A New System*, p. 213.

History shows that Dalton was right in this evaluation of his own work. Although he made quite a few mistakes in the determination of relative atomic weights, his *method* was extremely fruitful in its results. Dalton took the initiative in devising a method which has resulted in our modern atomic weights. Hence the value of his theory lies entirely in its connection with the chemical knowledge of his time. As a result of the application of this knowledge, certain properties were attributed to the atoms, and the mutual relations of these properties were determined. For instance, through analysis Dalton found that one unit weight of hydrogen combined with eight units weight of oxygen. Assuming that as a rule one atom of a substance would combine with one atom of another substance, his analysis showed eight as the relative atomic weight of oxygen. Although Dalton made a mistake because in reality water is formed of two atoms of hydrogen and one atom of oxygen, nevertheless in principle his method was correct. It needed only to be further developed. Other data also had to be taken into account to ascertain the true atomic proportions. Meanwhile Dalton was well aware of the fact that several combinations of two elements are possible. He even discovered an important regularity in this which greatly supported his atomic theory. It is formulated in what is now called Dalton's Law of Multiple Proportions: when the same weight of one element combines with different weights of another element these varying weights are to each other as small whole numbers. For instance, 100 gm. of tin combine with 13.5 and 27 gm. of oxygen. An interesting historical detail is that Proust who formulated the Law of Constant Proportions already knew that several combinations of certain elements were possible, but accidentally did not discover the above mentioned regularity because he expressed the relative weights in percentages of the whole. Thus he found that tin and oxygen combine in the proportions of 88.1% tin and 11.9% oxygen, and also of 78.7% tin and 21.3% oxygen. As expressed in percentages the numbers do not directly reveal the regularity in question. If, however, everything is arranged in reference to the same weight of tin, as Dalton indicated, the proportion of oxygen in both combinations stands out clearly. From the Law of Multiple Proportions Dalton naturally concluded that in one case one atom of tin combined with one atom of oxygen, and in the other with two atoms. Thus the law fitted in very nicely with his atomic theory. The same was true of Proust's Law of Constant Proportions, for constant composition is the result of the immutability of atomic proportions.

The Philosophic Background of Dalton's Atomic Theory. Now that we have seen how Dalton's conception of the atomic theory was determined by the chemical science of his time, the question may be raised whether Dalton was also influenced by philosophic motives. As with so many other questions, this one may be answered both in the affirmative and in the negative. It all depends on the meaning of the question. The answer will be negative if the question is taken to mean whether Dalton deliberately chose a philosophic position, i.e. whether Dalton expressed his own opinion in the matter only after a previous examination of the philosophic foundations of the atomism proposed by Democritus, Empedocles, and Anaxagoras, or that proposed by Gassendi, Descartes, and Boyle, and of the minima theory proposed by Aristotle or Sennert. The answer will also be negative if the question is taken to mean whether Dalton, without mentioning or even knowing of the existence of previous viewpoints, nevertheless deliberately turned his attention to the problems of smallest particles which had caused disagreement among philosophers in former ages. The question, however, can also have another meaning. Did Dalton more or less unconsciously take over some philosophic view of the past without trying to account for the motives or basis of this view? If the question is put in this form, we think that it must be answered affirmatively. But perhaps now the reader will be inclined to counter with another question. Does it still make sense to look for an answer if the question be understood in this form? Does not the philosophic setting belong definitely to the past, now that a scientific atomic theory has been born? In answering, we may first point out that even if this were true, the effort to determine the extent to which philosophic traditions of the past have contributed to scientific theories would still be jusified in a study such as ours. For initially these philosophic traditions, in addition to being philosophic, also fulfilled roles which later were taken over by specialized sciences. Therefore, they were also science-in-the-making *(Wissenschaft am Anfang)*. However, this aspect of continuity with the past is not the only reason why the question must be raised whether ancient philosophic theories exercised influence upon Dalton's atomic theory. The very history of the physical atomic theory compels us to ask this question. Much of the modern discussion around the atomic theory becomes incomprehensible if we do not take into account the philosophic background of Dalton's atomic theory. We use the term *background* to convey that it is an aspect which is rather presupposed than explicitly accounted for. Dalton accounts explicitly only for physical aspects.

It is not difficult to discover the philosophic background of Dalton's atomic theory. In his works a number of expressions are encountered which clearly recall the philosophic past.

> Chemical analysis and synthesis go no farther than to the separation of particles from one another, and to their reunion. No new creation or destruction of matter is within reach of chemical agency.

> All the changes we can produce consist in separating particles that are in a state of cohesion or combination, and joining those that were previously at a distance.[6]

Dalton conceived the union of the atoms in the compound as a simple juxtaposition.[7] The atoms lie against each other without undergoing any internal change. In this point the founder of the chemical atomic theory did not differ from the philosophic atomists, but simply continued as something quite natural the tradition of the preceding centuries. There is, however, a remarkable point of difference from the ancient philosophic atomism. Dalton's atoms are specifically different for every kind of substance. Even this is nothing new, for the prevailing medieval theory of smallest particles, the minima theory, knew minima of a specific nature, and it was in the circles of its supporters that the first efforts were made towards the more scientifically orientated corpuscular theories of the seventeenth century. The idea of specifically different smallest particles was already so firmly established that the official supporters of Democritus and Epicurus in the seventeenth century had made room for them in their atomic theory. Boyle's view is interesting in this regard. He remained loyal to the atomistic doctrine of atoms-without-qualities, but as a chemist worked with combinations of atoms which fully possessed the character of particles with a specific nature, because chemistry demanded them. In comparison with Boyle, Dalton shows still less philosophical orientation. His atoms are at once atoms of a specific nature. He does not even think of building these atoms from particles without qualities, as was demanded by the atomistic doctrine. His original atoms differ discontinuously. But he conceived this discontinuity against the background of contemporaneous atomism. The atoms are fragments of a matter which is uniform in its nature and in its qualities, such as attraction, weight, and size, but this matter possesses these fundamental

---

[6]*A New System*, p. 212.

[7]*A New System*, p. 216.

qualities in discontinuous measure.[8] This is an essential point of difference from Democritus, who had to exclude in principle every kind
of discontinuity in order to attain the goal which he envisaged with
his atomic theory. Hence it is not correct to put Dalton on one line
with Democritus, as is frequently done. On the other hand, neither is
it correct to deny all connection between Democritus and Dalton on
the ground that the former is purely speculative and the latter purely
empiric.[9] Dalton continued a tradition in which Democritus plays a
major part. It would not even be difficult to show that no empirical
data forced Dalton to conceive his atoms as intrinsically immutable. On
the contrary, many properties of the elements could not be found in
the compounds, and vice versa. It is difficult to see how this fundamental fact would agree with a simple juxtaposition of atoms. Nevertheless, there was nothing abnormal in the fact that Dalton accepted
it, because it was the general conviction of his time. It was a relic of
the philosophic setting in which the atomic theory had been placed in
the preceding century. Hence it is true that Dalton's atomic theory
was *to a large extent* determined by empirical data, but not entirely.
Its unmistakable philosophic background was *not* derived from these
data. Thus Dalton's atomic theory was a direct continuation of the
past in more than one respect. For he retained the general atomistic
view, which had been commonly accepted since the seventeenth century; but he also took over the idea of specific particles, which the
seventeenth century had inherited from the minima theory. And
finally, he completed the work which the Averroists had already started
and which the seventeenth century had pushed so vigorously—the
construction of an atomic theory upon a scientific foundation.

3. FIRST DEVELOPMENT AFTER DALTON

Berzelius. After Dalton the development went very rapidly. The
Swedish chemist Jons Berzelius (1779-1848) determined the relative

---

[8]Obviously, there are still traces of essentially different fundamental qualities in Dalton. Speaking, for instance, about heat he says: "Besides the
force of attraction, which, in one character or another belongs universally to
ponderable bodies, we find another force that is likewise universal, or acts
upon all matter which comes under our cognizance, namely, a force of repulsion. This force is now generally, and I think properly, ascribed to the
agency of heat. An atmosphere of this subtile fluid constantly surrounds the
atoms of all bodies, and prevents them from being drawn into actual contact."
A New System, p. 143.

[9]This is done, for instance, by Rousseau, *Histoire de la Science,* Paris 1944,
p. 55.

atomic weights with a surprising accuracy.   While Dalton had made rather arbitrary assumptions about the numbers in which atoms combine, Berzelius tried to derive these numbers from experimental data. One of these data was supplied by Gay-Lussac's chemical Law of Volumes which states that the volumes of gases in a chemical reaction are to each other as small whole numbers.   Connecting this law with the physical laws of Boyle and Gay-Lussac, Berzelius ventured to draw an important conclusion. As known, Boyle's law states that at a given temperature the product of pressure and volume of a quantity of gas remains constant. Gay-Lussac's physical law expresses the proportion between the volume at a given temperature (t) and the volume at 0°C., the pressure remaining constant:

$$V_t = V_o \left(1 + \frac{1}{273} t\right)$$

The fact that both laws apply to all gases without exception had led to the hypothesis that under the same pressure and at the same temperature the number of atoms in all gaseous substances is the same. Since hydrogen and oxygen combine in the constant volume proportion of two to one, Berzelius concluded correctly that two atoms of hydrogen combine with one atom of oxygen.

In this manner Berzelius succeeded in determining fairly accurately the relative atomic weights of a large number of substances.   This demand for accuracy became particularly urgent due to Prout's hypothesis[10] that all atoms are formed from the atoms of hydrogen. This implied that all atomic weights had to be whole numbers. Most of them, however, were not, but the question was whether the deviations were not the result of inaccurate analyses. When Berzelius analyses showed that with increasing accuracy the deviations from whole numbers became more and more manifest, Prout's hypothesis had to be shelved provisionally.

Berzelius also gave to chemistry its modern symbols. The idea itself of using symobls was already very old. Dalton too, used certain symbols to indicate his atoms, but Berzelius greatly simplified the existing systems by replacing the current signs with letters—the first letter of the Latin name of each element.

---

[10]The English chemist Prout (1785-1850), must not be confused with his French colleague Proust, whose name is attached to the Law of Constant Proportions of chemical compounds.

Thus much had been accomplished in a short time. However, within the limits of the then known problems, one great difficulty remained, against which Dalton had already struggled. From one volume of oxygen and one volume of nitrogen two volumes of oxide of nitrogen are formed. In the hypothesis of equal numbers of atoms in equal volumes this would imply that from one atom of oxygen and one atom of nitrogen two atoms of oxide of nitrogen would be formed. Hence the atoms would have to split, which was contrary to the hypothesis of the indivisibility of atoms. Now this indivisibility was a fundamental principle of the *chemical* atomic theory. It had been introduced into the theory, not for philosophic reasons, as was the case with Democritus' atomic theory, but because without indivisible atoms a firm basis would have been lacking for the entire chemical theory; for instance, for Proust's Law of Constant Proportions and Dalton's Law of Multiple Proportions. If the indivisibility of atoms had been introduced only for philosophic reasons, the chemists would not have worried very much about it.

Avogadro. Amadeo Avogadro (1776-1856), an Italian chemist, found the solution for the difficulties. He formulated the hypothesis that the atoms of one element could combine into compound atoms or molecules. Hence not only molecules of compounds had to be reckoned with, but also molecules of elements. According to Avogadro, the law which postulated an equal number of atoms in equal volumes of gas had to be understood as applying to an equal number of *molecules*. In this form, the law is still known as the Law of Avogadro. Although originally proposed in 1811, the idea of *compound atoms* of the same kind appeared too strange to be immediately accepted. It took several decennia before it found general favor. Meanwhile the work of Lavoisier, Dalton, and Berzelius, was followed by the discovery or the recognition of a large number of elements as such. This created the possibility to determine accurately a steadily increasing number of compounds. The chemical symbols proved of great value because they expressed combinations in a simple manner. Water, for instance, which is formed from two atoms of hydrogen (H) and one atom of oxygen (O) got the formula H_2O; sulphuric acid which consists of two atoms of hydrogen (H), one atom of sulphur (S), and four atoms of oxygen (O) was represented by H_2SO_4.

4. PERIODIC TABLE OF ELEMENTS

Lothar Meyer and Mendelejeff. The period around the seventies of the eighteenth century saw another important development in the atomic theory. Independently of each other Julius Lothar Meyer and Dmitri Mendelejeff drew up the periodic table of elements. Both discovered a certain periodicity when the elements were tabulated according to increasing atomic weights. Whenever a certain series of elements is passed, other elements occur which show a great analogy to the preceding elements. Their chemical behavior shows a large degree of similarity. For instance, the ninth element of the series, sodium (Na), strongly resembles the second, lithium (Li) ; the tenth, beryllium (Be), resembles the third, magnesium (Mg) ; and so on. The sixteenth, potassium (K), shows great similarity to sodium and magnesium (Mg), resembles the third, beryllium (Be) ; and so on. There seemed to be a fairly perfect natural table of elements. So strongly did this table suggest itself that its creators did not hesitate to leave a vacancy after calcium and put titanium on the next place, because according to its *properties* titanium should not come immediately after calcium. The vacant place meant an unknown element. Between zinc (Zn) and arsenic (As) even two places were left open, as can be seen on the next page in the systematic table of elements as originally proposed by Mendelejeff. Thanks to the great regularity in the system of elements, it became possible to predict fairly accurately several physical and chemical properties of the missing elements. For instance, on the basis of its place in the periodic table, an atomic weight of 72 had been predicted for the element germanium, which Winkle discovered in 1886.

PERIODIC TABLE OF ELEMENTS ACCORDING TO MENDELEJEFF[11]

Series	GROUP I — R_2O	GROUP II — RO	GROUP III — R_2O_3	GROUP IV RH_4 RO_2	GROUP V RH_3 R_2O_5	GROUP VI RH_2 RO_3	GROUP VII RH R_2O_7	GROUP VIII — RO_4
1	H 1							—
2	Li 7	Be 9.4	B 11	C 12	N 14	O 16	F 19	
3	Na 23	Mg 24	Al 27.3	Si 28	P 31	S 32		
4	K 39	Ca 40	—44	Ti 48	V 51	Cr 52	Mn 55	Fe 56, Co 59, Ni 59, Cu 63
5	(Cu 63)	Zn 65	—68	—72	As 75	Se 78	Br 80	
6	Rb 85	Sr 87	?Yt 88	Zr 90	Nb 94	Mo 96	—100	Ru 104, Rh 104, Pd 106, Ag 108
7	(Ag 108)	Cd 112	In 113	Sn 118	Sb 122	Te 125	I 127	
8	Cs 133	Ba 137	?Di 138	?Ce 140	—	—	—	—
9	(—)	—	—	—				
10	—	—	?Er 178	?La 180	Ta 182	W 184	—	Os 195, Ir 197, Pt 198, Au 199
11	(Au 199)	Hg 200	Tl 204	Pb 207	Bi 208	—	—	
12	—	—	—	Th 231	—	U 240		—

[11]From Fr. Dannemann, *Die Naturwissenschaften in ihrer Entwicklung und in ihrem Zusammenhange*, Leipzig[2] 1923, p. 348.

It was found to be 72.3. Many other properties could be predicted with a surprising amount of accuracy, as is shown in the following table:

	Predicted	Found
Atomic Weight	72	72.3
Specific Gravity	5.5	5.47
Formula of Oxide	XO_2	GeO_2
Specific Gravity of Oxide	4.7	4.703
Formula of Chloride	XCl_4	$GeCl_4$
Boiling Point of Chloride	below 100°C.	86°C.
Formula of Fluoride	XF_4	GeF_4
Formula of Ethyl Compound......	$X(C_2H_5)_4$	$Ge(C_2H_5)_4$
Boiling Point of Ethyl Compound..	160°C.	160°C.
Specific Gravity of Ethyl Compound	0.96	0.96

The accuracy is, indeed, striking. It did not fail to increase the authority of the periodic table notwithstanding the difficulties which kept confronting this system. Fortunately these difficulties did not all arise at the same time. For instance, in determining the order of elements in the periodic table Mendelejeff had followed the increase of atomic weight. Later it became clear that this principle could not be maintained consistently. There were some elements for which it had to be abandoned on account of their similarity with other elements, for example, tellurium (Te) with the atomic weight 127.61, and iodine (I) with the weight 126.92.[12] Tellurium is clearly related to sulphur, and iodine to chlorine. Sulphur, however, comes before chlorine in the periodic table. Hence it was obvious that tellurium should also come before iodine notwithstanding the atomic weights. It became clear that the principle of classification had to be sought not in the atomic weight itself, but in some other factor closely connected with it. Meanwhile this much at least had become certain from the periodic table of elements: the elements were certainly related to each other to a large extent. Hence there arose spontaneously the thought that every element was built of the same fundamental matter. Prout's hypothesis which pointed to hydrogen as this fundamental matter was still maintained as a possible explanation, although the fact that the atomic numbers of many elements were not

---

[12]This difficulty did not exist for Mendelejeff, because when he devised the atomic tables the atomic weights of these elements were only inaccurately known.

whole numbers remained a serious, and for the time being, unsurmountable difficulty.

Radioactivity.   Towards the end of the nineteenth century the
general idea that all elements consist of the same fundamental matter
found additional support in various discoveries and theories.   We
will mention only the most striking of these discoveries, which was
the phenomenon of radioactivity discovered in 1895 by Becquerel
(1852-1908), and the Curies.   Certain elements with a high atomic
weight were found spontaneously to disintegrate into elements of a
lower atomic weight.   This disintegration was accompanied by the
emission of rays.   Closer investigation revealed that the rays were of
three types, named alpha, beta, and gamma.   The alpha and beta
rays could be identified as rapid streams of material particles which
had respectively a positive and a negative electric charge and differed
considerably in mass and velocity.   The mass of alpha particles was
seen to be about four times that of the atom of hydrogen, whereas
the mass of beta particles was much smaller than the mass of hydrogen.   It was only about $\frac{1}{1840}$ of the atom of hydrogen and constituted
the smallest mass then known.   The velocity, however, of the beta
particles was very great and belonged to the same class as the velocity
of light.   The velocity of the alpha particles was considerably less,
but still greater than the velocity of any then known material particles.
The third type of rays, the gamma rays, did not consist of material
particles.   It appeared to be of the same kind as electro-magnetic
waves, but possessed an extraordinarily short wave-length.

The exact meaning of this discovery can be discussed only when
we have surveyed the development of several other branches of physics
and chemistry, because the connection between the various branches
of sciences is becoming more and more intimate.   Discoveries in one
branch have immediate consequences in another.   Provisionally we
want only to draw attention to the fact that the discovery of radioactivity gave strong support to the idea that the atoms of different
elements contain a common basic component.   Some atoms, at any
rate, were clearly composed.

5. ORGANIC CHEMISTRY

Origin of the Name.   The growth of organic chemistry was also
very important for the atomic theory.   The name *organic chemistry*
owes its origin to the ancient idea that there existed a group of

chemical compounds which could be produced only by living organisms. When, however, some compounds which certainly had to be considered as *organic* were successfully produced by synthesis in the laboratory, this idea had to be abandoned. Thus oxalic acid was synthetized in 1824, urea in 1828, both by Woehler, and acetic acid in 1845 by Kolbe. Hence it became obvious that as far as production is concerned, there was no essential difference between *organic* and *inorganic* chemistry. Continued research, however, showed that there was reason to maintain the difference between the two branches of chemistry, but that the name *organic* chemistry could be fittingly changed into *carbon chemistry*. It became clear that carbon compounds occupied a special place, not so much because they are the building material of living organisms, but rather because of the peculiar properties of the element carbon and its compounds. For instance, the number of its compounds is about twice as big as that of all other elements together. This appeared to be a **result of the tendency** of carbon to form compounds which contain chains of many atoms of carbon.

Isomerism. It was most remarkable that organic chemistry knew compounds which were combinations of the same atoms, but possessed different properties. This phenomenon, which is called isomerism, occurs, for instance, in the so-called saturated hydrocarbons. They are a series of substances which can be grouped under the common formula C_nH_{2n+2}. In this formula n can have a value of 1, 2, 3, 4, etc. While there is only one substance with a combination of CH_4, one of C_2H_6, and one of C_3H_8, there are two with the combination of C_4H_{10}, and three with C_5H_{12}. But C_6H_{14} already has five isomers, C_7H_{16} nine, and thereafter the number increases rapidly. For $C_{10}H_{22}$ there are 72. The explanation of this and other remarkable phenomena was given by Jacob van 't Hoff (1852-1911). Assuming that carbon is tetravalent, i.e. that one atom of carbon combines with four atoms of hydrogen, van 't Hoff formed a hypothesis about the spatial arrangement of a molecule composed of carbon and other atoms. For the sake of clarity we will limit ourselves to the series of compounds of carbon and hydrogen. Van 't Hoff conceived the first term of this series (CH_4) as spatially arranged in such a way that the atom of carbon is located in the center of a tetrahedron, the four corners of which are determined by the four atoms of hydrogen. Thus the valence of the atom of carbon is arranged in four spatially different directions. In the compound C_2H_6, two tetrahedrons are joined in such a way that in either tetrahedron three atoms of hydrogen occupy their normal position while the two remaining bonds of the compound, one for each tetrahedron, are joined to each other. In this atomic model only one combination of C_3H_8 is possible, two of C_4H_{10}, three of C_5H_{12}, etc. This agreed perfectly with the number of isomeric combinations which are found in nature or can be synthetized in the laboratory. Moreover, other more complicated isomeric phenomena could be explained by the hypothesis of the tetrahedral model. It goes without saying that this simple explanation of a spatial atomic model offered a strong argument in favor of the reality of atoms. We will come back to this later in connection with another problem.

6. THE KINETIC THEORY OF GASES

Revival of the Theories of Impact. Another contribution to the development of the atomic theory came from physics in the form of the kinetic theory of gases. Its purpose was to derive the gas laws from the motions of the hypothetical molecules. We do not intend to survey all the theories which were advanced in the course of the eighteenth century, but will mention only that, under the influence of Newton, the mathematician-philosopher G. Boscovich (1711-1787), devised a system of atoms without extension. For him atoms were sort of point-centers of energy. Ampère, Cauchy, and Laplace, proposed similar theories. Even the phenomena of impact were treated according to the theory of forces acting from a distance. Later, however, due to the influence of Maxwell's theory of electromagnetic fields,[13] the mechanical theory of impact became again preponderant. The reason was that the same mathematical law which holds for gravitation appeared to apply to the mutual attraction and repulsion of electric charges with the proviso that in the formula mass be replaced by charge. Hence the formulas were respectively

$$K_{gr} = \frac{m_1 \times m_2}{r^2} \text{ (Newton)} \quad \text{and} \quad K_{el} = \frac{e_1 \times e_2}{r^2} \text{ (Coulomb)}$$

Later, however, it became clear that Coulomb's formula is not complete. Another important factor had to be added in order to account for the influence of the medium, i.e. of the matter which is between the charges that attract or repel each other. This factor led to the hypothesis that in the immediate surroundings of a charge, the medium undergoes a gradually spreading change. Thus the

---

[13]See below p. 154.

mathematical formula of a force acting from a distance got a physical interpretation which reduced it to the mutual influence of juxtaposed spatial particles. Henceforth the idea of action from a distance was but a concise expression for a series of processes by means of which the distance is in reality only gradually bridged. This same thought was now transferred to the motions of colliding particles so that the classical theory of impact was restored to honor. Research scientists such as Clausius, Maxwell, and Boltzmann, definitely succeeded in deriving the behavior of gases, as described in the empirical laws of Boyle and Gay-Lussac, from the motions of the individual molecules of gases. Of course, the motions of each individual molecule were not known, but with the aid of the calculus of probabiltiy, a reasonable assumption about the average velocity of the particles could be made. From this assumption, combined with the hypothesis of perfect elasticity, it was possible to derive certain conclusions about the behavior of gases.

All this acquired special importance in view of the fact that between 1840 and 1850, R. Mayer, Joule, and Helmholz, had arrived at the conclusion that heat is also a form of energy. By different methods they had tried to determine the so-called mechanical equivalent of heat which corresponds to a definite amount of energy (1 cal. $= 4.2$ x 10^7 ergs). Already in 1824 Carnot had turned his attention to similar problems, but he had conceived heat as a special kind of matter in accordance with the then current concept, which was held also, for instance, by Dalton. Although by itself this equivalence of heat and energy had not yet revealed anything about the nature of heat, nevertheless the speculations about energy acted as a stimulating force on the theory that heat is not a special form of matter, but a certain state of motion of matter. In the kinetic theory of gases, heat was subsequently identified with the energy of random molecular motion, and thus a natural explanation of many facts had become possible.

Controversy about the Reality of Atoms and Molecules. Critical views, however, of the kinetic theory of gases were not lacking. But they were directed not against the theory itself, but against its interpretations. Was it really necessary to admit molecules and atoms because of mathematical formulas expressing the phenomena of gases? Was it not sufficient to admit the mathematical formulas which the kinetic theory of gases had established? Was it absolutely necessary to admit the real existence of motion in molecules which no one had ever observed? Were there not a large number of thermodynamic formulas which gave an accurate description of chemical and physical processes without any necessity or even possibility of reducing these formulas to the motion of particles?[14] How should these particles and their motion be conceived in solids, to which the thermo-dynamic laws were also applicable? Since these atoms and molecules had always escaped observation and were only admitted hypothetically, were they not, perhaps, only a last vestige of the metaphysical period? Did not physical science owe its enormous progress in the last century to the fact that it had been based exclusively upon empirical data? Should not everything which is not subject to experience be removed from it? To use the famous phrase of Kirchhoff, was it not true that *"the purpose of physical science is to describe as perfectly and as simply as possible the phenomena occurring in nature?"* The objections were not so much against the use of the terms *atom* and *molecule* as heuristic concepts, nor against the atomic hypothesis as a simple model from which many data could easily be derived, but rather against the idea that in view of the successes of the atomic theory atoms and molecules had to be admitted as really existing in nature. While for many physicists and chemists the atomic theory came first in importance, because it gave an insight into the real structure of matter, for others it was only a more or less successful aid in describing the behavior of substances.

The Twofold Aspect of the Critique. At the present stage of our study we must resist the temptation of entering more profoundly into this problem. It is mentioned here only because it constitutes an important moment in the history of the atomic theory. Meanwhile it should be clear that this problem does not belong exclusively to physical science, but also to philosophy. The worry expressed by the series of questions above did not result from mere doubts about the physical existence of atoms and molecules.[15] A difference of view about the value of *any and every* physical theory contributed to it. To a certain extent the doubt sprang from that mentality which in the history of philosophy is called positivistic. In the last

---

[14]An example of a basic thermodynamic rule is the Principle of Conservation of Energy. All processes take place in such a way that this principle is observed.

[15]As an example of a doubt which is really based upon physical science we may point to the difficulty of forming an idea of the motions of atoms and molecules in solid substances.

chapter we will have an opportunity to revert to this philosophic problem.

Best known in this struggle about the atom are two outstanding scientists, W. Ostwald and E. Mach. The latter wrote:

> The atomic theory has in physical science a function which is similar to that of certain mathematical auxiliary representations. It is a mathematical *model* used for the representation of facts. Although vibration is represented by sine-curves, the process of cooling by exponentials, and the length of fall by squares of time, no one would admit that vibration *itself* has anything to do with angular or circular functions, or fall with squares.[16]

Famous too, are the attacks of Ostwald who would have liked to remove the concept *atom* entirely from physical science. The reaction of his friend van 't Hoff against this view is interesting. In a letter to Arrhenius he wrote:

> You write about the anti-kinetic utterances of Ostwald. I too, must say that with a fairly large expenditure of mathematical development the kinetic theory barely gives the current 4% interest on capital, and I think that even this theory should be measured by its fruits. The representations themselves, atom, molecule, their dimensions, and perhaps their shapes, are after all something doubtful, as is the tetrahedron itself. But as long as something good comes *from* it, one can console oneself and believe that there is also something good *in* it. Here, however, applies the proverb: "Virtue must show itself."[17]

It is easy to understand that the man who had devised the tetrahedral model saw more in it than an auxiliary for the description of isomeric phenomena. However, one may be inclined to ask: How could a chemist such as Ostwald be in favor of denying not only all real value to the concept *atom,* but even of banishing it entirely from physical science? What would happen to concepts, so important for chemistry, such as can be quantitatively determined, as atomic weight? The difficulty is not as great as it appears. The concept *atomic weight* could be maintained, although its definition would have to be reworded. Instead of saying "the number which indicates how many times heavier one atom of an element is than one atom of hydrogen" we would have to say: "the number which indicates the proportion of weight between the smallest quantity of a substance that takes part in a reaction and

---

[16]E. Mach, *Die Mechanik in ihrer Entwicklung,* Leipzig[9] 1933, p. 467.

[17]Quoted from E. Cohen, *Vijftig jaren Revolutie,* Amsterdam 1939, p. 10.

the smallest quantity of hydrogen which takes part in a reaction."
Thus this difficulty could be overcome, but it would remain true that
man would ask himself the obvious question why substances react
in such minimal quantities.

The Brownian Motion. As mentioned, the opposition to the atomic
theory had a twofold basis, one physical and the other philosophical.
Mach was the principal exponent of the philosophic difficulties. Ostwald's objections were directed rather against many really obscure
points of the atomic theory which were essentially physical in nature,
for instance, the immutability of the atoms and the disappearance of
the properties of an element in a compound; although even for Ostwald
philosophic and scientific objections were closely united. Fortunately
the course of history has been kind enough to separate these two kinds
of difficulties. We cannot mention all the details, but will have to be
satisfied with one important datum, namely the investigation of the so-
called Brownian motion. This term indicates the phenomenon, discovered by Brown in 1827, that extremely small particles which are
barely visible under a microscope begin to move in a zigzag pattern
when suspended in a liquid. Accurate observation showed two facts:
first, that this motion could not be due to some external cause; and
secondly, that quantitatively it could be explained fully by the hypothetical motion of the molecules of the liquid (Perrin 1909). For if
with the kinetic theory of gases one admits that the molecules of a
liquid are in constant motion, it follows that they must continually
collide with particles suspended in the liquid. The form of this
motion corresponded exactly to the size, mass, and average velocity
of the molecules, as admitted by the kinetic theory of gases. Practically speaking, therefore, one could say that the motion of molecules
had been observed indirectly. This made such an impression that
even Ostwald declared himself convinced of the existence of something like a grainy structure of matter. Meanwhile many experiments were made in which the behavior of separate particles could
be observed more or less accurately, so that no physicist *as a physicist*
could be in doubt any longer about the real existence of atoms and
molecules. Philosophic difficulties might still be raised against the
reality of atoms and molecules, but it would no longer be possible
to find support for them in the physical atomic theory. According
to physical standards the smallest particles had been observed more
or less directly. Hence our previous remark that the course of history
has been kind enough to separate philosophic and scientific difficulties. The special nature of these philosophic difficulties will be

considered in the last chapter. Provisionally we mention only that on account of their different nature, they could continue to exist when the physical difficulties might seem to have been solved.

7. THE ELECTROMAGNETIC LIGHT THEORY

The Difficulties of the Old Theory. In order to get a true picture of the position occupied by the atomic theory at the end of the nineteenth century, it is necessary to survey briefly the evolution which took place in the views about electric and magnetic phenomena. Two theories especially will be of importance. The first is the electronic theory, which is directly connected with the atomic theory. The second is the electromagnetic theory of light, which provisionally had only an indirect bearing upon the atomic theory. Since the seventeenth century two classical theories of light had opposed each other, Huygens' wave theory and Newton's corpuscular theory. The crucial experiment for the two theories was the determination of the velocity of light in the so-called optically denser media. According to Newton the well-known phenomenon that a ray of light is broken in the transition from one substance into another, for instance, from air into water, is explained by the attraction which the optically denser substance (water) exercises upon the particles. Hence their velocity had to be greater. However, Foucault was able to establish experimentally that this is not the case (1854). Because this experimental datum agreed with the wave theory, and the latter, moreover, gave an easier explanation for the phenomenon of motion and interference than Newton's corpuscular theory, Huygens' view seemed definitely to have been confirmed. One big difficulty, however, remained in the wave theory: What was undulating, what was vibrating? The answer was not difficult in the case of the prototype of all undulation, the waves of water; for one could safely say that particles of water executed the upward and downward motions. As regards sound waves, one could fittingly point to the molecules of air as the vibrating substance. But what substance vibrates with waves of light? Of old, many theories of natural philosophy were in possession of concepts indicating a special kind of matter, called quintessence, ether, special fluid, very fine splinter matter, and the like. Hence there seemed to be no objection against placing the vibrations of light in some such medium, different from ordinary matter. However, due to the development of mechanics it became possible to indicate a connection between the mechanical properties of a substance and the vibrations of which it is capable. As the knowledge of this kind of phenomena increased, the hypothetical ether began to give all kinds of difficulties. On one hand, it had to possess the constitution of a very fine gas; otherwise it could not penetrate into everything. On the other hand, the fact that light waves are transverse, i.e. vibrate perpendicularly to the direction of propagation, indicated that the ether possessed the properties of a solid with a very high degree of elasticity. Thus the theory found itself in a predicament.

J. C. Maxwell. A provisional solution of the difficulty was offered by J. C. Maxwell (1831-1879), when he succeeded in making it acceptable that light is an electromagnetic undulation. According to his hypothesis the vibrations would be the periodic changes of electric and magnetic field intensities. Several reasons led Maxwell to this hypothesis. In the first place, the experimentally established velocity of light corresponded to the velocity of the electromagnetic waves in Maxwell's theory. Secondly, light possessed several properties which corresponded accurately to Maxwell's formula of electromagnetic waves.

A few words may be added here about Maxwell's electromagnetic wave theory which caused such a radical change in the problem of light. It owed its origin to the desire to give an explanation of electric and magnetic phenomena. For some time already it had been known that electric charges attract each other according to a formula which corresponds to that of Newton, provided that mass be replaced by charge.[18] The formula applying to magnetic charges, likewise, was entirely similar. In view of the then current interpretation of Newton's ideas, it was only natural to conceive this force of attraction as acting from a distance. When, however, Faraday discovered that the medium between two electric charges exercises influence upon the interaction of the forces, the picture of electric attraction changed.[19] Henceforth the attraction between two charges was seen as the resultant of a whole group of physical influences which gradually expand through space. This expansion, the gradual change of state, requires time. Maxwell's formulas gave an accurate account for this matter. Another matter for which his theory accounted was formed by a group of phenomena which refer to the interaction of electric current and magnetism. An electric current causes magnetism (Oersted, Ampère, Arago, about 1820), and a magnet under certain conditions causes an electric cur-

---

[18]See above, p. 148.

[19]Likewise, the concept of gravitation, as already mentioned.

rent. These facts and the connected phenomena of induction were summarized by Maxwell in his famous equations which express a quantitative connection between the changes in a magnetic field and the electric field caused by it, and vice versa. According to his theory these changes take place as undulatory motions of both field intensities. Shortly afterwards several successful experiments of Herz confirmed Maxwell's theory that there exist electromagnetic waves of the same nature as light. Herz, first, succeeded in producing electric waves, and then showed that these waves produced the same phenomena as light waves.

The importance of Maxwell's theory lies in this that it enables us to survey in one comprehensive grasp a large group of physical phenomena. It became clear that the X-rays which were discovered at the end of the nineteenth century, the radioactive gamma rays, the light rays and their extensions of ultraviolet and infrared rays, the heat rays, and Herz's electromagnetic waves (radiowaves), all possess the same physical character and differed, physically speaking, only in wave length. Between the wave length of X-rays (6×10^{-11} cm) and that of radiowaves (2×10^5 cm) are the light waves with wave lengths of 4×10^{-5} cm for violet and 8×10^{-5} cm for red light. Within the limits of the whole there is room on both sides of light for infrared and ultraviolet light, heat rays, etc. Henceforth the theory of light no longer occupied any special place, but was integrated into electrodynamics. Thus there remained practically only two large branches of physics at the end of the nineteenth century, namely mechanics and electrodynamics. Maxwell himself had tried to give a mechanical basis to his theory of electromagnetic waves, but did not succeed very well. Notwithstanding the clear connection between the two branches of physics, it was not possible to devise a mechanical model of the electromagnetic wave theory.

8. THE ELECTRONIC THEORY

The Electron. The advance in the knowledge of electric phenomena has thus resulted in a wave theory exhibiting the typical continuity proper to such a theory, for waves travel through space with continuity. The atomic theory, on the other hand, is characterized by discontinuity. When various data became known which showed a close connection between the theory of electricity and the atomic theory, the latter gave rise to the electronic theory. The *electric atom,* the electron, was discovered rather gradually. The first step towards its discovery was taken by chemistry. In 1833 Faraday discovered that in electrolysis, i.e. in the decomposition of certain compounds by means of electric current, chemically equivalent weights of different substances were decomposed by the same quantity of electricity. Since chemically equivalent quantities consist of an equal number of particles, or if the compounds are multivalent, of $\frac{1}{2}$ or $\frac{1}{3}$ of this number, Faraday's law already pointed towards the existence of a minimal quantity of electricity, of an elementary charge. More important, however, was the discovery of cathode rays which occur when a discharge takes place under very low pressure of gas. By close investigation of these rays, J. Thomson discovered that these bundles of rays consist of very fast particles each of which has a negative unit of charge and $\frac{1}{1840}$ of the mass of hydrogen. Thanks to the improved technique of the Wilson cloud chamber it became possible to study accurately the behavior of a single particle of the current.[20]

The Ionic Theory. The proof of the reality of electrons, in turn, had important consequences for chemistry. In 1887 the Swedish chemist Arrhenius had introduced his so-called ionic theory. The concept *ion* had come from Faraday who understood by it the 'fragments' of a compound which is decomposed by an electric current. He called those fragments ions, because they 'walked' (the Greek ἰω means *I go*) with an electric charge towards one of the poles. In his theory Arrhenius specifically made the hypothesis that the ions of a compound do not come into existence when a solution of a compound is exposed to electric current, but that a large part of the molecules already have split into ions when the compound is dissolved in water. When, for instance, NaCl is dissolved in water, it splits into Na-ions with a positive charge and Cl-ions with a negative charge. These ions, therefore, differ from the respective atoms of Na and Cl by their charge. Thus chemistry and the theory of electricity became very intimately connected, because the ionic theory was accompanied by the hypothesis that the forces of attraction between the various atoms of a molecule are of an electric nature. When shortly after Arrhenius had

---

[20]The Wilson cloud chamber is an apparatus which makes it possible to observe indirectly the path of a single electron or of another small particle. One of the properties of an electron is that it causes ions to form in the gas through which it passes. Thus its path is, so to speak, marked by ions. Although it is not possible to magnify ions and to make them directly visible, they can be observed indirectly. If the gas in which the ions are formed is saturated with water vapor and made to expand at the exact moment when the electron draws its 'path of ions,' the result will be that the water vapor will condense around the ions so that a visible 'fog track' will accompany the 'path of ions.'

proposed this theory the electron passed from the status of a hypothesis to that of an observed reality, Arrhenius' negative ions were considered as atoms or group of atoms with one or more electrons, and positive ions as atoms or groups of atoms from which one or more electrons had been expelled. This agreed with the new theory of electricity in which what used to be called negative electricity was identified as 'real' electricity. For the electron was seen to possess a negative charge. A positive charge meant that the number of electrons had suffered a decrease below the normal level which is characteristic for the electrically neutral state of matter.

Thus the results obtained towards the end of the nineteenth century were very encouraging, not only as regards the progress made in the various branches of physical science, but especially with respect to the connections between these branches. They had been definitely established by apodictic experiments. Let us restate this briefly. The phenomena of heat could be incorporated in the atomic theory by means of mechanics. Chemistry had been drawn into the sphere of the science of electricity. The phenomena of light also could be treated within the same sphere because light had revealed itself as an electromagnetic undulation.

The Electron as the Building Block of the Atom. The theory of electricity had created the possibility of establishing the relations between matter and the light which is emitted by matter under certain conditions. In 1896 Zeeman discovered a phenomenon that for some time had been anticipated—namely, a change in the wave length of the light emitted by a sodium flame when the flame is placed in a strong magnetic field. Immediately afterwards, Lorentz was able to give the exact explanation of this phenomenon by means of the electronic theory that had been developed shortly before. He reasoned as follows: If light is an electromagnetic undulatory motion, it must be caused by electric vibration within matter. Therefore, the electrons within the atom are responsible for these vibrations. If this is true, then the wave length of the light emitted by incandescent matter must change when this matter is placed in a strong magnetic field. For a magnetic field exercises influence on the motion of the vibrating atoms. Lorentz could even calculate the precise change in wave length which Zeeman had found. The support which this offered to the electronic theory was obvious. For the fruitfulness of a physical theory does not reveal itself primarily in the explanation of phenomena which the theory explicitly intends to explain. True, any theory that provides a natural explanation for many phenomena, especially those of a highly divergent nature, impresses us profoundly by which it introduces in plurality. However, a theory will be far more convincing if it allows us to explain phenomena unknown when the theory was formulated. Such was the case with the electronic theory. When it was introduced, it was not known that spectral lines shift their position under the influence of a magnetic field.

As a result of the connection which the theory of electricity had established between the different branches of chemistry and physics, there were available at the beginning of the twentieth century theoretical and experimental materials for the construction of a new atomic theory which would endeavor to penetrate into the interior of Dalton's atoms. We mean the atomic model of Rutherford and Bohr (1911-1913), in which the electro-magnetic theories and the theory of matter meet each other. This model considers every atom as built of a nucleus with a positive charge around which as many electrons circle in fixed orbits as indicated by the charge of the nucleus. In the following chapter we will see more details of this model which forms the terminus of the development of the atomic theory in the nineteenth century and the starting point of the twentieth century atomic theory. Around 1900 the finer details of this model showed already the marks of a new development which had not been foreseen. For this reason we shall make a study of the mentality of the physicists at the end of the nineteenth century, especially in regard to the atomic theory, before we consider this new development and its bearing upon the mentality of the physicist.

9. THE DEVELOPMENT OF THE PERIODIC TABLE

Before we can analyze the mentality of the nineteenth century physicist we must mention a few other important discoveries. These discoveries were very valuable because they supplied numerous new data, especially as regards our knowledge of the periodic table of elements. The first discovery which extended and deepened our knowledge of the periodic table dealt with the so-called noble gases, helium, argon, etc. At first there seemed to be no room for them in the periodic table, because they could not be placed in any of the vacant spaces, as had been the case with the other elements. However, this difficulty existed only because of insufficient consideration. The close mutual connection of these elements and the fact that they did not form any chemical combinations suggested that they should be considered as a special group. The place of this group was then seen to be between that of the alkali metals (Li, Na K), which have a strong tendency to form univalent positive ions, and that of the halogens (F, Cl, Br, I), which easily change into univalent negative ions. This position, which corresponded to their inert character, also agreed with their atomic weight. Hence there really were places reserved for them in the atomic table. No attention had been paid to this, because when the periodic table was composed no representative of the group was yet known.

A second important extension of the periodic table took place when isotopes were discovered. This discovery also was destined to be of great importance for the theoretical foundation of the table. The existence of isotopes became evident from the study of radioactivity. In radioactivity the atom disintegrates through the emission of alpha and beta particles. The result is a new atom. Remarkably enough, these new atoms did not always correspond to the atoms which were already known. For example, from radium, which has an atomic weight of 226 and occupies the 88th place in the periodic table, an element is formed which has an atomic weight of 206, and according to its properties should occupy the 82nd place in the table. But that place is taken by lead (atomic weight 207). Hence ordinary lead and lead formed by radium were called isotopes (from the Greek ἴσος and τόπος, the same place). Closer investigation showed that isotopy was a common phenomenon. Moreover, it became clear that the elements whose atomic weights were not whole numbers consisted in reality of a mixture of isotopes, each of which had an atomic weight that could be expressed by a whole number. For instance, chlorine with an atomic weight of 35.5 is composed of two isotopes with the atomic weights of 35 and 37. Thus Prout was right after all.

Still another difficulty with the atomic table could be cleared. It will be recalled that the places assigned to tellurium and iodine by reason of their relationship to other elements, did not correspond to their atomic weights. The same had been true of some other elements, such as argon (atomic weight 39.994) and potassium (atomic weight 39.096). Hence the original criterion for the order of elements in the atomic table, that of increase in atomic weight, could not be maintained as such. Meanwhile, however, another fundamental property of elements had been discovered in the formula which expresses the

frequency of some determinate characteristic line in the X-ray spectra
of all elements (Mosely 1913). This formula is

$$v = \tfrac{3}{4} \, K \, (Z-1)^2$$

in which v is the frequency, K some determinate constant, and Z the
series of ascending whole numbers. For every element Z corresponds
to its place in the periodic table, and it was clear therefore that Z
can be used as the criterion of this place, i.e. of the ordinal or atomic
number.

Herewith we end our sketch of the history of the atomic theory in
the nineteenth century. If occasionally we have trespassed the bounds,
we should be excused since it was done only for the purpose of
mentioning in general some data which flowed immediately from
the nineteenth century theories. We will now interrupt our historical
explanations to investigate what was referred to above as the mentality
of the nineteenth century physicist. We could just as well have called
it the philosophic background or the undercurrent of the atomic theory
around the year 1900. Perhaps we may not find any such undercurrent at all, but at any rate the fact that this theory descends
directly from that of Dalton obliges us to investigate.

10. THE PHILOSOPHIC BACKGROUND OF THE ATOMIC THEORY AROUND 1900

The Difficulty of Determining a Philosophic Background. To
determine the philosophic background of a physical theory is an
arduous task, since its object is something which is, to say the least,
not clearly stated, but at most, only tacitly assumed. One may
object that although physicists and chemists themselves abstain from
mentioning their philosophic background, the philosophers of the
same period would do so all the more explicitly. According to this
viewpoint we should consult the philosophers of the period around
the turn of the century to discover the philosophic background of the
physical atomic theory in that same period. They would explicitly
declare whatever philosophic principles are implied in the scientific
theory. We should consult, of course, especially those philosophers
who were at the same time either students of physical science or at
least thoroughly acquainted with it. This view is not entirely wrong.
We must indeed consult the philosophers, but not in the manner
suggested by the above objection. For the philosophers of 1900 did

not take scientific data as the basis of their speculations about the philosophic implications of scientific theories. They had their own setting of problems, and in respect to these problems the various trends of the nineteenth century, such as Kantianism, Hegelianism, positivism, empiricism, realism, and many others, were divided both according to basic principles and ultimate conclusions. The conviction of philosophers, therefore, is determined primarily by their solutions of philosophic problems. Subsequently, this conviction also determines their view on physical science. This applies also to those philosophers who are at the same time scientists. Hence they are not directly useful for the object of our present inquiry. However, this does not mean that they are of no use at all. For example, a careful analysis of the manner in which E. Mach proposes his philosophic theses concerning the atomic theory, clearly reveals not only the conclusions which he accepts as true in the light of his philosophic principles, but it also shows what according to him ought to be rejected in the commonly accepted view which he attacks. When Mach asserts that a mechanical model is nothing but an auxiliary representation, a simple expression of our experiences in the manner most suitable for our way of thinking, it is clear that he attacks the view that such a mechanical model is an image, though an imperfect one, of reality. Thus frequently we find a reflection of the basic principles of non-philosophic scientists in the expressions used by philosophers. It is, however, the non-philosophic scientist who interests us most. For we are investigating the philosophic background of the atomic theory around the year 1900, and this means nothing else than that we are looking for the philosophic views which were assumed tacitly, or at least without conscious philosophic reflection on the tenets of this theory. Of course, we do not mean to claim that there are no philosophers who in their philosophy do not consciously think that they must admit the implicit philosophic conviction of the non-philosophic scientist. Such philosophers also exist, but prudence remains necessary when one intends to use them as authorities. For, as we will see in the last chapter, physical science has progressively freed itself from the bonds of philosophic settings, so that it can easily be placed in different philosophic perspectives. It is, as it were, indifferent to them, because it does not commit itself. Hence in general great prudence is necessary with regard to the philosophic interpretations of physical science by philosophers or philosophizing scientists, at least when the purpose is to discover whether there exists a philosophic background for physical science in a given period, and if so, what that background is. It can easily happen that these philosophers interpret the data according to their own convictions, without doing any obvious violence to physical scince. An intelligent reader may venture to remark that this applies equally well to the interpretations of the author! He is right. Let the reader be careful. However, the reader's conviction that the author did not embark upon this problem carelessly and unsuspectingly will perhaps be strengthened by the author's assurance that he realizes the difficulty inherent in any philosophic evaluation of physical science.

But now the question whether it be possible or not to speak about the philosophic background of the atomic theory becomes even more problematic. Suppose that such a background were discovered; would it not most likely be nothing but the product of the imagination of a philosopher who arbitrarily interprets the data of physical science? Before answering this question we must first state exactly what we mean by the vague term *philosophic background*. Without anticipating the discussion of the difference between philosophy and physical science, which will be made in the last chapter, we may give here a provisional answer. It is the answer which history itself provides.

The Nature of Physical Science. In the first chapter we examined in detail the reasons which led Democritus to propose atomism. Atomism was a general answer to the question why change is at all possible. All change had of necessity to be a change in position of intrinsically immutable atoms. A physical theory, however, which accepts particles in order to explain certain changes is an entirely different thing. Assuming that a gas consists of moving particles endowed with certain properties, such as size, velocity, and elasticity, the physicist can deduce the laws of gases. He does not say that molecules are intrinsically immutable, he does not assert that every change has to be explained in this manner. He states only that those changes which occur in gases are explained by the atomic theory. Or to express the same differently, the physicist tries to create an intelligible connection between certain facts which he provisionally accepts as the basis of his explanations—let us call them fundamental facts—and other facts, say between the fact that a gas consists of molecules, and the visible properties of a gas. We call them *facts* because in principle they can be verified by sense experience. This is immediately clear as regards the visible properties of a gas, and it is also true for the fundamental facts. The nature of a molecule is such that its characteristics are in principle subject to experience, or rather the properties of molecules fit into the frame of the physical methods of measurement and argumentation. Thus the object of the physicist differs greatly from that of Democritus. The properties of his atoms were primarily admitted in order to make apparent change intelligible and not to explain certain well-defined phenomena.

The mere fact that Democritus attributed different sizes and shapes to his atoms does not make his theory a physical one, although it may be admitted that in principle such properties belong to a physical sphere. The foundation which Democritus gave to his theory shows clearly that his setting of the problem was not physical. His atoms had to be endowed with the properties mentioned above in a continuous variation, in order to bring apparent change into harmony with the denial of real change. He was concerned with the philosophic problem of the possibility of change in general. The question whether or not philosophic speculations, such as those of Democritus, still have value nowadays, does not concern us here. The only point which demands our attention is whether the atomic theory of 1900 possessed the above-mentioned purely physical orientation or still showed traces recalling the philosophic setting of problems. As we have seen, the latter was the case with Dalton's atomic theory.

The Philosophic Background of the Nineteenth Century Atomic Theory Does Not Differ From That of Dalton's Theory. The view of the Universe offered by the nineteenth century atomic theory does not really differ much from that of Dalton's theory, although at first sight the difference appears to be fairly large. Dalton's atoms, upon which the nineteenth century theory had been built, were no longer considered as immutable. Radioactivity had shown that some atoms disintegrated spontaneously. Molecules were no longer seen as a mere juxtaposition of unchanging atoms. Yet those differences are only accidental. For in what did those changes consist which the atoms underwent in these two cases? In the first case the atom emitted other small particles. In the second the atoms became ions, which according to the atomic theory amounted to the addition or the loss of electrons. In other words, there were still immutable particles, though on a lower level than assumed by Dalton's atomic theory. His atoms revealed themselves as composed of several intrinsically immutable parts so that the loss or exchange of these component parts could account for the possibility of change on a sub-atomic level.

Thus the general picture of physical science had remained practically the same. The world was thought to be composed of smallest particles which differed in nature and which in certain definite ways could form relatively stable structures (atoms). These structures, in turn, were able to form new combinations (molecules) by exchanging certain component parts (electrons). The whole process was ruled by well known mechanical and electrodynamic laws.

It would not be easy to find a treatise of physics or chemistry which claims that every physical explanation must ultimately be reduced to some explanation based on the motion of immutable particles, although it is true that there were some physicists who more or less held this view.[21] Well-known especially is Lord Kelvin's statement that to understand a physical problem means to be able to make a mechanical model of it. However, it is not so very important whether this idea was explicitly formulated or not. It is far more important that the whole mentality of physical science showed this tendency. The Universe was conceived as an agglomeration of primitive particles, big ones and small ones, ruled by fixed laws. All the aspirations and ideals of the nineteenth century lie revealed in Laplace's famous concept of physical science:

> We must, therefore, conceive the present state of the Universe as the effect of its preceding and the cause of its future state. An intelligence which knows at a given instant all forces acting in nature and the respective position of all things which compose the Universe, would be able to embrace in one and the same formula the motions of the biggest bodies in the Universe as well as those of the smallest atoms, provided it were powerful enough to submit all these data to analysis. Nothing would be uncertain to it, future as well as past would be present before its eyes. In the perfection it has been able to give to astronomy the human mind offers a feeble image of such an intelligence. Man's discoveries in mechanics and geometry together with that of universal gravitation have enabled him to embrace the past and future states of the celestial system in the same analytic expressions. By applying the same method to other objects of knowledge he has succeeded in reducing observed phenomena to general laws and in foreseeing the phenomena which are bound to result from given conditions. All his efforts in this quest of truth tend to bring him nearer and nearer to that intelligence which we have described above, although he will remain forever infinitely far from it. It is this tendency, proper

---

[21] See J. H. Poincaré's objections against this view in *Science et Hypothèse* IV, ch. 10.

to the human race, which makes man superior to animals. Special achievements in this field distinguish nations and centuries, and constitute their true glory.[22]

Unwittingly every problem was placed against this mechanistic background, even though the latter was far from being deliberately accepted by all. Yet whoever applied himself to the study of physical science began to see the world as described by Laplace, unless for religious or philosophic reasons he deliberately took a different point of view and thus gave another philosophic interpretation to the data of physical science than that given by mechanism.[23]

We may now ask ourselves: What was the origin of this mechanical view of the world? The answer must be the same as that given in our study of Dalton: it came from tradition combined with the attraction of the mechanistic conception of the Universe and its astounding success in physical science. This success especially gave mechanism inexhaustible credit in the eyes of physicists. They had no doubt that whatever difficulties were to be found in their conception of the Universe would eventually be conquered. The time would come when everything could be mechanically explained whether it belonged to the field of physical science or not.[24] It will be clear now why we prefer to speak of mechanism as a *background*. The fundamental tenets of mechanism remained somewhat in the dark in the nineteenth century atomic theory, but full light was thrown upon the physical aspect of the theory and upon everything which by means of this theory could be completely or partially explained. Thus the idea was suggested that all explanations of physical phenomena had to be sought in a mechanistic conception of nature. Naturally this suggestion remained vague and was bound to lead to difficulties upon closer analysis. Not without reason had Democritus recognized only shape and size as fundamental properties of his atoms. Any other property was bound to come into

---

[22]Laplace, *Essai philosophique sur la probabilité,* used as *Introduction* to his work *Théorie analytique des probabilités, Oeuvres* VII, Paris 1847, p. VI.

[23]As an example of a different interpretation which upholds the scientific atomic theory we may cite P. Hoenen, *Filosofia della natura inorganica,* Brescia, 1949. In this book Hoenen interprets the scientific data as a specification of the Aristotelian minima theory. Although the book is based upon the twentieth century atomic theory, its author shows also that the nineteenth century atomic theory does not necessarily have to be interpreted mechanistically. Hence we may cite him here as an example.

[24]Typical of the vigor which emanated from the mechanistic conception of physics is the nineteenth century attitude towards free will. The freedom of the will was denied on the basis of determinism. We will come back on this in the next chapter. For an extensive treatment of the problem see Ph. Kohnstamm, *Vrije wil of determinisme,* Haarlem 1947.

conflict with the basic idea of the theory. Modern mechanism, how-ever, relied on other mysterious properties, such as elasticity and at-traction or repulsion. Undoubtedly, such properties were very useful as physical hypotheses, but they seemed strange customers in a wholly quantitative theory of atoms-without-qualities. In a more profound philosophic analysis these contradictions were bound to betray them-selves. We may, therefore, conclude: although the nineteenth century atomic theory was connected with the doctrine of mechanism, both at the beginning and at the end of that century, mechanism itself re-mained in the background, or to use an alternative expression, mechanism was only the undercurrent of the atomic speculations.

Before finishing this chapter let us make one more remark. After a superficial study one might be inclined to see a certain relationship between the views of, say Boyle, and the atomic theory at the end of the nineteenth century. We are not alluding to the mechanistic back-ground which, undoubtedly, was the same. But there is some point on which one might be inclined to think that the development of the atomic theory in the nineteenth century did justice to Boyle precisely insofar as Boyle's theory was different from that of Dalton. Contrary to Boyle who conceived the 'atoms' of chemical elements as composed of more primary elementary particles, Dalton considered the atoms of the elements as the most primitive particles. Hence it may seem that the atomic theory switched again to Boyle's view at the end of the nineteenth century. However, this is only apparently so, for Boyle for the avowed purpose of remaining loyal to the atomic theory admitted that primary concretions, the atoms of his elements, were composed of more primitive particles. The particles which formed his primary concretions were of *many different* shapes and sizes. The component parts of the atom as admitted by the nineteenth century atomic theory were only two-fold: the nucleus and the electron. To make matters worse from an atomistic point of view, the protons, as the nuclei of hydrogen are called, and the electrons were qualitatively different. They had different fundamental properties insofar as one had a positive and the other a negative charge of electricity.

Once more, this should make it clear that the atomic theory of the nineteenth century was primarily a physical theory. Certain prop-erties were attributed to the smallest particles not on account of philosophic speculations, but because of hypotheses postulated by ex-perimental data. We should never lose sight of this fact, even though it remains true that the atomic theory of the nineteenth century had a mechanistic background.

CHAPTER FIVE

THE ATOMIC THEORY IN THE TWENTIETH CENTURY

1. THE ATOMIC MODEL OF RUTHERFORD AND BOHR

A Fundamental Difficulty. As already mentioned, Lord Rutherford and Bohr by their construction of an atomic model successfully established a bridge between the electromagnetic theory of light and the theory of matter. It was a fitting conclusion to the development of the atomic theory in the nineteenth century, but it also meant the start of something new. For when speculating upon the problem which he wanted to solve, Bohr encountered a very peculiar difficulty. Let us have a close look at their atomic model. Rutherford and Bohr conceived the atom, analogous to a planetary system, as a nucleus around which a number of electrons move in different orbits. While planets are kept in their appointed orbits by the equilibrium between the centrifugal force of their orbital motion and the gravitational pull of the masses, the latter is replaced in the atom by the force of attraction between the positive charge of the nucleus and the negative charge of the electrons. It is in this negative charge that lies the peculiar difficulty to which we alluded above. According to electrodynamics the moving electrons ceaselessly emit electromagnetic waves which represent a certain amount of energy. According to the Law of Conservation of Energy this energy would have to be subtracted from the atom; in other words, the atom would not be stable but always losing energy. Hence the motion of the electrons around the nucleus would gradually decrease and finally cease entirely, since the process of loss of energy would continue as long as there would be any motion of electrons around the nucleus. This constituted a very fundamental difficulty. We say *fundamental* because it was caused by the fundamental idea of classical electro-dynamics—that periodically moving electricity emits an electromagnetic undulation. However, Bohr did not abandon his theory, for notwithstanding this difficulty the atomic model offered many possibilities of explaining fundamental data that there was no choice left. The theory—too fruitful—had to be maintained. Moreover, the classical conception of electro-dynamics had already caused difficulties on other points, as we shall see, and had to be revised anyhow.

Bohr's Postulates. In order to give the required stability to his atomic model, Bohr admitted some postulates which originally had no other purpose than to record the required deviations from the classical theory. These postulates are the following:

1) Electrons can move only on definite orbits of different energy levels, i.e. at different distances from the nucleus. The possible orbits had to fulfill the condition that the product of the impulse of an electron in a given orbit and the total length of that orbit be a whole number times a certain constant about which we will hear more presently. As long as an electron remains in the same orbit it does not emit any energy.

2) Emission of energy occurs only when an electron 'jumps' from one orbit to another. In that event an electromagnetic wave is emitted whose frequency is not in direct relationship to the frequency of the electronic motion. In order to understand this second postulate properly, it is to be noticed that according to electrodynamics the frequency of the emitted wave coresponded to the frequency with which the emitting electric charge performs its periodic motion. By frequency, usually indicated by ν, we mean the number of vibrations per second. According to Bohr, however, the frequency was determined by the following formula:

$$\nu = \frac{E_1 - E_2}{h}$$

in which E_1 and E_2 indicate the respective energy levels between which an electron jumps, and h the constant which is called Planck's constant.

Planck's Quantum Theory. This constant had been discovered a few years before by Planck when he solved another problem in which the classical theory had proved itself equally insufficient—namely the calculation of the distribution of energy over different wave lengths in the radiation of an incandescent body. According to calculations based on the classical theory this energy would lie for the greater part in the ultraviolet part of the spectrum. But this is contrary to fact. Planck solved this anomaly by formulating the hypothesis that the energy of vibrating sources of energy can be only a whole multiple of an elementary quantity of energy, $h\nu$; ν being the frequency of the source of energy, and h a constant with the dimension of a work[1] and a numerical value of 6.6×10^{-27} erg. $\times$ sec. Till about 1900 there had

---

[1]In mechanics the unit of work means the product of power and time during which the work is done.

been no reason for physicists to conceive the exchange of energy as discontinuous. The classical theories had all supposed that energy could pass through all values with continuity. Now it became clear that in energy also there existed a certain 'atomization'. Thus the physical concept *atom* got again an increase in extension. While the concept originally expressed only that space was not filled with continuous matter, or that matter could not be divided infinitely, later the concept had to be extended to include the atom of electricity, or electron, when it became clear that there was a definite minimum of electric charge and that every charge represented a multiple of that minimum. Remarkably enough, it also became clear that this minimum of electric charge was united to a definite amount of matter, the matter of an electron. Thus the concept of the 'ordinary' atom and that of the atom of electricity became closely connected. Factually the electron could be considered as one of the primordial material particles and thus as one of the material atoms. Now the idea of a *minimum of energy* was added to these material atoms. It was remarkable that the number of minima of energy was found to be equal to that of the possible frequencies. Hence it is better to speak of a *minimum of work*, which then is equal to h, so that we have to do with only one minimum.

Post factum, it should not surprise us that the discontinuous structure of energy had escaped observation by classical mechanics. The scale of sizes with which mechanics works, not only in the movement of planets, but also in the study of phenomena in bodies with a mass of some grams or milligrams, is such that the discontinuous structure cannot reveal itself. Processes which take place on such large scales appear entirely continuous. Hence however revolutionary Planck's idea may have been, it did not touch classical physics and mechanics. The only thing that changed was the insight that the experimentally well-founded laws of the classical theories applied only to the field in which they were discovered. Only the endeavor to extrapolate them outside this field met with difficulties. In fact, therefore, the situation amounted to the retention of the classical theory as a particular instance of the new, more general, theory.

Perhaps it is not entirely useless to remark that this is the normal course of affairs. As a rule the many new theories which arose in physical science during the course of the last century did not mean the destruction of the old theory, but only its incorporation in a more embracing theory. If anything is rejected in an old theory, it is usually only the explicit or implicit endeavor to extrapolate it over **a wider field than is** warranted by observation. This shows how solidly classical physics is founded on experimental data. At the same time it shows how easily man is inclined to generalize and extrapolate without sufficient reason. We shall see more about this in the last chapter, for we must limit ourselves here to the theory under consideration.

This theory, which is known as Planck's theory, was the key to the solution of many difficulties in diverse problems, which is a splendid confirmation of its exactness. We have seen, for example, how Bohr made a grateful use of Planck's constant in his atomic model. Obviously, it would be impossible to describe here all the theoretical possibilities offered by his model. They may be found in numerous modern works. We will give here only one application as an example.

The Atomic Model and the Spectra of Light. For some time certain regularities had been discovered in the spectra of several elements which could be expressed by the simple empirical formula

$$\mathbf{v} = K \left(\frac{1}{m^2} - \frac{1}{n^2} \right)$$

The formula expresses series of correlated spectral lines. A first series is obtained when m is given a value of 1, and n successively 2, 3, 4, 5, etc. Since K is a constant, a new frequency is obtained for every value of n, and therefore also a new spectral line which is characterized by this frequency. A second series results if m is replaced by 2, and n by 3, 4, 5, etc. With the aid of his atomic model Bohr succeeded in deriving this empirical formula theoretically up to, and inclusive of, the numerical value of the constant K.

The spectral lines of one series (one value for m and different values for n) correspond according to Bohr to the 'jumps' of electrons from different energy levels to one and the same final level. The special meaning of m and n is that they are numbers which represent the different possible energy levels on which the electrons may be found in the atom. Since these energy levels depend on the distances of the electrons from the nucleus, m and n characterize the different orbits around the nucleus. Accurate study, however, of the spectra showed that more numbers were needed to characterize the motion of the electrons. We shall not enter into details, but mention only that four quanta numbers are required to account also for the lesser details of the spectra.

The Atomic Model and Chemistry. A few remarks remain to be made about the results which the work of Bohr and his collaborators achieved as regards chemistry. In a truly amazing manner the regularities of the periodic table and simultaneously many typical differences in the chemical behavior of the elements were accounted for. According to Bohr's atomic model every atom consists of a nucleus around which one or more electrons move in different orbits. These orbits represent different energy levels. In one atom there are as many electrons as there are units of positive electricity in the nucleus. The charge of the nucleus increases always by units equal to the ordinal number of the element in the periodic table. Thus hydrogen consists of a nucleus with a charge of 1 around which one electron moves. The second element in the periodic table, helium, has a charge of 2, and therefore also 2 electrons in the shell. The term *shell* is preferably used to indicate the whole of associated orbits in which electrons move. It implies that the place in which the electrons move in a definite energy level is not a two dimensional figure, such as a circle, but a three dimensional figure, such as a sphere and the like. The third element, lithium, has a nuclear charge of 3 and 3 electrons. And so on. In the periodic table on p. 222 the elements are arranged according to atomic numbers. Hence from this number one can read at once the nuclear charge and the total number of electrons.

Beginning with lithium, something special happens. From theoretical considerations which we will not examine, it follows that the three electrons of lithium cannot move on the same energy level. The first energy level is 'full' with two electrons. Hence the third electron moves on the second level. Such a level should be conceived as a complex of connected levels rather than as a single level. Even within one level the electron can travel on several closely juxtaposed shells and jump from one to another. For the sake of convenience, however, we speak of one level or shell to indicate such a complex of closely juxtaposed shells. In lithium, then, two electrons are in the first level which now is full. The third electron begins to build a new level. Ascending in the periodic table, for each new element a new electron is added to this level. For instance, the 9th element, fluorine, has 7 electrons in the second shell, and the 10th element, neon, has 8. Now the second shell is also full. With sodium, the 11th element, a new level is started, so that its electrons are distributed as follows: 2 in the first, 8 in the second, and 1 in the third shell. We could continue in this manner, but what we have seen thus far suffices to derive some important properties of the elements. As seen in chapter IV, in the periodic table, the properties of lithium return with sodium. The cause of this phenomenon lies in the electronic configuration: like lithium, sodium has only one electron in the outermost shell. The same is true of all the elements in the first group. Potassium, for example, also has only one electron in the outermost shell, as can be seen in the table below which gives the electronic configuration of certain elements.

The elements related to fluorine, Cl, Br, and I, have each 7 electrons in the outermost shell; hence their relationship in chemical behavior is clear. The same applies to all the elements which, because they are placed in one group of the periodic table, have closely related properties: in every element of such a group the electronic configuration of the outermost shell is identical or almost identical. But there is more. In helium the outermost shell is full. In neon likewise. This explains the inert character of these elements. The outermost shell which shows itself responsible for chemical behavior possesses a

		LEVELS						
Number	Element	1	2	3	4	5	6	7
1	H	1						
2	He	2						
3	Li	2	1					
4	Be	2	2					
5	B	2	3					
6	C	2	4					
7	N	2	5					
8	O	2	6					
9	P	2	7					
10	Ne	2	8					
11	Na	2	8	1				
17	Cl	2	8	7				
18	Ar	2	8	8				
19	K	2	8	8	1			
35	Br	2	8	18	7			
36	Kr	2	8	18	8			
37	Rb	2	8	18	8	1		
53	I	2	8	18	18	7		
54	X	2	8	18	18	8		
55	Cs	2	8	18	18	8	1	
56	Ba	2	8	18	18	8	2	
57	La	2	8	18	18	9	2	
58	Ce	2	8	18	19	9	2	
59	Pr	2	8	18	20	9	2	
71	Cp	2	8	18	32	9	2	
72	Hf	2	8	18	32	10	2	

stability which does not allow the reception or the loss of electrons.[2] This also explains why elements with a single electron in the outermost shell, such as Li, Na, and K, show such a strong tendency to form univalent ions. The single electron can easily be lost, because it is relatively loosely connected so that little energy is needed to remove it. A second electron, however, would have to come from a stable shell, and that would require much energy. We customarily express this by saying that the atoms have a tendency to assume the configuration of a noble gas, i.e. a configuration with a 'full' outermost shell. In elements such as F, Cl, Br, and I, which have 7 electrons in the outermost shell this tendency to the configuration of a noble gas will express itself by the inclination to assume one electron and thus to form a stable shell. In other words, they will easily change into univalent negative ions.

For a proper appreciation of the importance which must be attributed to the explanation of chemical properties by electronic configuration it should be kept in mind that the distribution of electrons among the shells had been made for theoretical reasons based on the spectral data of the diverse elements. The distribution had not been inspired by the desire to account for the above mentioned chemical properties. The fact, however, that this distribution gave an explanation for the *chemical* behavior of the elements was a splendid confirmation of Bohr's atomic model. New light was thrown on the natural relationship of the different elements as recorded in the periodic table. This relationship was connected with the internal structure of the atoms of different elements. Relationship in structure was shown to be the cause of relationship in chemical behavior.

By means of the atomic model another striking difficulty of the modern periodic table was solved. In a single place of the table, in the 7th series of the 3rd group, where the 57th element could be expected, no less than 15 elements, the so called rare earth metals, had to be placed. That they belong there is immediately clear from the respective atomic weights of the numbers 56 and 72 which show a difference in weight of about 51, although they are only two places distant. Although there was no doubt that the 15 rare earth metals with their 15 different nuclear charges had to occupy only one place in the periodic table, the reason was far from clear. The Bohr atomic model solved the difficulty. The chemical qualities

[2]The number of electrons in stable outermost shells is 2, 8, 18, or 32.

which determine the place in the periodic table depend mainly upon the electronic configuration of the outermost shells. A look at the table on p. 171 shows that the 15 elements in question have the same number of electrons in the two outermost shells and differ only in the fourth shell. Thus it is clear why they should occupy only one place. There are several other chemical and physical problems which are nicely solved by Bohr's theory, but for them we must refer the reader to textbooks of chemistry and physics.

Meanwhile it is interesting to note that the development of the atomic model in the sense indicated above remained entirely within the frame of the nineteenth century mechanistic conceptions. The additions to our knowledge of atomic structure was projected against this background, as is clear, for example, from such terminology as electronic *orbits,* etc. Nevertheless the quantum postulates of Bohr's theory were bound to rock this mechanistic background. After all, these postulates were really in flagrant contradiction to the classical theories. The situation was far from satisfactory. Hence there was a tendency towards a new, more general, theory which would both embody the classical theories and provide natural surroundings for Bohr's postulates. For although they contradicted each other on certain points, both had proved their good right to existence.

The conjecture of Planck and Bohr had been fortunate, but needed a broader and more solid theoretical foundation. It was going to be provided by a more profound insight into the phenomena of light.

2. THE DUALISTIC CHARACTER OF MATTER[2a]

The Dualism in the Theory of Light. Shortly after Planck had proposed his sensational theory, a remarkable phenomenon was discovered, which is called the photoelectric effect. When ultraviolet light falls on a metal plate it liberates electrons from the plate. In itself this is not very remarkable. According to the accepted theories there are in a metal plate electrons which can move freely in it and therefore should also be able to leave the plate when sufficient energy is supplied for the purpose. But what is remarkable is that the occurrence of this effect does not depend on the intensity of the light but on its frequency. Only if the light is of a certain frequency, even though its intensity is very weak, does the effect take place. The only effect of the weakness in intensity is that the number of electrons which are liberated from the plate is very small. According to the intensity of

---

[2a]See p. 193 for footnote.

the light few or many electrons are liberated, but they all possess the same kinetic energy. This may be expressed by the formula

$$h\nu = \tfrac{1}{2}mv^2 + T$$

in which T represents the amount of energy required to liberate one electron from the plate. If $h\nu$ is smaller than T, nothing happens. If it is greater than T, $h\nu - T$ indicates the kinetic energy of the electrons which are liberated from the plate.

These remarkable experimental data could not be explained by the wave theory. According to this theory intensity is a measure of energy of radiation. As a result of this contradictory experiment Einstein reverted somewhat to Newton's corpuscular theory in order to explain the photo-electric effect. In doing so he made use of Planck's quantum theory, which thus gained new support and a new interpretation. According to Einstein light should be conceived as a bundle of particles each of which possess the energy $h\nu$. Hence instead of being distributed with continuity over a wave, the energy is concentrated in certain particles. If the light is monochromatic, i.e. has only one frequency, all particles have the same energy. If the light is not monochromatic, the particles represent as many energies as there are frequencies of light. The photo-electric effect must be considered as the result of a collision between such a particle of light (a photon) and an electron. If the photon has more energy than the threshold value required for the liberation of an electron, the photo-electric effect occurs; otherwise not. When light has a greater intensity there are more photons per unit of time; therefore, there is more chance of collision and more electrons are liberated.

Soon other similar phenomena were discovered which could all be explained if light were conceived as a bundle of photons. Now according to the theory of relativity the connection between energy and mass may be expressed by the following fundamental proportion:

$$m = \frac{E}{c^2} \text{ (c is the velocity of light in a vacuum)}$$

Hence it was possible to ascribe a definite mass to the photons. Their energy is $h\nu$, therefore their mass is

$$\frac{h\nu}{c^2}$$

Other mechanical units, such as impulse, could also be brought into a sensible relationship with the photons. Impulse is mass $\times$ velocity; hence as regards a photon

$$\frac{h\nu}{c^2} \times c = \frac{h\nu}{c}$$

This would have meant a victory for the atomistic view if there had not been a complication which we shall see presently. According to the photon theory there must be practically as many smallest particles as there are frequencies. Thus it begins to look somewhat like the original philosophic atomic theory.

However, as we said, there was a complication. The reasons which formerly had settled the issue in favor of Huygens' wave theory against Newton's corpuscular theory still retained their value. There are certain physical phenomena which seem irreconcilable with the photon theory. When, for instance, light is thrown upon a screen through two slits we get the well known phenomena of interference. They are easily explained by the wave theory. Likewise, they do not cause any unsurmountable difficulties to the photon theory as long as the intensity of the light is high enough. In that case we may assume that there are many photons in the light. Hence we can easily imagine that they work together so as to produce a continuous image of interference. Where many photons strike the screen there will be much light, where no photons strike there will be no light, and in between there is room for all possible nuances. Hence the regular variation of light and darkness can be explained without great difficulties, provided there is a large number of photons. Remarkably enough, however, when the intensity of the light is decreased, even to such an extent that only one photon may be presumed to pass through the slits during a given time, the same image of interference results, although it remains very weak. According to the photon theory we could expect that light would be visible only there where the one photon would strike the screen, and that the rest of the screen would be in darkness. Some time later a second photon would show another spot of light, so that eventually the interferential image could be built successively. But experience shows otherwise; immediately there is a weak but complete interferential image. In this case, therefore, the one photon seems to spread itself with continuity over the whole amplitude of the wave. This agrees with the wave theory, but other processes, such as the photo-electric effect, are contrary to this theory. Hence the physicist faces the situation that certain behavior patterns of light can be explained only by a corpuscular theory, others only by a wave theory, and a fairly large number of phenomena by both theories. The fact that these two theories contradict each other on certain points makes it difficult to see how a synthesis would be possible. At any rate, none has been found, so that the physicist has no other choice but to reconcile himself with the thought that his theoretical considerations will exhibit a dualistic character.

The Dualism of Matter. In 1924 it occurred to the French physicist Louis de Broglie that the same dualism might very well apply to the particles of matter. There were mainly two considerations which led him to this hypothesis. The first was that of the Bohr postulates, which deviate from the classical theories, but are necessary to obtain a satisfactory theory of the atom. According to the Bohr postulates only certain orbits are possible to an electron, and these orbits must fulfill certain conditions which resemble the conditions under which a so-called standing wave is stable. De Broglie's second consideration was of a more general nature. He was struck by the great similarity between certain basic formulas of geometrical optics on one hand, and of classical mechanics on the other. In geometrical optics, which describes the path of lightrays with the aid of mathematical figures, there is applied the so-called principle of Fermat, according to which a lightray always travels the 'quickest' way. In an optically homogeneous medium this means that the lightray takes a straight path, but in an optically non-homogeneous medium the path generally must be described as a curved or a broken line. To this curved or broken line the rule applies that the sum of the segments divided by the respective velocity in each segment, is smaller than the sum which would be obtained if the light were to choose a different path.

A similar principle applies in mechanics. A motion always takes place in such a way that the 'work' is minimal. The relationship between the two principles is especially striking when expressed mathematically.

Thus de Broglie was induced to apply to the motion of material particles the wave functions which had rendered such excellent services in the problem of light. When speaking about the photon theory we saw, thanks to the relationship between mass and energy expressed by the theory of relativity, that it is not difficult to convert the characteristic units of the wave theory, such as frequency (ν) and wave length (λ), into units which are characteristically mechanical, mass (m) and impulse (mv). It was not surprising that the Bohr postulates could logically be derived from de Broglie's theory, for these postulates had been one of the reasons why the wave theory had been applied to the motion of matter. However, a splendid confirmation was obtained in 1927 when Germer and Davisson succeeded in producing with electronic rays phenomena of diffraction which correspond totally to the diffraction of X-rays. The importance of this discovery may be gauged from the fact that less than twenty years previously science had succeeded in distinguishing alpha, beta, and gamma rays in radioactive rays, and had admitted as the fundamental difference between the first two and the last one that the former were streams of matter particles and the latter an electromagnetic wave. The most amazing fact, however, was that the wavelength, calculated from the diffraction pattern of the electronic rays, corresponded exactly to the length these rays should have according to de Broglie's speculative hypothesis.

As has happened so frequently in the most recent history of physics this striking experimental confirmation was soon followed by others. The most important one of these was that under certain conditions the change of photons into electrons and vice versa was seen to be possible. In 1933 Blacket and Occialini performed the experiment successfully. It may be mentioned that the various phases of this experiment had been predicted by the theory. In 1930 Dirac concluded from his electronic theory that there must exist also positive electrons (positrons). They were discovered in 1932. A second conclusion was that it ought to be possible to produce such a positive electron together with an 'ordinary' negative electron from the energy of electromagnetic rays, i.e. from photons. The experiment of Blacket and Occialini confirmed this conclusion and at the same time supplied an additional confirmation of de Broglie's theory. It was clear that the latter's conjecture had been fortunate notwithstanding all the theoretical complications it caused. Moreover, these complications should not cause us to close our eyes to the great advantage that henceforth at any rate the physicist will be able to consider from one and the same point of view the formerly separate fields of electromagnetic and corpuscular radiation.

True, the unity of this theoretical viewpoint may demand much of our power of visualization, because we are not able to see one and the same reality both as an undulatory motion and as matter particles, but mathematically it can be expressed by the same formulas.

Shortly afterwards Schrödinger perfected de Broglie's mathematical formalism. Following in the footsteps of his predecessor he started with the Bohr atomic model. From the fact that a wave function is connected with every moving electron he deduced mathematically the conditions under which electronic orbits are stable.

Quantum Mechanics. W. Heisenberg tackled the problems at the same time as Schrödinger, but from an entirely different angle. Although it is not possible for us to sketch this mathematically complicated theory in detail, nevertheless we must consider for a few moments its general tendency because it contains some interesting aspects in relation to the problems which hitherto have held our attention. Heisenberg's basic idea is that in the description of the atoms, primarily those units should be used which can be directly determined by experiments.

Such units are, for example, the different possible energy states of an atom, and the intensity and frequency of its specific spectral lines. The electronic orbits which are typical of the Bohr theory do not fulfill these conditions. They owe their origin to a mere hypothesis which is not without great difficulties. Moreover, the various units which determine these orbits cannot be measured directly.

Hence Heisenberg dropped the whole idea of electronic orbits and restricted himself to the mathematical expression in one schema of all the states of vibration which are typical of an atom. In this manner he obtained, just as well as had de Broglie and Schrödinger, a closed theory which in the end equalled the other in value notwithstanding the difference in mathematical treatment. Certain arithmetical units in Heisenberg's theory have the same function as the space coordinates of the theory which works with electronic orbits, while other units express what corresponds to the velocity of electrons in the old theory. Hence nowadays the so-called wave mechanics of Schrödinger and the quantum mechanics of Heisenberg are used indiscriminately, except insofar as preference is given to that method which is simpler in the treatment of a given problem. The equivalence of the two theories reveals itself very strikingly in a remarkable conclusion from quantum mechanics, the so-called Principle of Indeterminism. According to this principle it is impossible to determine accurately at the same time the position and the velocity of a particle. The inaccuracy is of the same order of size as Planck's quantum of energy. Thus theoretically it is possible to determine with absolute accuracy the position of a particle at a given moment, but in that case nothing can be known about its velocity. If, however, the velocity is determined with absolute accuracy, it is impossible to determine the position.

Mathematical methods clearly show that this remarkable conclusion is in complete agreement with the speculations of wave mechanics. Although we cannot explain these methods within the scope of this study, we may indicate some point which shows to a certain extent that this consequent of quantum mechanics is essentially the same problem which we encountered above in dualism as the consequent of wave mechanics. In a rigid corpuscular theory the individual particles appear to us as objects which are accurately determined in time and space. A particle at a given time is in an accurately determined place, and shortly afterwards is either still in the same place or in another. In case it has moved, we can accurately indicate the velocity with which it has moved from one place to another. However, we have seen above that this is but a one-sided representation of a physical reality. There are physical processes in respect of which this corpuscular representation is deficient, so that an appeal has to be made to an undulatory representation. Now in an undulatory representation there is never such a sharp definition of time and place, because a wave expresses continuous expansion in space and not concentration in a sharply defined place. We will not enter into further details here, but will refer the reader who may be interested to our work, *The Philosophy of Nature,* Chapter VII (Pittsburgh, 1954).

3. NUCLEAR PHYSICS

The evolution of the atomic theory in the twentieth century was not limited to the more profound theoretical penetration into the Bohr atomic model sketched in the preceding pages. The twentieth century saw also the birth of a new branch of physical science, so-called nuclear physics, i.e. the science which studies the changes to which the atomic nucleus is subject. Till that time this had been unknown territory. All the 'ordinary' chemical and physical processes take place, in Bohr's theory, in what are called electronic shells. The spectrum of visible light is caused by jumps of electrons in the outermost shell, the X-ray spectra are the result of jumps in more central shells, chemical reactions are explained by an exchange of electrons in the outermost shell, etc. All these processes leave the nucleus intact and untouched. The same is true of all those physical phenomena in which the atom or the molecule does not change as a whole but only in its state of motion, as for example, in the phenomena of heat.

The Transmutation of Nuclei. The first acquaintance with the new branch was made in radioactive radiation. It was immediately noticed that this radiation continued without change when the substance in question entered into a compound or was exposed to certain physical influences. Whether a radioactive element was present as an element or in combination with another element, as Ra in $RaCl_2$, whether the temperature was low or high, the radiation did not undergo any change at all. It seemed to be a process which stood entirely outside the sphere of hitherto known phenomena. Hence, as an official confirmation that such phenomena were totally different from all others, radioactivity was attributed to the *nucleus* when the atomic model was constructed. Through radiation the nucleus changed in charge and mass and thus became the nucleus of another element. In opposition to all other known processes in nature and in the laboratory this was a *transmutation,* a change from one element into another. The physicist could not exercise any influence upon the process, he was but a spectator, albeit that a large amount of both experimental and theoretical ingenuity was required to be a spectator. Some elements transmuted steadily and without any variation, while others did not, till Rutherford in 1919 succeeded in effecting an 'artificial' transmutation of nuclei. He 'bombarded' nitrogen with alpha particles, i.e. he shot a stream of alpha particles from radioactive nuclei through nitrogen gas. The result was surprising. When a nitrogen nucleus was struck by a helium nucleus (an alpha particle), the result was a split into an isotope of oxygen and one hydrogen nucleus. With the Wilson cloud chamber Rutherford was able to make visible the path of the individual particles. By all kinds of ingenious means it was possible also to identify the particles. The transmutation of nitrogen did not remain an isolated case, for soon it became clear that other transmutations also could be effected in this manner.

The Neutron and the Composition of the Nucleus. Of special importance was a transmutation which did not produce hydrogen nuclei, but particles having the same mass as the hydrogen nucleus, yet no electric charge (the neutron). Its importance was twofold. In the first place, it gave a new insight into the composition of the nucleus. Originally it was thought that an atomic nucleus consisted of a hydrogen nucleus and electrons. Two reasons pleaded for the presence of electrons in the nucleus. First, there were electrons in the radioactive radiation which is caused by the nucleus. Secondly, the mass of the nuclei did not correspond to their charge if it was assumed that a nucleus consists entirely of hydrogen nuclei. For instance, the nitrogen nucleus has a mass of 14 and a charge of 7, the silver nucleus a mass of 107 and a charge of 47, etc. Hence the view took hold that nitrogen consists of 14 hydrogen nuclei and 7 electrons. The presence of the latter left the mass of the nucleus 14, because the mass of an electron is practically negligible, but the charge was decreased by 7. For a silver nucleus the combination would be 107 hydrogen nuclei and 59 electrons.

However, there was a basic difficulty, for certain physical properties of the nucleus seemed to exclude the presence of electrons (the so-called *spin*). But the recently discovered neutron came to the rescue. Since it had the same mass as the hydrogen nucleus but no charge, a nucleus could be conceived as consisting of a certain number of protons and neutrons. The protons would be equal in number to the ordinal number in the atomic table, and the number of neutrons to the difference between the number expressing the mass and the atomic number. The fact that electrons come out of the nucleus the theory explains by admitting that a neutron shows itself capable of disintegrating into a proton and an electron. The term *disintegrating*, strictly speaking, is not correct, for it more or less suggests that a neutron consists of a proton and an electron. Not without reason did we mention the mechanistic background of the atomic theory. Here again it shows itself in the terminology. Some physicists prefer the term *creation* to show clearly that the electron does not pre-exist as an electron in the nucleus.[3] Something new comes into existence which did not exist as such before. Of course, it is not a creation from nothing, because there was a neutron before. It is what the ancient philosophers would have called a *generation*.

The importance of the discovery of the neutron was not limited to the possibilities if offered for theoretical physics. It was also a very fortunate acquisition for the laboratory. Hitherto all particles used in research work on the transformation of nuclei had always been charged, and the use of such charged particles suffered under a great handicap. Since the nuclei which were to be struck by alpha

---

[3]For example, L. Rosenfeld, *De ontsluiting van de atoomkern,* Amsterdam 1946, p. 61.

particles or protons had a positive electric charge they repelled the approaching projectiles according to the Law of Coulomb. In the case of nuclei of light elements with a corresponding light charge this did not cause any serious trouble, because the tremendous energy of the alpha particles was strong enough to overcome the relatively weak repulsion, although heavier nuclei could not be transformed by the alpha particles or protons. In the latter case the repellent forces are too strong for the projectiles to reach the heavy nucleus. Now the use of neutrons as projectiles eliminated this difficulty. Because of their neutral charge these particles have a far greater capacity of penetration so that even the heaviest nuclei can be transformed.

For theoretical reasons it is assumed that this process of transformation takes places in different phases. First the nucleus is struck by a neutron. Let us take an Ag-nucleus as an example. This nucleus with a mass of 107 and atomic number 47 receives one neutron and becomes an isotope of Ag with a mass of 108 and atomic number 47. The new nucleus, however, is unstable so that under the emission of one electron it changes into a nucleus with one additional electric charge (Cadmium) and the same mass of 108. In this way artificial radioactivity was successfully produced.

Concerning the stability of the nuclei to which we referred above, since the theory is still in its infancy we may be satisfied with mentioning that stability appears to require an equal number of neutrons and protons in the lighter nuclei, i.e. a mass which is twice the atomic number. For instance, He 4 (mass) and 2 (atomic number), 0 16 and 8, S 32 and 16. But in the heavier nuclei a surplus of neutrons is normal and increases steadily (Cu 64 and 29, Ag 107 and 47), so that there in a considerable surplus in the heaviest nuclei such as Ra (226 and 88), and uranium (238 and 92).

It seems that the increasing concentration of positive charges has to be kept together by a relatively increasing surplus of neutrons. When a nucleus is not stable because it contains too many neutrons, as for example the isotope of Ag, a neutron changes into a proton and a negatively charged electron is emitted. If, however, the instability is caused by a lack of neutrons, a proton disappears by being changed into a neutron, and a positively charged electron is emitted. Thus the latter process is the reverse of the former. Other emissions also are possible. For example, it can happen that a surplus of neutrons is overcome by a secondary emission of neutrons. The possibility of shooting neutrons into nuclei becomes particularly interesting in the case of uranium. This element has the highest atomic number (92) of elements found in nature, although there would be room in the periodic table for elements with a higher atomic number. If a uranium nucleus catches a neutron, it possibly could happen that this nucleus would not be stable, but would emit one electron and change into a nucleus with one additional positive charge and therefore also with a higher atomic number. As a matter of fact, this has happened. A so-called transuranium, neptunium (with the atomic number 93) and another one, plutonium (with the atomic number 94) were successfully produced by this method. More recently americium (95), curium (96), berkelium (97), californium (98), einsteinium (99), fermium (100), mendelevium (101) and nobelium (102) were added to the list.

Nuclear Fission. Meanwhile the production of transuranium is not the only effect obtained by bombarding uranium with neutrons. Another hitherto unknown phenomenon takes place, namely nuclear fission, through which a nucleus disintegrates into two parts. Of course, the transmutations to which we referred above may also be called nuclear fissions: the silver nucleus disintegrates into cadmium and an electron. This, however, is not much more than chipping a 'splinter' from the original nucleus. In the present case of nuclear fission the nucleus splits into two large 'chunks,' for example into barium (at. number 56) and krypton (at. number 36). It should be clear that this is a special kind of fission if we pay attention to the enormous accompanying surplus of neutrons. To keep to the same example, barium has an atomic weight of 137, and krypton of 84, which together makes 221. Therefore, the barium nucleus contains 137 — 56 or 81 neutrons, and the krypton nucleus 84 — 36 or 48 neutrons, which gives us a total of 129. But for the 'chunks,' barium and krypton, which are formed from the fission of uranium, there are 238 —92 or 146 neutrons available. Hence there is a surplus of 17 neutrons so that the 'chunks' in turn will emit particles, such as electrons and neutrons. According to circumstances, either electrons or neutrons will prevail. If the conditions are chosen in such a manner that the emission of neutrons prevails, a chain reaction takes place. A neutron splits a nucleus, the 'chunks' emit several neutrons which in turn split other nuclei, etc. The atom bomb, in which enormous quantities of energy are liberated, rests upon this principle. We must now briefly consider these quantities of energy.

The Relationship of Energy and Mass. When speaking about the dualism of light and matter we mentioned the equivalence of energy and mass in the relationship $E = mc^2$. On account of the very high value of c (the velocity of light in a vacuum), 186,000 miles a second, every mass represents an enormous quantity of energy. One gram-mass corresponds to an energy of 9×10^{20} ergs, or to use a measure which is more familiar, the energy of 30,000,000 kilowatt hours.

A so-called mass defect occurs in nuclear fission, i.e., the mass of the fragments is not equal to that of the uranium nucleus. The loss amounts to about 0.2% or 0.1% of the whole. Hence per gram of matter about 0.001 gram-mass disappears, which corresponds to a production of energy of about 10^{18} ergs or 30,000 kilowatt hours. Therefore, the enormous amount of energy produced by these nuclear reactions, which is so many times greater than the energy released in 'ordinary' chemical reactions, comes from the loss of mass.

One more point deserves our attention. In calculating the amount of energy which corresponds to the loss of mass we again used the relationship[4] of the theory of relativity $E = mc^2$. Although it was originally proposed for an entirely different purpose, here too this relationship proves how much it stands for physical reality. In its original setting this formula appeared only as a theoretical construction, a mathematical relation between the quantity of energy and that of mass. It could hardly have been surmised that a few decennia later scientists would succeed, so to speak, in effectuating this formula, not only as an imposing confirmation of the universal connection which unites all branches of physical science, but also as a striking demonstration that a certain physical reality corresponds to mathematical formulas notwithstanding the fact that they are difficult to visualize.

4. THE PHILOSOPHIC BACKGROUND OF THE CONTEMPORANEOUS ATOMIC THEORY

Insufficient Data. As usual, we will add to this description of the most recent phase in the development of the atomic theory a short consideration of what on previous occasions we called the philosophic background. This will not be easy—for the simple reason that at the end of the above description we should have to write "To be continued." The story is cut short while the events continue. Of course, it is true, as we have pointed out several times, that every division into periods is somewhat artificial. Nevertheless there is a big difference between the present case and previous occasions. Form-

---

[4]On p. 175 it was used to calculate the theoretical wave length of a bundle of moving electrons.

erly we could look back upon more or less associated facts and theories, and distinguish the whole into periods according to tendencies which really dominated these periods and set them apart from others. Now we must break off right in the middle of a period of development. We may make some conjectures about the tendencies which dominate the present development, about the forces which are behind it, but it will be possible to determine what really is most important only when these forces have accomplished their work, when their achievements belong to history. In other words, only he who knows the future evolution of the atomic theory will be able to write the evaluation which both readers and author would like to see here. We must point out especially that the relatively simple concept which admits in the nuclei a composition of electrons, neutrons, and protons, is without doubt inadequate. In recent years quite a few new particles have been either discovered or at least hypothetically admitted in order to explain certain phenomena. The most important of these are the neutrinos and various kinds of mesons.[4a]

The Difference Between the Nineteenth and the Twentieth Centuries. For the time being all we can do is to make an effort to emphasize that aspect of the twentieth century atomic theory which differs from that of its nineteenth counterpart. From a scientific viewpoint we have already done this on the preceding pages. Now we must investigate to what extent the most recent developments imply consequences with respect to the philosophic background which was undoubtedly still present in the nineteenth century. Fortunately it is possible to say something about that, and this section will not have to consist only of arguments to prove a confession of ignorance.

Above we have seen that the philosophic background of the nineteenth century atomic theory was mechanistic. All phenomena ultimately were reduced to local change, to a change in position of intrinsically immutable particles. This mechanistic viewpoint was accompanied by another characteristic, namely determinism. Every situation of the primordial particles at any given moment was determined by an inner law abidance and by the situation at another moment. Hence a mind which knew both the laws and the situation at a given moment would have been able to calculate and to know the entire past and the entire future.

[4a]For a recent survey of these particles, see A. Salam, *Elementary Particles and Space-Time Symmetries,* in *Endeavour,* vol. xvii, April 1958, pp. 97ff.

We may briefly remind the reader why we called mechanism a *philosophic background*. We called it a *background* because the basic principles of mechanism and determinism with their absolute and universal character did not find any support in strictly physical theories; on the contrary, the physical theories were projected against this background. A so-called closed physical system, i.e. a system which is not subject to any known external influences, was seen as the prototype of a mechanistic universe, but in reality no such entirely closed system was known. We called it a *philosophic* background because of the absoluteness with which it was admitted. Scientific thinking seemed to postulate this conception of reality. However, this does not mean that the physicist clearly realized this philosophic reasoning as such. Otherwise it would not have been a philosophic *background* but a philosophic *theory*. This philosophic background revealed itself strikingly with respect to the problem of free will. Without further consideration, as something which was quite obvious, free will was held to be impossible, although from a purely physical viewpoint there was little reason to place the phenomena of free will within the frame of physical science. The frame was more or less unwittingly extended.

This conception of the universe, if we may use that term for the philosophic background, received a serious blow from the most recent developments in physical science, because it became clear that such a conception could not be maintained in those parts of physical science which were being studied in the twentieth century. In the nineteenth century it was still possible to foster the illusion that what applied in some sections of physical science, for example in the motion of planets or the functioning of mechanical apparatus, could be considered as ideal for the *whole* of physical science. In other words, strictly from the viewpoint of physical science it was possible to believe that the program of physical science could be consistently enlarged, and that as time went on an ever larger number of phenomena could be explained by the local motion of primordial particles which in their physical aspect are immutable. By physical aspect we mean that the properties which the scientist considers as characteristic of these particles are not subject to change. Of course, even the consistent extension of this program would not imply anything about such a phenomenon as free will, for physics simply is not concerned with it. Possibly some reasons could be given also why non-physical branches of knowledge and theories should be projected against a deterministic background, but that is an entirely different matter and does not concern physical science as such.

Hence in itself the failure of the mechanistic program in physics has consequences only for physics and its philosophic background. It is due merely to the fact that the mechanistic conception of the universe was incorrectly thought to be supported by nineteenth century physics that the change within the frame of physical science may seem to have consequences outside this frame.

We insist upon this point because in our opinion it happens frequently nowadays that an appeal is made to the evolution of physics in order to solve, say the problem of free will. However grateful we may be that contemporaneous physical science has liberated itself from the narrow frame of its background, we must never forget that this narrow frame had not flowed from physical science as such. In the final chapter we will have an opportunity to revert to this problem upon a wider plan. Apart from other reasons, something had to be said about it here because it may have surprised the reader that at the beginning of this section we emphasized that the time is not yet ripe for saying much about the philosophic background of the most recent developments in physical science. The remark could be made that as a result of contemporaneous physics very many philosophic studies are published. Undoubtedly these studies are very interesting, but they are born from *reflex philosophic* interpretations, and that is not what we mean by the philosophic background of a physical theory. Of course, in the long run such interpretations could become a background. However, this cannot happen as long as they are being developed explicitly as philosophic interpretations, but only when they have become, as it were, unwittingly incorporated into one whole together with scientific theory itself. By means of illustration we may refer to Dalton. His atomic theory was a scientific theory. Its atoms were characterized by definite physical and chemical properties by means of which Dalton explained a number of chemical phenomena. The *immutability,* for example, of the atomic weight was, within the framework of Dalton's theory, a scientific hypothesis, which consequently exercised influence also upon the proportions of weight in which substances could combine with each other. But his supposition that a compound could be formed only by simple juxtaposition was something not demanded by physical science. It was the consequence of the mechanistic viewpoint common in Dalton's days. Dalton mentioned it in passing as something which was quite obvious. It is true that this supposition was the result of philosophic speculation in the preceding centuries, but in Dalton's time it had become practically unwittingly incorporated into the scientific theory.

Therefore, if we want to speak about the philosophic background of the contemporaneous atomic theory, the above-mentioned philosophic interpretations, precisely because they are explicit, are not what we are looking for. However, let us repeat again, it is not our intention to belittle these studies. On the contrary, we consider them very important philosophic endeavors, as we intend to show in the final chapter.

Meanwhile, however, our attention is directed towards the philosophic *background* of the contemporaneous atomic theory. The first question we face is: To what extent does this background differ from that of the preceding century? The answer to this negative aspect is not very difficult. The hypothesis of immutable primordial particles in the sense of 'fragments of matter' has disappeared. Electrons, for example, can be entirely transformed into gamma radiation, as the physicist is wont to say. True, gamma radiation nowadays has also a corpuscular aspect, but this does not mean that positive and negative electrons can be conceived as becoming juxtaposed and then disintegrating into photons. Such a description of the process of dematerialization would be very unfortunate because the electron would have to be conceived as being composed of photons or parts of photons. Moreover, we have seen that neither the electron itself nor the photon can be wholly characterized as corpuscles, for there are processes in which a bundle of electrons and a bundle of light must be conceived as a continuous whole. In order to describe the data of modern physics more forceful expressions must be used than that of motion of pre-existing particles. There are transformations for which some authors do not hesitate to use the terms creation and annihilation. These terms may seem somewhat exaggerated, but they indicate sufficiently the direction our thought should *not* take, and that is the direction of immutable particles.

Thus, though the concept *smallest particle* is retained for many reasons, it receives a far more relative meaning. Particles can be absorbed into a greater whole in which they lose their individuality. In our opinion that is all we can say about the question for the time being. Molecules, atoms, neutrons, electrons, and protons are undoubtedly concepts of physical realities, of relatively smallest particles, but they are not particles which either in themselves or in their components lead an independent existence. And thus the main point in the philosophic background of the former atomic theory has disappeared.[4b]

Meanwhile we venture to add another comment. The reader will remember our statement that every man is a Democritus, i.e. the physicist will always try to understand the multiplicity of phenomena through the interaction of as few primordial elements as possible. This is true also in our own time. Even though our conception of particles shows itself deficient, physical science in the construction of the whole continues to work with certain primordial elements, such as elementary wave functions. It is, we think, the only course open to the physicist; hence we may suppose that he will continue to travel on it. Nevertheless it makes a big difference whether these primordial elements are considered as entirely independent beings which more or less accidentally become incorporated in a greater whole, or are taken at once to be components of a whole. It would not surprise us if the latter view would reveal itself as a permanent trait of the future physical conception of the universe. Perhaps it is true that the knowledge of the nineteenth century, which in the light of modern science was after all relatively superficial, could allow itself to neglect this aspect of the whole precisely on account of its superficiality. Contemporaneous science on the other hand, has so profoundly penetrated into the world of matter that such a neglect would immediately avenge itself even in its physical aspect. The future, however, will show whether this surmise is correct or not, for every generation has the tendency to overestimate its own importance. (See *Supplementary Note* on p. 193.)

The nineteenth century physical conception of the universe suffered another severe defeat in respect to the determinism which accompanied its mechanism. As mentioned before, contemporaneous physical science denies in principle that it is possible to know exactly all the data which are required to describe the situation of the various particles. Thus there remains no possibility for absolutely accurate predictions. Although the concepts *predictability* and *determinism* are not identical[5] the fascination of determination lies pre-

---

[4b]See p. 193 for footnote.

[5]It is beyond the scope of this book to enter into the problems of causality, determinism, and predictability. The interested reader may consult our study, *The Philosophy of Nature*, Ch. VII.

cisely in the possibility to predict future events. Hence the reverse suffered by this aspect of the mechanistic conception of the universe deprived it of a large part of its assets.

While the answer to the problem of the philosophic background of modern physics is not difficult when we restrict ourselves to the difference from the nineteenth century, more difficulties are met when we try to determine the present background more positively. The first question to arise is whether there is still any background or not. This is a very interesting question because the failure of mechanism could very well have resulted in the disappearance of any philosophic background. An all-over view suggests that progressive recession from philosophy is the main theme in the history of the concept *atom*. Hence this supposition could very well be true to a large extent. Nevertheless we have definite reasons to doubt its exactness, as we shall explain in the final chapter. Provisionally the physicists still project their atomic theories against a mechanistic background, although they make some essential corrections. These corrections are of such a nature that one may ask whether a profound reflection on them would still allow it to be called mechanism. However, this difficulty is less formidable than it may seem because it is characteristic of a background that there is no conscious reflection upon its consequences. Dalton too, made essential corrections. It should not be forgotten that mechanism offers great opportunities for visualization and has always been the traditional background. Hence the idea of immutable particles is maintained as long as possible, and at the same time it is pointed out that occasionally this conception falls short. The emphasis itself with which this is stated shows that the mechanistic background is still there.

Positivism. One may perhaps be inclined to ask: Are these not the last spasms of philosophy within physical science? Has not the development of physical science increasingly shown the correctness of the positivistic viewpoint which is a denial of philosophy? In the words of P. Jordan:

> Two things should be seen as inseparately connected: the new physics is inconceivable without the influence of the positivistic theory of knowledge, and reversely only when thinking in objective processes was replaced by the new thought form of comple-

mentarity[6] could positivism become stabilized and rendered precise.[7]

Numerous scientists and philosophers express themselves in similar terms. We do not think that their opinion is correct, but even if it were true that modern physical science and the positivistic theory of knowledge are insolubly united, this could not at all be put forward as a proof that modern science has no philosophic background. For in that case positivism itself, which is a very definite philosophic theory, has succeeded in becoming that background. Meanwhile we do not think that positivism has succeeded in accomplishing this. Certainly, it is true that many outstanding scientists and philosophers interpret modern physical science in a positivistic manner, but here again the fact that it is done so explicitly, proves our thesis. There is too much *interpretation* and not enough *projection* without many words. Moreover, we are convinced that positivism, especially in its modern form, is too complicated a philosophy ever really to become the philosophic background for the majority of scientists. A scientist will always see an atom as a real particle and not as a logical symbol whose only function is to group together certain observable data, as positivism would require (see Chapter VI).

Therefore, regardless of the truth or falsity of positivism, which does not concern us here, it is not likely that it will ever become the philosophic background of physical science. With this remark we may close this chapter about the latest developments of the atomic theory. Many questions remain unanswered because the answer belongs to the future. However, there is one more question to which we have promised an answer: must there always be a philosophic background for the atomic theory? In order to give a well-founded answer we must first investigate the proper nature of both physical science and philosophy. This investigation will culminate in the crucial question whether or not, in view of the development of physical and other sciences, there still remains room for another science in its

---

[6]By the thought form or principle of complementarity is meant that two theories of the same reality must be held to be complementary, i.e. to supplement each other insofar as the exclusive application of one theory would cause insurmountable difficulties in the explanation of certain phenomena which can be explained only by the other theory. Examples of its application are the undulatory and the corpuscular theory of the photon, and Heisenberg's principle of indeterminism, according to which it is impossible accurately to measure position and velocity at the same time. See the author's study *The Philosophy of Nature*, Pittsburgh, 1954, Ch. VII. (Translator's note.)

[7]*Die Physik des 20 Jahrhunderts*, Braunschweig 1936, p. 132.

own right, which we call philosophy. Only after answering this second question will it become possible to answer the first, namely whether every physical atomic theory will always have a philosophic background. The next chapter is devoted to these questions.

FOOTNOTE FOR P. 174:

[2a]For a detailed historical account of the theoretical developments, mentioned in this section, which make the third decade of the twentieth century one of the most important periods in the history of science, see E. T. Whittaker, *History of the Theories of Aether and Electricity*, vol. 2, New York, 1954, Chs. VI–IX.

FOOTNOTE FOR P. 190.

[4a]Recently Heisenberg sketched the present situation in these words: "The transmutation of matter into energy is, so to speak, the fundamental principle of elementary particle physics. This state of affairs may be expressed also in the statement that all elementary particles consist of the same primordial substance—namely, energy or, if you prefer, simply matter. Therefore, strictly speaking, one cannot make a distinction between qualitatively different particles but should say that these particles are merely different forms of one and the same primordial substance, matter, or energy." *Vom Atom zum Weltsystem*, p. 55.

SUPPLEMENTARY NOTE FOR P. 190:

Perhaps we may add also the following remark. The physicist of our times will no longer conceive the mechanical models with which he works and could hardly avoid working as representations of reality in the same light-hearted way as his predecessors. He will be more aware of the fact that his models are *human* models, i.e., models depending on man's cognitive possibilities, because all our concepts are connected with sense representations. This connection is the very reason why mechanism could become the philosophic background of physical science and in all likelihood will always remain its background, at least to a certain extent. However, the partial collapse of mechanism in twentieth century physics will have as a consequence that henceforth even *unconsciously* only a relative value will be attached to the mechanical models. In other words, the feeling that only a relative realtive value can be attached to physical models will, we think, become a permanent feature of the philosophic background proper to physical science.

CHAPTER SIX

SCIENCE OF NATURE, PHILOSOPHY, AND PHILOSOPHY OF NATURE

1. INTRODUCTION

In the introduction to this study a brief historical sketch of the concept *atom* was given. Then the question arose whether nowadays philosophic speculations, such as those of the Greek thinkers Democritus and Aristotle, still make sense. The same question arose again at the end of the preceding chapter. For the question whether or not the scientific atomic theory must of necessity have a philosophic background coincides with the question: Is there apart from the physical setting of problems another setting which, although not considered in the science of nature itself, nevertheless forces itself irresistibly upon the *man* who devotes himself to this science so that it forms the background against which he projects his physical theory? Upon closer examination this question about the meaning and necessity of philosophy can be broken down into two questions. We can ask ourselves, first, whether or not after the separation of autonomous specialized sciences from the single science of the Ancients there still can be question of a *general* science in its own right, which is called philosophy. Only when this question has been answered in the affirmative may the second be raised: Is there alongside general philosophy and the science of nature room for still another science which may be called philosophy of nature or a philosophic science of matter? In view of the scope of our present study it is obvious that the answer to the second question is of special interest; for the history of the concept *atom* is a subject in which the progressive shift from the ancient philosophic speculation to the modern scientific view has taken place. Logically, however, the question about the right to existence of philosophy in general must be given priority, not only in order to determine whether it should be answered affirmatively or negatively, but also in order to understand the reason for this answer. For the answer will reveal something about the nature of philosophy, and that is exactly what we need for the reply to the second question.

194

2. THE RIGHT OF PHILOSOPHY TO EXIST AS A SCIENCE IN ITS OWN RIGHT

The reader who is more or less a stranger in philosophy will perhaps find our introduction somewhat peculiar and mysterious. It seems as if such a simple thing as the gradual recession from philosophy has to be shrouded in mystery because otherwise it would be too simple. This impression is not incorrect, but the expression "shrouded in mystery" is deceptive. Perhaps the best way to express the nature of philosophy is to say that its function is to make us think about that which we find extremely simple, but which on second thought is not really so simple. Using the same figure of speech we may say that rather than shrouding an ordinary thing in mystery, philosophy takes away the customary shroud so that the ordinary thing is suddenly no longer such an ordinary thing. One may justifiably remark that this is something which holds for every science. For instance, physical science makes problems from what in everyday life is quite ordinary. The Greek philosophers used to say that "science is born from wonder." No doubt this applies to all science. For whoever does not wonder about the facts of daily life will not go very far in any science. Nevertheless, this characteristic applies in a special way to philosophy because it cultivates wonder more radically than any other science. To explain this let us use a concrete example.

What is a Material Thing? In science as well as in daily life we use ideas which indicate material things, such as plants, animals, minerals, utensils, instruments, etc. Likewise, we have ideas which indicate those properties of material things which we clearly distinguish from each other. Concerning these material things various questions may be asked. For instance: What is their composition? What are their properties, and how do these properties depend on their composition? Physical science gives an answer in its atomic theory. However, another question also can be asked: What is implied by the fact that in our language we classify certain concepts under a common denominator "material things," and others under "properties of material things?" This usage is maintained also in physical science where molecules and atoms are classified under "material things," and where there is question of "properties of material things." Provisionally, however, we will limit ourselves to "ordinary" material things, and abstract from concepts which are derived from physical science. The reason for this procedure will become clear later.

To repeat our question: What is the reason why we speak of material things? What do we mean by it?

It seems beyond dispute that in ordinary life we call a horse a thing because we attribute an independent existence to it. A horse is something which exists without depending on us and which has properties that can be observed. The fact that we can observe them we consider to be the result of the existence of these properties and their power to exercise influence upon our organs. The same conception is the basis of Aristotle's philosophy. It shows itself, for instance, in his distinction between substance and accident. It may be called the realistic conception. Let us mention a few others. The so-called empiricists, whose principal exponent in the past we may consider David Hume (1711-1776), thought that only that may be accepted as really existent which has been observed by the senses. Now, the empiricists say, that what we observe with our senses is separate impressions and never "complete things." To use ordinary terminology, the sum total of impressions a horse makes on us is a very complex whole of impressions on our hearing, sight, touch, etc. Normally we perceive only a few of these impressions at a time, but we say that they come from a horse because we are convinced that eventually the other impressions also could be obtained. For instance, when we see a horse, we are already convinced that certain impressions of touch and smell can be obtained. According to empiricists the meaning of the concept *horse* is nothing but a compact and brief expression of that expectation. Because in the past we have observed the association of certain impressions on hearing, sight, touch, and smell we have chosen a certain name to indicate and to facilitate the memory of the entire complex. Moreover, the name does not mean that the complex is always the same. There is always variation, but there is also always a permanent core which we indicate as "the thing." This view was opposed by Kant (1724-1804). He too, thought that the concept *substance* has its origin in man, but he was not satisfied with Hume's theory of association. Kant sought its origin in the structure of the human mind, which, according to him, classifies the impressions received from outside in a fixed pattern. The mind cannot do otherwise. This classification of impressions according to fixed categories of concepts is a necessary condition for intellectual knowledge. The concept *substance* is one of these classifying and synthetizing concepts. According to this view a material thing is not an extra-mental reality, but a construction of the mind for the purpose of classifying our impressions. This does not mean that Kant denied the existence of an extra-mental world. On the contrary, he considered such a world necessary as a source of sense impressions, but "the thing in itself" *(Das Ding an sich)*, Kant warns, is unknowable. Our concept of it is determined by the cognitional form of the mind.

Finally, we may mention a fourth conception, the so-called neo-positivistic view. According to neopositivism, a material thing is nothing but a logical symbol. This means that the word *material thing* has been fixed in our usage of words according to the rules of language in such a manner that it bundles together impressions which are closely associated in time and place. Every sentence containing, say, *horse* can be replaced by another sentence in which the word *horse* does not occur, but is replaced by symbols of impressions obtained from a horse.

Thus a certain amount of difference is possible in the interpretation of the concept *material thing*. Before drawing an important conclusion from this possibility of differences in interpretation we must make a few remarks to prevent misunderstandings. In the first place, our exposition of these interpretations had to be very schematical, so one might get the impression that these different views are somewhat superficial. That, however, is not the case. They are based on profound thinking; but since a proper exposition would require a special volume for each of these views we must be satisfied with a schematical exposition. In passing, it may be mentioned that these four conceptions—to which several others could be added—are not irreconcilable under all aspects. For instance, logical analysis must occupy a fundamental position in any view. Kant admits the existence of a "thing in itself" which is independent from our knowledge, so that his view in this respect coincides with realism. Secondly, it is to be noted that the first of these four views, which we called the realistic view and which we described only as being both the more or less unconscious view of every man and the conscious view of certain Greek philosophers, is not adequately represented by the term *naive realism*. Even in modern philosophy it offers impressive arguments. However, it is not our intention to enter here into this fascinating problem, except indirectly insofar as it contains one point of fundamental importance for our present query: the whole of the theses and concepts which compose physical science is, to use a mathematical expression, invariant with respect to these philosophic views. It is a whole which is closed in itself. Whether this science is evaluated as a more or less adequate knowledge of a really existing world, or as a construction of our mind in which the data of sense impressions are classified according to the basic structure of the mind, or as a purely logical embodiment, all this does not make any factual change in physical science, but is only a difference in view as regards the evaluation of *all* human knowledge and of reality *as such.*

The Inevitableness of Philosophy. From these considerations we deduce the important conclusion that alongside physical science and all other specialized sciences there is, in any event, room for several philosophic visions. The question may and must be raised whether or not the speculations upon which these visions are built can still claim the name of science. We will not be able to examine this interesting problem in detail, but must mention that neopositivism has used a lot of clever arguments upon the negative answer to this question. Its supporters think that so-called philosophic speculations are based upon insufficient logical analysis of language, so that propositions in which terms are used for things are understood as if they refer to autonomous realities. Mindful of our resolution we will not enter into any discussion of this view. It is not necessary anyhow, because as a matter of fact the publications of its supporters more convincingly than anything else demonstrate the existence of philosophy as a science. These publications cannot be classified under any of the specialized sciences. Nevertheless, they possess unmistakably a scientific character, and this character is philosophic. Several neopositivists realize it. For instance, the English author, A. J. Ayer, frankly admits it in the extensive introduction to the second edition of his work *Language, Truth, and Logic.* While in the work itself he continues to show that there cannot be any question of philosophy in the proper sense of the term, in the introduction of the second edition, which he wrote ten years after the first, he admits that his entire work is after all philosophic.[1]

---

[1]"It used to be said by the positivists of the Viennese school that the function of philosophy was not to put forward a special set of 'philosophical' propositions, but to make other propositions clear; and this statement has at least the merit of bringing out the point that philosophy is not a source of speculative truth. Nevertheless I now think that it is incorrect to say that there are no philosophical propositions. For whether they are true or false, the propositions that are expressed in such a book as this do fall into a special category; and since they are the sort of propositions that are asserted

The fact that the neopositivists advance philosophic theses which differ from those advanced by others can at most imply that their theses are wrong, but does not mean that they are not *philosophic*. It is not our task here to decide which of the different philosophic views is right, but the fact that a philosophic science still exists is a sufficient answer to our question. At the same time it does justice, to a certain extent, to the proper nature of this science. It considers the truly most universal aspects of human experience. It asks, for instance: What is *experience*? Is experience limited to a registration of separate impressions or does the mind exercise a synthetic function in the production of an experience, and if so in what manner? The dispute about the true nature of a material being is based upon essentially the same question.

Although the foregoing constitutes a sufficient answer to our original query, a few additional remarks may be made. We have steadily avoided entering into the problem which of the various philosophic views is correct. Because of this, someone may perhaps get the idea that the issue cannot be decided, so that he would consider all these views as equally relative. That is an attractive idea, but on second thought it cannot be maintained. For by declaring all these views to be relative one could not escape having one's own very definite view. The more this relativity of the different philosophic viewpoints is stressed, the more forcefully the *absolute* character of one's own position in philosophic problems reveals itself. Perhaps it could be called a *super-viewpoint,* but nevertheless it remains a *viewpoint*. It offers no escape from a decisive, absolute, choice of position in philosophic problems. Man has endeavored to escape from philosophic problems in many ways and with a considerable display of intelligence. This endeavor is quite natural because, contrary to what happened in the empirical sciences, no agreement could be reached in philosophy. While every science knows apodictic proofs, crucial experiments, decisive discoveries, etc., which according to the unanimous consent of its students put an end to a scientific dispute, there seems to be nothing in philosophy which can really force its students to come to an agreement. Hence the effort to declare philosophy senseless because its problems cannot be solved in the manner in which physical science

---

or denied by philosophers, I do not see why they should not be called philosophical. To say that they are, in some sense, about the usage of words, is, I believe, correct but also inadequate; for certainly not every statement about the usage of words is philosophical." *Language, Truth, and Logic,* London[2] 1947, p. 26.

and other empirical sciences solve theirs. Yet even this effort to get rid of philosophy is in vain. For to declare that only the judgments of physical and other experimental sciences make sense because they can be experimentally verified is ultimately nothing but a philosophic utterance which is certainly very interesting and worth investigation. We call it a *philosophic* utterance because it contains a definite and irrevocable judgment concerning all possibilities of human knowledge and their relationship to what is knowable.

It would be worth while to give here a more detailed description of these efforts to "get rid of philosophy," but it is beyond the scope of our book. One other point, however, must be mentioned. Sometimes it is asserted that the choice of a philosophic trend of thought is a question beyond discussion, because the choice is dictated by inclination or character. There are temperaments which have a certain need for so-called metaphysical speculations, and others which are satisfied with what is taught by experience; hence according to the inclination of one's temperament one chooses one's philosophic system.[2] It is easy to see that this escape also is blocked, because in this case also a judgment is pronounced from a super-viewpoint. An absolute connection is admitted between someone's temperament and one's philosophic view. No matter what else becomes relative in this process, certainly the connection will not.

Some reader may be inclined to say: But what is the use of insisting upon all this which seems to have little bearing upon the atomic theory? We answer: because it clearly demonstrates the following points:

1) *There is no escape from philosophy.* Man may twist and turn, but he always makes an ultimate and absolute judgment about what is called reality and our cognitional relation towards it.

2) The basic philosophic viewpoint is *not determined by physical science.* On the contrary, *philosophy judges physical science,* for it judges all human cognitional activity.

3) Philosophy is based on reflection upon what our mental activity itself reveals to us, specifically on reflection upon that which it reveals *always and under all circumstances.* Thus it became clear, for example, that when man makes a judgment, his judgment, even the most relative one, always contains an absolute element which he intends to pro-

---

[2]For example, H. Feigl, *Logical Empirism,* in *Twentieth Century Philosophy. Living Schools of Thought.* Edited by D. D. Runes, New York, 1947, p. 373.

nounce. For its relativity is known to him, the relative is stated *as relative,* and it is precisely in this that the absolute element of the judgment reveals itself in such a manner that it cannot be explained away if the judgment is to retain any meaning at all. Let the reader reflect again quietly upon the above-mentioned efforts to declare all knowledge relative. Moreover, he will arrive at the same conclusion if he tries to attribute no certainty but only probability to human knowledge.

In all this we find a confirmation of the conclusion which is so important for the subject of our study, namely, that *alongside the specialized sciences there is still room for philosophy.*

This conclusion, however, does not answer another question which falls within the scope of this study and which was already casually mentioned. We mean the question whether or not *ancient* philosophic speculations such as those of the Greeks and in the Middle Ages, to mention only the most remote in time, possess real value. The question is important for us because of the nature of our study which forced us to spend much time with these thinkers. However, this is not the only reason to ask the question, for as we shall see presently, the question is also important in itself.

3. THE IMPORTANCE OF ANCIENT PHILOSOPHIC SYSTEMS AS REGARDS NATURAL SCIENCE AND GENERAL PHILOSOPHY

Although it is beyond the scope of the present study fully to investigate the philosophic value of the systems proposed by the ancients, nevertheless some indications can be given about the nature of the answer. At the same time it will illustrate from a different angle the specific character of philosophy.

Scientific Value. By way of contrast let us first make a few remarks about the value which, from a scientific viewpoint, must be attributed to the theories proposed by philosophers in former ages, say up to 1600.

In judging this value we must distinguish between what we may call the stimulating and the material value. Obviously the latter is very small. As a rule, a profound study of antiquated views is meaningless if one's purpose is to obtain a correct insight into the sciences of nature. Whatever good points they contained have been wholly incorporated into our modern views so that it is sufficient to study the latter. We do not intend to deny that it certainly is an advantage to see our modern theories in their historical perspective, but generally speaking this does not mean that we have to go back more than fifty or a hundred years. Whatever came before that will teach us materially very little as regards physical science itself. Of course, the history of science has a value of its own, but that is a point which does not concern us now.

While it is true that the modern student of natural science will learn materially very little from ancient conceptions, we should not forget that this is but one aspect of the value of these conceptions. There is also another aspect, namely, the stimulating power which these conceptions exercised. We owe our better insights to the fact that we took our starting point from the less good insights of our predecessors. Because they proposed certain theories and hypotheses it was possible to check and to correct them if faulty. Thus even a faulty theory can have a great value for physical science. In our opinion it is not subject to doubt that the ancient philosophy was valuable in this sense. Its doctrine incorporated theses and theories that were valuable for the physical science which developed later, although it may be admitted that in general these theories appear materially very deficient to us. A brief reflection on the nature of physical science will make our assertion clear.

Science of Nature Proceeds by Successive Stages. The science of nature has what may be called a successive character, i.e. its problems appear only gradually. For instance, the presently so actual problem of nuclear physics could only be raised in the present state of physical science. It would be senseless to reproach Dalton for having omitted the problem of atomic nuclear structure from his considerations. Likewise nobody will think of censuring Huygens because he did not interpret the undulatory motion of light as an electromagnetic wave. As things are in physical science, one thing has to wait for another. Chemistry could be developed only when various physical methods of measurement had been learned. The physics of the seventeenth and eighteenth century was possible only when the more mathematical methods of differential and integral calculus had been developed. Biology could open new vistas only when physics had given it the microscope as a tool. Now that chemistry has solved many of its problems, biology can advance even farther. Moreover, traditional problems receive an entirely new solution now that the biologist knows how the various functions in plants and animals are chemically influenced and regulated. Thus we see everywhere in the science of nature either a successive rising of new problems or a more profound solution of the same problems. The order in which these problems rise depends on the matter itself, for one thing has to wait for another. This is the reason why above we spoke of the successive character of the science of nature.

Difference From Philosophy. Of course, we do not want to claim that this successive character is wholly lacking in philosophic problems. That would not be correct. On the other hand, it would be still less correct if we did not point out that succession occupies a much less important position in the problems of philosophy. In order to illustrate this we must revert to the answer we gave above to the question whether nowadays there is still room for philosophy as a science. In that answer we indicated as a typical characteristic of philosophy that it is directed towards the universal aspects of human experience, i.e. towards that which is always and of necessity present in experience. We saw, for example, how *every* judgment contains some absolute element. It is this absolute element which is the very object of philosophic analysis. Without any further discussion it should be clear that this element was just as clearly present for, say, Aristotle, as for Descartes, Kant, or Bergson. For insofar as this aspect of the problem is concerned it does not matter whether the judgment contains an assertion about the four elements of Aristotle or about the nuclear structure of the atom; the point is only what the judgment as such reveals. One might object that nevertheless there is a big difference between the character of the judgments Aristotle was wont to make and those which are formulated by the modern physicist. Aristotle's judgments expressed an absolute certainty, whereas the judgments of a modern scientist are far more modest. For instance, by the judgment "the atomic nucleus consists of neutrons and protons," he merely wants to express that the present state of our experiences can be expressed in this manner. This distinction, indeed, can be made, but it does not affect the judgment as a judgment. It may be granted that the modern scientist always includes this element of relativity in his physical judgments, but this does not change the simple fact that he explicitly affirms that element in his mind. It is a *certainty* for him, which—let us remark it in passing—many defend just as absolutely as the ancient Greeks defended their assertions.

Hence it is not difficult for one who is at home in ancient and modern philosophy to find many of the modern philosophic discussions back in earlier periods, though perhaps in a different form. And we must emphatically add that this applies also to those fundamental discussions which seem to find their origin in the development of modern sciences. For instance, the problem of the relativity of all human knowledge can be found almost literally in the discussions of the Greek philosophers.

After these preliminary remarks we may now revert to the questions which were raised at the beginning of the chapter. The answers will no longer be difficult to find.

The Importance of the Ancient Systems With Respect to General Philosophy. The first question was: What value have the philosophic speculations of the past, say, of the ancient Greek philosophers? It cannot be denied that, apart from their stimulating value, these speculations still possess a great material value even for the present time, for they went to the very core of the philosophic problems. Hence it is a simple matter of fact that no one can abstain from studying the great masters of Greek philosophy without serious harm to his own philosophic vision. The same holds for the speculations of the Middle Ages and of the seventeenth, eighteenth, or nineteenth century. Meanwhile we do not have to restrict ourselves to the observation of the fact, we can also point out the reason. From the very nature of philosophy it is perfectly clear that its *central* problems could be posed without the knowledge of modern specialized sciences. The reader, no doubt, suspects already why we put the word *central* in italics, but we shall come back to that presently. However strange it may sound to certain ears we must add that their ignorance of modern science was not only no unsurmountable obstacle for the Greek and medieval philosophers, but in a certain sense it even was an advantage. They were able to concentrate more upon the philosophic problems because their attention was not divided by the numerous divergent facets which modern science holds up before the philosopher. Obviously, we do not at all intend to claim that their ignorance was an unmixed advantage for the representatives of ancient philosophy. On the contrary, even when we leave out of consideration the progress in purely philosophic thought during the course of centuries, it is obvious that the development of specialized sciences opened up many illuminating vistas on philosophic problems. The most important of these is perhaps the new datum of experience that such more or less autonomous sciences *do exist*. Although we called it an advantage that in former ages the philosophic problems occupied a far more central position in scientific interests, it had also its drawback. The philosophic problems were far too frequently mixed with problems we have learned to consider as belonging exclusively to the physical sciences. The difference was not clearly perceived, and as a result the philosophic insight suffered.

4. THE RIGHT TO EXISTENCE OF NATURAL PHILOSOPHY

Natural Philosophy as the Meeting-ground of General Philosophy and Natural Science. If we want to formulate all this more precisely, we raise practically the second question mentioned in the introduction to this chapter: Is there still room for a philosophy of nature alongside modern science of nature? Although our answer to the first question may have convinced the reader that there is room for philosophy alongside the many specialized sciences, perhaps it has also given him such an idea of philosophy that now he will give a negative answer to the second question. Philosophy was presented as the science which studies the most universal aspect of human experience, but leaves all special problems to the various specialized sciences. Though this idea is true, it does not necessarily imply a negative answer to the second question. For the universal, the most fundamental aspect which constitutes the object of philosophy, is not an abstract colorless thing that is not subject to any shades of differences. On the contrary, the general theses of philosophy naturally branch out into all fields of reality. Let us illustrate with an example.

In preparing the way for the answer to the first question we made use of the philosophic problem contained in the term *material thing*. We observed that the philosophic view about the meaning of the concept *material thing* was determined by the more universal view on human experience. Now, even without any further explanation, it should be clear that if instead of the idea *material thing* we had chosen another concept with a general meaning, say, the concept *perceiving subject,* we would likewise have encountered very different views, varying from a realistic concept of person to a comprehensive symbol for a conscious stream of sense impressions. If we had done so, we could have made the same remark that these views spring from the same basic convictions which we have met in the answer to the question: What is a material thing? This is an interesting discovery, for it shows that these general philosophic considerations have consequences in the philosophic interpretation of the fundamental concepts in different sciences. As regards the above examples, the concept *material thing* is a basic concept of natural science, and *perceiving subject* is a basic concept of empirical psychology. This, however, should not be misunderstood. We do not mean that the concept *material thing* in its philosophic interpretation is a basic concept of natural science. As stated before, the physical theses remain untouched regardless of their philosophic interpretation. When the concept *material thing* is used in physics, it is not taken according to its possible philosophical meaning. As far as the physicist is concerned the concept is characterized by specifically physical concepts, such as mass, energy, charge, etc. However, the physicist is aware that these concepts more closely determine the material things which for him comprise material reality. Although in physics he is directly concerned only with these determinations, nevertheless the very fact that these concepts are further determinations of material things makes the concept *material thing* itself a basic concept for him, albeit only indirectly.

It is clear, however, that at the very moment when the physicist explicitly evaluates his scientific knowledge, the implications of this fundamental concept become of decisive importance. On the other hand, it is also clear that the physicist in evaluating his scientific knowl-edge has entered into the field of philosophy,—specifically that part of philosophy in which he will meet those philosophers who after starting from the general theses of philosophy have devoted their attention to the problem of the fundamental characteristics of matter as such. It is this boundary region which constitutes the field of natural philosophy, and therefore the physicist and the philosopher will meet one another in the philosophic considerations of nature.

Physical Science Fails to Realize its Philosophic Implications. In order to determine the position of natural philosophy somewhat more accurately, it will be useful to reflect upon a remarkable property of natural science which has not yet received sufficient attention in the foregoing considerations. We mean the fact that physical science does not realize all its implications. No doubt, this assertion will cause surprise, for a scientist does not at all give the impression of proceeding without realizing the implications of his work. He proceeds, indeed, very deliberately in his experimentation, and careful study precedes each new experiment. In numerous examples of the last chapter we have seen how new experiments are literally thought out as consequences of a new theory; witness for instance, the interferential phenomena of electronic rays after de Broglie had proposed his theory, or the experiments of Zeeman which had been prepared theoretically by Lorentz. These cases are not exceptional, but show the normal course of affairs. Hence the assertion that it is characteristic of physical science not to realize its implications seems very unfortunate not only as regards the experimental part of natural science, but especially as regards its theoretical aspect. To say that the implications of the theoretical part are not realized is almost a contradiction in terms, for theory presupposes a conscious complex of thoughtfully considered ideas.

Nevertheless the expression makes sense provided it be properly understood. Let us use again as an example our question: What is a material thing? Is it an extra-ego reality of which we know certain properties, or a construction in accordance with the innate cognitional forms of our mind, or a logical symbol? The answer is not without importance for the view taken of natural science as a whole, yet the question does not arise within the science of nature. Other questions could be asked to which the same remark would apply, viz. that various possible answers leave the scientific theories and data untouched; they do not add anything to them in the physical order, but they are important for the view taken *of* physical science as a whole.

Let us give an example of such a question. What is a scientific explanation? One will answer, the knowledge of the causes of a physical phenomenon; another, the logical comprehension of a series of experiences; a third, the classification of the phenomenon in one of the cognitional forms of the mind, etc. We must apologize for the brevity of these formulas which more or less force us to mutilate the answers. Whoever has thus far understood the chapter will be able to make them more complete. At the same time he will understand what we mean by the lack of realization of physical science. When a physicist proposes or considers an explanation, he does not enter into the problem of what is meant by explanation, but he simply sees some connection between what is offered as an explanation and the phenomenon which needs to be explained. Whoever, for example, reflects upon the phenomena of isomerism in organic chemistry sees that the different isomers follow with necessity if the spatial structure of carbon compounds proposed by this model is accepted. He also sees that no explanation is given by a structure which places the different atoms in one plane. Such explanations may require a large measure of knowledge and insight on the physical and mathematical level, but the mind surrenders spontaneously to the evidence, the perspicuity itself of these explanations. This matter is ruled by its own laws, which are clear enough in themselves, but which, on the other hand, leave quite a few questions unanswered, questions which center around the problem: What exactly is an explanation? Why is it that in one case our intellect submits to an explanation but not in another? Obviously, we do not mean the arguments proposed by the chemist in favor of the theory of the tetrahedron model and against that of a plane, for those arguments are precisely chemical. We mean the answer to the question: What makes an argument an argument, and an explanation an explanation? That question goes unanswered, and does not have to be answered within the science of nature. This is clear already from the fact that the answer to these philosophic questions leaves every scientific explanation as such entirely untouched.

Accordingly, in respect of these and other philosophic questions natural science proceeds more or less without realizing its implications. It accepts spontaneously the evidence of an explanation without realizing the peculiar problem which the use of explanations implies. Insofar as a physicist is aware of this problem, which of course is not at all an imaginary case, it is to his advantage to bar it from his mind as long as he is engaged in the search for some physical explanation. Paying attention to it would not only be useless for the solution of the physical problem, but could even be harmful because it is a well established psychological fact that we cannot without loss divide our attention between two different problems.

Upon second thought, therefore, there is good reason to speak about a certain lack of realization in the science of nature. Obviously, the state of affairs which we indicated by the term *lack of realization* could be expressed also in a different manner and perhaps even better. We could say, for instance, that when man works as a *physicist* a certain aspect of reality must remain outside his field of consciousness. This formula has the advantage of stressing that the lack of realization does not apply to the specific sphere of natural science, although it is true that it is closely connected to it.

The Twofold Character of Natural Philosophy. This lack of realization proper to natural science brings us back to our point of departure, to natural philosophy as the boundary area between the science of nature and philosophy. For nothing prevents the physicist from reflecting upon the philosophic side of the problems which hold his attention. But in doing so he is no longer in natural science but in philosophy, specifically in that part of philosophy which is closely allied to natural science. He finds himself in a boundary region where, as mentioned, he will meet the philosopher who started from the other side and investigates the special form which the general problems of philosophy assume when they are applied to the various branches of human knowledge. In keeping with the classical division of philosophy it will be considered preferable when there is question of, say, the philosophic interpretation of what is meant by *explanation*, not to speak about philosophy of nature but about the philosophy of natural science. Theoretically at least, these two may be sharply distinguished, although the distinction cannot always be equally maintained. In order to clarify this let us first indicate the basis for the distinction and then the objections which can be raised against it.

When on page 205 we explained that the philosophic problems of the true nature of a material thing really belong to the philosophic science of matter, we indicated that science by the term *philosophy of nature*. By this term we mean the philosophic consideration of what is called matter or material being. The object of this science, therefore, is matter,—not matter in its internal relations, which are studied by the science of nature, but matter placed in the broader philosophic setting which is concerned with such problems as: What is the difference between *matter* and objects which are not *material*? As an opposite of *material being* we indicated above, for example, *perceiving subject*. Obviously, we do not want to anticipate an essential difference between a material being and a perceiving subject, but provisionally there is plenty of reason to make a distinction, whatever may be its nature. A specific problem of natural philosophy is, for example, the investigation of mutability as an essential characteristic of matter, such as that made by Aristotle.

When, however, we pose as a philosophic problem the question as to what is really meant by an explanation in natural science, the object is no longer *matter* under its philosophic aspect, but the *science* of nature. Hence the attention is focused upon human knowledge as revealed in natural science. This kind of philosophic consideration belongs to what is called science of knowledge or logic (in a wider sense), and frequently also epistemology or the theory of science.[1]

Although this distinction between natural philosophy and the philosophy of natural science appears to be clear and well founded

---

[1]Sometimes the term *critique of science* is used. For instance, in the title of Renoirte's book *Éléments de critique des sciences et de cosmologie*, Louvain 1945.

upon an obvious distinction in their object, nevertheless it is open to several objections. In the first place, whether emphasis is laid upon this distinction or not is intimately connected with one's fundamental philosophic view. The distinction certainly makes sense for any one who considers a material thing as a reality which exists outside the perceiving mind. But for those who think that a logical analysis is the only function of philosophy, so that a material thing is seen only as a logical symbol, the distinction loses all reason for existence. In such an analysis *material things* disappear, so to speak, in thin air, they appear as having no proper being; hence it only makes sense to speak about *material things* as logical symbols which possess an accurately defined function in the science of nature and in daily life. Thus there is no room for a philosophic consideration of matter, and only a philosophy of natural science remains possible.

Moreover, as a matter of fact the distinction will be theoretical rather than practical for those who make room for natural philosophy alongside philosophy of natural science. For the very reason that natural philosophy is a boundary area between natural science and philosophy, the data of natural science will form an important part of the discussion, and thus the question of philosophic interpretation of natural science is bound to be considered. Moreover, whoever wants to do fruitful labor in either field must not only be acquainted with the data of natural science, but also completely at home in general philosophy. Hence for both fields of study the same requirements must be met, which in itself is already a sign of their intimate connection. For the sake of convenience, therefore, we will indicate the boundary area between the science of nature and philosophy by the single term *philosophy of nature,* while taking due cognizance of the fact that this term now embraces also the philosophy of natural science. (See *Supplementary Note* on p. 217.)

From all this it should be clear that there is a proper field of activity for the philosopher of nature. Yet, this answer does not wholly satisfy us. For here again we may raise the problem whether or not there is still any value in the speculations of ancient *philosophy* of nature, such as those of Democritus and Aristotle, to which we had to devote so much time at the beginning of our study.

5. THE VALUE OF GREEK PHILOSOPHY OF NATURE

From the fact that the philosophic speculations of the Greeks still retain their value with respect to the most central problems of philosophy, we cannot conclude that the same is true of their natural philosophy. Because in our eyes their science of nature is very primitive, one would rather be inclined to apply the same qualification to their philosophy of nature. Yet upon closer examination it becomes clear that their scientific conceptions exercised less influence upon their philosophy of nature than we would have expected. We got evidence of this in the course of the present chapter. Democritus' philosophic speculations on matter continued to pervade the philosophic views of the scientists for a very long time, so that in the scientific atomic theory we had to point continually towards a background inspired by Democritus. Hence the core of his ideas must have been relatively loosely connected with his scientific insight; otherwise his persistent influence, or rather the concordance between Democritus' basic idea and the philosophic background of the nineteenth century atomic theory, could not be explained if we keep in mind that the scientific speculations of the fifth century before Christ differ fundamentally from those of the nineteenth century. Moreover, in order to explain the agreement between the philosophic conception of Democritus and those of the nineteenth century atomic theory, we made reference to the eternal Democritus who reveals himself in every scientist, and this expression alone is already an indication that Democritus did touch some essential point. The objection may be raised that the most recent developments in physics have resulted in a break from the mechanistic view. This is true, but it does not mean that now we are outside the domain of Greek philosophy of nature. Whoever nowadays hears a scientist emphatically announce that an electron which leaves the nucleus was not present in it before as an electron, but is created, cannot help thinking of Aristotle's fundamental speculations *On Generation and Corruption,* at least if he is somewhat at home in Greek philosophy of nature. If one reads this treatise of Aristotle on philosophy of nature with a sense for the philosophic backgrounds of natural science and with the latest knowledge of the data of this science, one becomes more fascinated by the profound analysis of change than annoyed by the faulty scientific views. Aristotle's conclusion that change belongs essentially to the structure of matter, i.e. characterizes matter as matter, appears in a remarkable light if we take into consideration the recently discovered phenomena of so-called materialization and dematerialization. Although these terms are rather unfortunate, for a gamma quantum is just as material as an electron, nevertheless they express the radical change in matter which occurs in this process. Now the philosophic analysis of the possibility of *radical* change is exactly that which constitutes the core of Aristotle's philosophy of nature.*

These few remarks may suffice to show why we do not so easily dare to give a negative answer, at least not without close reflection, to the question whether or not the speculations of the Greek philosophers of nature still possess value for us. For the above mentioned conceptions of Democritus and Aristotle are not laboriously gathered together and ingeniously connected with the contemporary problems of philosophy of nature. On the contrary, the problem of change was undoubtedly the cardinal problem for the Greek philosophers of nature, and the fact that the undeniable radical changes which occur in matter undermined the mechanistic view of the physical universe constitutes likewise one of the major problems in the contemporaneous philosophy of nature. Hence one cannot exclude the possibility that the study of classical theories of natural philosophy may be able to teach us something concerning the philosophic problems which are raised by the modern science of nature. Neither is this possibility excluded by the fact that, because of the close ties between science of nature and philosophy of nature, the value of the classical philosophy of nature will be less than that of the general philosophic speculations of the Greek thinkers. In the classical philosophy of nature much will be found that bears clearly the stamp of the primitive science of nature proper to those times. A reader who is well versed in the science of nature will be less surprised by this admission than by the fact that we attribute value, even for our times, to the classical speculations. However, it is not so surprising after all. Whatever form natural philosophy may assume (see p. 208ff.), it is above all a *philosophic* science. Therefore, its method is philosophic, which means that it starts from the most universal aspects of matter. One of these aspects is, for example, mutability. The science of nature, which studies this mutability in the concrete forms in which it manifests itself, can only successively penetrate into them because one thing has to wait for another. Natural philosophy, however, investigates change as such and the conditions which matter must fulfill in order to be at all subject to change. Or to express the same in less realistic terms, philosophy of nature investigates the exact meaning of the term *change* and the cases in which it should be used. Hence in speculations of natural philosophy the point is not the special character of a certain change, but that which makes a change a change, or in other words,

---

*See *Supplementary Note* on p. 218.

why exactly a certain phenomenon is *change*. Now since the Greeks did not have more difficulty than we have in observing the existence of change, their lack of scientific knowledge did not have to be an obstacle for the correct philosophic analysis of the *mutability* of matter.

Perhaps someone will remark that this is a very abstract argument because in science we are never concerned with the phenomenon *change in general,* but always with some concrete change. And since the views of the Greeks about these concrete changes differed from ours, their analysis of *change in general* will show signs of this difference.

No doubt, this remark goes to the heart of the question. The answer, however, is not difficult. Why do we call all these concrete changes *changes?* Only because they possess a common element, i.e. an element which is found in all cases of change. Otherwise to speak of change would simply be an abuse of language and a cause of confusion. Of course, such an abuse of language does occur occasionally, but it remains exceptional. Let us illustrate this with a very modern example, the so-called process of dematerialization. Since it was discovered only in the twentieth century, it certainly is something of which Aristotle did not even dream. Nevertheless in this process we speak of change in just the same sense in which Aristotle spoke about change. For the concept change expresses at the same time two elements, namely, a thing-remaining-what-it-is and a thing-being-different. That which first was such is now different. Hence the scientist says: the electron is changed and transformed into gamma quanta, because he sees a special connection between this electron and those gamma quanta. He explains, for example, that the energy of the latter corresponds exactly to the mass energy of the electron. In other words, nothing has totally disappeared, nothing was annihilated to be replaced shortly after by something else which has absolutely nothing in common with the former. The physicist is profoundly convinced that the gamma quanta came from the electron, and this is the reason why he calls this process a change. Accordingly, he calls dematerialization a change because this phenomenon exhibits all the essential characteristics of change; in other words, this concept of change is available before its new concrete application. However, this answer does not yet settle the issue, for one may make the objection: Do you want to assert that from the very beginning all concepts are immutably fixed? We certainly do not want to make any such claim, for obviously it is not true. Nearly all modern physical concepts came gradually into existence and were subject to frequent change. But the concept *change* is not a physical concept if by this term we mean a concept which could come into existence only within the frame of natural science. It is far more primary, and forces itself upon our attention as a concept which is needed even for the classification of our most primitive experiences. Without the concept *change* no human knowledge is possible, and consequently neither any knowledge of natural science. For this reason an analysis of change without accurate knowledge of all possible changes *can* be correct provided it is based upon the characteristics of change as change. (See *Note* on p. 217

Perhaps some reader is not yet fully satisfied, and justly so, for it is indeed rather mysterious that speculations on the philosophy of nature which date from a time when natural science was very primitive would still be worth while. This reader will point out that the explanation of change touches after all a problem of general philosophy rather than a problem of natural philosophy. We fully agree with him. Speculations of natural philosophy do, indeed, derive their strength from general philosophy. Upon accurate analysis of modern discussions about natural philosophy one comes to the conclusion that the basic points of difference flow from a difference in fundamental philosophic views. It is sufficient to recall our previous remarks about the true nature of a *material thing*. It would not be correct to put too much stress upon the difference between general philosophy and the philosophy of nature. Philosophy of nature cannot be anything else but the application of general philosophic principles to the sphere of what is called *matter*. This is the reason why there are parts with a permanent value in the most fundamental speculations of the classical philosophy of nature. At the same time, however, it is clear that the detailed elaboration of this natural philosophy will show the traces of the special knowledge of matter which the science of nature provides. Consequently it cannot be otherwise than that philosophy of nature will bear the seal of time far more clearly than a treatise of general philosophy.

This brings us to the end of our study of the various aspects of value in ancient natural philosophy. For a more profound study we would have to go into the details of a modern philosophy of nature, compare it to some important natural philosophies of the past, and investigate to what extent the difference must be attributed to a change in physical insight. Or we would have to investigate accurately whether the natural philosophy of Aristotle and Democritus depended perhaps on the contemporaneous knowledge of natural science. Either alternative would be beyond the scope of this study.[2] Moreover, the reason why we have spoken rather extensively about the possible value of ancient natural philosophy was not to obtain a detailed answer concerning Plato, Aristotle, or Democritus, but to show the proper setting of problems with respect to modern natural philosophy. We hope that our effort has been successful. Even nowadays there is still room for speculation on natural philosophy. Although these speculations differ in nature from those which belong strictly to the science of nature, nevertheless they are part of the intellectual assets of our time.

6. THE PHILOSOPHIC BACKGROUND OF THE SCIENCE OF NATURE

There is still another reason why we dwelled so long upon philosophy of nature. As we pointed out in the introduction to this chapter, the question whether philosophy in general, and natural philosophy in particular, have a right to exist is closely connected with the problem whether or not there will always be a philosophic background in the scientific atomic theory. We are now in a position to answer this question. The starting point of the answer lies in what we have called the lack of realization in physics. Certain aspects of reality are left out of consideration by the science of nature, not only as a matter of fact inasmuch as this science does not yet extend to everything within its field, but also as a matter of principle. Natural science limits itself to the creation of an intelligible connection between certain facts which can be verified by the senses.[1] It does this more or less spontaneously. There are many questions which are not raised by the science of nature, for the simple reason that it does not have to raise them in order to reach its goal. For example, questions like: What exactly is an intelligible connection? What is a *fact*? What is the value in reality of such entities as are indicated by the physical concepts atom, molecule, and their properties? Nevertheless these and other similar questions exist, and they are raised explicitly in philosophy, specifically in the philosophy of nature.

---

[2]The different problems are discussed in our study, *The Philosophy of Nature*, Pittsburgh, 1954.

[1]See p. 162f.

On the other hand, it is clear that even the scientist, who does not formally philosophize, gives a more or less unconscious answer to these questions. It is this unreflected answer, this more or less spontaneous conviction, which forms the philosophic background against which he projects his science of nature. This background will always continue to exist because natural science is born from an abstraction which apprehends only certain aspects of reality. What is missing is added by the mind of the scientist, whether consciously or unconsciously. If unconsciously, we get a philosophic *background;* if consciously, the result will be a philosophic *theory.* Both are the philosophic perspective in the light of which scientific theories are considered.

It should be clear that important contributions to the unrealized philosophic background are made by every day language, which continues to be an important factor in every science. Because of the realistic tendency of this language we think that the philosophic background also will always show a realistic trend. However, this is not the only reason, or at any rate not the ultimate reason, for we can always ask why every day language shows and has always shown this realistic trend. Without attempting to give a full reply to this question, we may indicate in a few words what direction the answer will take. As we have seen above, physical science always starts from certain philosophic presuppositions. These presuppositions are neither investigated nor even explicitly formulated by physical science, but lie concealed in its fundamental methods. Because these presuppositions cannot be the result of physical science, they have to originate in a different sphere—namely, the sphere of general experience which lies at the basis of every science. But this general experience has its repercussions also in language.

7. RECAPITULATION

The considerations of this chapter were not intended primarily as a careful study of the ultimate problems of philosophy. That would have been beyond the scope of this book. Our purpose was only to show that outside all empirical sciences there still remain problems which these sciences do not solve and are not able to solve. Hence there will always be room for philosophy alongside the sciences of nature. But there will also be always in the science of nature something which we indicated as the *philosophic background.* This conclusion is very important for an exact evaluation of the ancient philosophic theories, which occupied such a large place in our study for the simple reason that they occupied also a large place in history.

SUPPLEMENTARY NOTE FOR P. 210:

The intimate connection between the two realms may be clarified also in a different way. The part of physical science which interests the philosopher is not primarily the results achieved by this science but the method by means of which these results have been reached. Thus the philosopher will be most interested in the experimental methods, because they give rise to such questions as: Why is the experimental method so marvellously effective? What does this effectiveness teach us about the nature of the object and the nature of man's cognitive power? For, if a method is to be effective, it must be adapted to both the object investigated and the cognitive power of the investigating subject. The important point here again is to realize that physical science itself cannot undertake this reflection on the experimental method. The reason is that this method constitutes the fundamental procedure of physical science; hence any analysis aiming at this method ceases to be a reflection of physical science itself and belongs to the philosophy of physical science, i.e., epistemology or the philosophy of knowledge. However, this philosophy will automatically assume in part the character of a philosophy of nature, because one of the questions that will arise is why the experimental method is so particularly well-adapted to the object to be studied. Thus it will be impossible to escape reflecting on the general character of nature. Let us consider this point somewhat more in detail.

The Presuppositions of Physical Science. If the experimental method is to be fruitful, it presupposes that the object to which it is applied satisfies certain conditions. Thus, for instance, the method presupposes that the object possesses at the same time a certain mutability and a certain immutability. Mutability is required because, if the object is to become better known through experiment, it should in principle be capable of reacting in different ways to the varied conditions supplied by a series of experiments. Otherwise the experiments would not supply any information. On the other hand, the experimental method presupposes also immutability in the object. In the different replies the object gives to the changed conditions of the experiments it must be that fundamentally the same nature reveals itself. Otherwise the different experiments would stand unrelatedly alongside one another without giving together any information about the object. If, for instance, experiments are made with copper, this metal is exposed to all kinds of influences. In many cases the copper reacts differently, but all these reactions are seen as flowing from the identical and immutable nature of copper. Likewise, the same law of gravitation reveals itself in such divergent events as the celestial motion of bodies and the earthly phenomena of fall.

Accordingly, certain presuppositions about the general nature of matter are implied in the basis of the experimental method. For this reason one who investigates the philosophical presuppositions of physical science, which primarily belong to the philosophy of physical science, will be led quite naturally to a philosophy of nature.

SUPPLEMENTARY NOTE FOR P. 212:

In this connection we may point also to Aristotle's concept of matter. In a certain sense this concept is being constantly more closely approximated by the conceptions of present-day physical science. Science acknowledges something that remains in every change, but at the same time this permanent something more and more losses its concrete character. It is no more immutable particles than mass or energy, but something which underlies all these things as their common substratum.[1]

[1]Cf. p. 190, footnote 4a.

SUPPLEMENTARY NOTE FOR P. 214:

In other words, as was already pointed out, the concept "change" belongs to the sphere of presuppositions of physical science. It is not difficult to see that concepts pertaining to the reflection on the presuppositions of physical science are much less subject to revision than concepts originating in an ever-developing and self-correcting physical science. For physical science owes this development precisely to the results obtained through the constant application of always the same fundamental method—experiment.

CHAPTER SEVEN

EPILOGUE

The preceding chapter took our attention away for a while from the history of the concept *atom* which we endeavored to sketch in this book. However, the digression was fully justified because it accounted for the peculiar characteristic which sets philosophy apart from physical science. Without any understanding of the relationship between philosophy and physical science it would hardly be possible to acquire a comprehensive view of the *entire* development that took place in the concept *atom,* for this development can be divided into two more or less distinct periods, one scientific and the other philosophic. Strictly speaking, this division is not correct because there are no two distinct successive periods. We do not mean this in the sense of the general correction which must be made in every division into periods, namely that there is no sharp division, but we allude to something more fundamental. What we mean can be expressed most suitably as was done in the introduction: two periods may be distinguished, with a transition period from the seventeenth to the nineteenth century, but these periods cannot be adequately characterized by the adjectives *philosophic* and *scientific.* It is not true that before the seventeenth century there was question only of a purely philosophic theory. The philosophic atomic theory was already interwoven with something which later was to develop into an autonomous scientific atomic theory. Neither is there in the period after 1800 question only of a purely scientific theory, for in the background there remains something of the philosophic atomic theory.

The very first atomic theory which we analyzed extensively, that of Democritus, clearly exhibited this twofold character. Without any doubt, its center of gravity lay in the sphere of philosophy, but there were also links with the later physical atomic theory. However, precisely because its center of gravity lay in its philosophic views, contemporary and subsequent Greek philosophers judged Democritus' atomic theory primarily upon its general philosophic value and rejected it. Thus its promising links with a physical atomic theory were lost for centuries. This is the correct view of the matter, for in Aristotle's theory smallest particles occupied only a very secondary place. Undoubtedly, there were possibilities for a development of his minima theory, and as a matter of fact this development did take place, but it took centuries. Not before the Averroists was the Aristotelian

218

minima theory ripe for application in a physical setting. Before that time there was often question of the minima, but it was always in the general frame of the philosophic problem of change.

We may ask ourselves whether this retardation in the development of the physical concept of the atom could have been avoided or not. It would be difficult to give a satisfactory and adequate answer to this question. Since the investigation of the actual historical development is already full of difficulties, how much worse would it be to draw a reasonably convincing picture of the eventual development if history had taken a different course. Hence we shall not attempt to formulate an answer, but modestly limit ourselves to point out a certain aspect which in our opinion should be taken into consideration if the answer to this question were attempted. We mean the necessity which the Greeks faced to construct first a scientific method. This method was bound to be connected with that aspect of experience which was accessible even at the initial stage of science, and that aspect was formed by the most general data of experience. Hence it coincides with what we came to know in the preceding chapter as the object of philosophy.*
Only very gradually did man discover that it was possible to consider some sector of experience as a separate and closed branch of science. Before this discovery was made, too few physical data were known to find a sufficient number of intelligible connections for the construction of a separate autonomous science.

Hence we may describe the situation as follows. Among the Greeks the urge to find intelligible connections could not yet find sufficient scope in the consideration of the mutual relations among physical phenomena. Therefore, the few available scientific data were drawn into the sphere of philosophic problems; for there were sufficient data to construct a philosophic setting. This is the reason why Grecian science exhibited such a preponderantly philosophic character, both in method and in object, especially in Democritus' atomism. His atoms have properties that are adapted to the setting of a problem of natural philosophy and to the solution which he wanted to give to that problem. The Greeks who rejected his solution as unsatisfactory should not be blamed for not paying attention to the physical aspects of atomism, for only much later did it become possible to judge these aspects upon their own merits. It could not be done before enough physical and chemical data had been gathered to make a specifically scientific setting possible. Whether or not this should have taken *as long as it did take,* is a question which we are not prepared to answer. Yet, it is easy to see why it did take a *long*

---

* See *Supplementary Note* on p. 224.

time. The necessary data had to be supplied by the technical arts, which without the basis of an adequate theory could advance only step by step. Whatever theory these arts contained was nothing but a philosophic superstructure. In view of its twofold character philosophy certainly did contain elements which could be utilized as a scientific theory in the technical arts. But the very requirement which philosophy imposed upon Democritus' atomism (all particles had to be of the same kind) made his atomism less suitable for this purpose. Initially Aristotle's minima theory was equally unsuitable, but this theory gradually developed in such a way that it became capable of supplying the demand for a corpuscular theory when chemistry felt the need for it. For even in the Middle Ages the situation was still such that philosophy had to fulfill the role of the theoretical part of science. It is in connection with this that great importance must be attributed to the Averroistic minima theory, because it was far closer than atomism to chemical practice which worked with qualitatively different substances. Hence the first manifestations of a theory of smallest particles which was suitable for the formation of physical concepts was found among the Averroists. True, the entire background of their minima theory was still philosophic, the concepts still showed the seal of the philosophic setting from which they had come forth, but the idea *smallest particles* had been recognized as fruitful in physical problems. This explains why at the revival of Democritus' atomism the physical aspects came almost immediately to the fore. To some extent they were noticeable already in Gassendi, whose atomic combinations were based upon specific smallest particles, but they were clear in Descartes, whose particles had a different *mass,* and in Boyle, who in practice worked only with primary concretions (specific smallest particles). We find this confirmed in another representative of the seventeenth century theory of smallest particles, namely Sennert. Being older than the others, he followed the traditional minima theory more closely, but his corpuscles had a philosophically neutral character. He was interested only in the idea *smallest particle* and developed it according to the requirements of chemical practice.

It is always dangerous to characterize a complex situation in a single sentence. Nevertheless we will attempt to do so, trusting that the reader will see these brief conclusions in the light of the explanations that have been offered in the course of this study. With this proviso, we would like to characterize the events of the seventeenth century as follows: in this century two methods met: the deductive method, which up to that time had been developed only in the setting of philosophy and mathematics, and the inductive method, which had been developed in the practice of the technical arts.

We do not intend to imply that previously no connection had been 'constructed' between these two methods, but rather that it had been no more than a construction. Chemistry, for example, was wholly seen within the frame of some philosophic conviction, and reversely natural philosophy was illustrated with examples from chemical practice. But all this was a more or less arbitrary, extrinsic connection. There was no inner contact between the result of the experiment and the imposing philosophic vision which was supposed to satisfy the man of science. Such an inner connection was not yet possible. For philosophy apprehends aspects of experience other than experimental data of technical arts. On the other hand, the discovery had still to be made that a scientific method was possible which was not philosophic and nevertheless scientific, that it was possible to have a true science which gives general principles which are applicable only in a limited field of knowledge. That discovery was made in the nineteenth century.

The discovery that it was possible to devise a scientific theory which was immediately connected to the data of experience and which had value only insofar as it was immediately connected to them, constitutes one of the most important discoveries in the history of scientific thought. It was the discovery of physical science as an independent, autonomous science. It was not made all at once, but the events of the seventeenth century may be said to have made an essential contribution, at least insofar as the atomic theory was concerned.

The fact that the science of nature is considered as an autonomous science must never make us forget that the philosophic problems remain present in the background, but it offers the possibility to see them as *separate* problems. In the past philosophic and scientific problems were interwoven, just as is reality itself. Hence we should not be surprised that the Greeks were not able adequately to treat all these aspects. Long experience had to precede, not in the discovery of facts, but in methodological possibilities. Thus the history of the concept *atom* is a fascinating datum of experience which can teach us much about the nature of man's cognitional possibilities. It was the purpose of this study to give the reader some idea of this.

THE PERIODIC TABLE OF ELEMENTS

GROUP / PERIOD	I	II	III	IV	V	VI	VII	VIII			O
I	1 H 1.0080										2 He 4.003
II	3 Li 6.940	4 Be 9.013	5 B 10.82	6 C 12.010	7 N 14.008	8 O 16.000	9 F 19.00				10 Ne 20.183
III	11 Na 22.997	12 Mg 24.32	13 Al 26.97	14 Si 28.06	15 P 30.98	16 S 32.066	17 Cl 35.457				18 A 39.944
IV	19 K 39.096	20 Ca 40.08	21 Sc 45.10	22 Ti 47.90	23 V 50.95	24 Cr 52.01	25 Mn 54.93	26 Fe 55.85	27 Co 58.94	28 Ni 58.69	
IV	29 Cu 63.54	30 Zn 65.38	31 Ga 69.72	32 Ge 72.60	33 As 74.91	34 Se 78.96	35 Br 79.916				36 Kr 83.7
V	37 Rb 85.48	38 Sr 87.63	39 Y 88.92	40 Zr 91.22	41 Nb 92.91	42 Mo 95.95	43 Tc 99	44 Ru 101.7	45 Rh 102.91	46 Pd 106.7	
V	47 Ag 107.880	48 Cd 112.41	49 In 114.76	50 Sn 118.70	51 Sb 121.76	52 Te 127.61	53 I 126.92				54 Xe 131.3
VI	55 Cs 132.91	56 Ba 137.36	57-71 Lanthanide Series	72 Hf 178.6	73 Ta 180.88	74 W 183.92	75 Re 186.31	76 Os 190.2	77 Ir 193.1	78 Pt 195.23	
VI	79 Au 197.2	80 Hg 200.61	81 Tl 204.39	82 Pb 207.21	83 Bi 209.00	84 Po 210	85 At (210)				86 Rn 222
VII	87 Fr (223)	88 Ra 226.05	89-102? Actinide Series								

Lanthanide Series														
57 La 138.92	58 Ce 140.13	59 Pr 140.92	60 Nd 144.27	61 Pm (147)	62 Sm 150.43	63 Eu 152.0	64 Gd 156.9	65 Tb 159.2	66 Dy 162.46	67 Ho 164.90	68 Er 167.2	69 Tm 169.4	70 Yb 173.04	71 Lu 174.99

Actinide Series														
89 Ac 227	90 Th 232.12	91 Pa 231	92 U 238.07	93 Np (237)	94 Pu (239)	95 Am (241)	96 Cm (243)	97 Bk (245)	98 Cf (246)	99 E (253)	100 Fm (254)	101 Mv ?	102 No ?	

TABLE OF SUBATOMIC PARTICLES[1]

Particle	Symbol	Spin	Rest Mass	Mean Life	Transformation
Photon	$h\nu$	1	0	—	
Electron	e^-	$\frac{1}{2}$	1	Stable	$e^+ + e^- \longrightarrow 2h\nu$
Positron	e^+	$\frac{1}{2}$	1	—	$\nu + p \longrightarrow n + e^+$
Neutrino	ν	$\frac{1}{2}$	<0.01	—	
Proton	p	$\frac{1}{2}$	1836	Stable	
Neutron	n	$\frac{1}{2}$	1838	12 min	$n \longrightarrow p + e^- + \nu + 0.78$ Mev
Mu meson	$\mu^\pm$	$\frac{1}{2}$	206	2.2×10^{-6} sec	$\mu^\pm \longrightarrow e^\pm + 2\nu + 105$ Mev
Pi meson	$\pi^\pm$	0	273	2.5×10^{-8} sec	$\pi^\pm \longrightarrow \mu^\pm + \nu + 33$ Mev
Pi meson	π^0	0	264	5×10^{-14} sec	$\pi^0 \longrightarrow 2h\nu + 133$ Mev
K meson	$K_\mu{}^+$		950	10^{-8} sec	$K_\mu{}^+ \longrightarrow \mu^+ + \nu$
Tau meson	$\tau^\pm$		975	10^{-9} sec	$\tau^\pm \longrightarrow \pi^\pm + \pi^+ + \pi^- + 75$ Mev
Tau meson	$\tau^\pm$		975	10^{-9} sec	$\tau^\pm \longrightarrow \pi^\pm + \pi^0 + \pi^0$
Tau meson	τ^0		975	10^{-9} sec	$\tau^0 \longrightarrow \pi^0 + \pi^+ + \pi^- \ 50$ Mev
Theta meson	θ^0		975	1.5×10^{-10} sec	$\theta^0 \longrightarrow \pi^+ + \pi^- + 210$ Mev
Kappa meson	κ		1000	2×10^{-9} sec	$\kappa \longrightarrow \mu + 2\nu + 350$ Mev
Chi meson	$\chi^\pm$		1000	10^{-9} sec	$\chi^\pm \longrightarrow \pi^\pm + \nu + 220$ Mev
Neutral hyperon	Λ^0		2180	4×10^{-10} sec	$\Lambda^0 \longrightarrow p + \pi^- + 37$ Mev
Charged hyperon	$\Lambda^\pm$		2300	6×10^{-11} sec	$\Lambda^\pm \longrightarrow n + \pi^\pm + 130$ Mev
Charged hyperon	Λ^+		2300	3×10^{-10} sec	$\Lambda^+ \longrightarrow p + \pi^0 + 120$ Mev
Charged hyperon	Λ^-		2600	5×10^{-10} sec	$\Lambda^- \longrightarrow \Lambda^0 + \pi^- + 65$ Mev

[1] Courtesy Robert S. Shankland, *Atomic and Nuclear Physics*, Macmillan, New York 1955, p. 509. By permission of the publisher.

SUPPLEMENTARY NOTE FOR P. 219:

The same idea could be expressed also in this way. Before it was possible to build specialized sciences, man had first to reflect on the general conditions of science for, as we have seen above, every science starts from certain presuppositions. In this way, the struggle of the Greeks (Heraclitus, Parmenides, Democritus, Plato, Aristotle) with the problem of mutability and immutability assumes the form of a struggle for clarity with respect to what has to enter science as its presupposition. Thus the entire intellectual activity at first bore the stamp of a philosophic reflection on the essence of nature and the essence of man. It was thought that a clarification of these philosophic problems was a *sine qua non* condition of all science. This view was right insofar as philosophy could not be dispensed with in the search for the scientific attitude and method. It was wrong, however, insofar as the philosophic clarification of the philosophical problems is no longer strictly necessary for science itself, once the method of science has been discovered. But the ancient Greeks could not know this, for at that time no autonomous science of nature was known.

BIBLIOGRAPHY

At the request of the editor and for the convenience of the reader we add here a bibliography which may be useful for a more detailed study of our subject. The list does not aim at completeness. As a rule books which are important only for specialists are not mentioned. This applies especially to purely scientific works.

Translators Note

As far as possible English equivalents have been substituted for Dutch works mentioned in the original bibliography, because the latter would be of little interest to the general reader. These substitutions are marked with an asterisk.

Other additions to the bibliography also are marked with an asterisk.

PHILOSOPHY

History of Philosophy

General Works

Friedrich Ueberweg: *Grundriss der Geschichte der Philosophie.* 5 vol. 12th ed. Berlin 1924-1928. Reprinted Tübingen, 1955.

This basic work is an almost infallible book of reference. It contains an extensive bibliography about every philosopher of the past.

*Of the earlier editions English translations are available under the title: *History of Philosophy.*

Emile Bréhier: *Histoire de la philosophie.* 7 vol. Paris 1945.

Less documented than Ueberweg, but still very complete.

Frederic Copleston, *A History of Philosophy,* Vol. I-III, Westminster, 1950 ff. Vol. IV, London, 1958.

A comprehensive history, still incomplete. Vol. IV ends with Leibniz.

*Bertrand Russell: *A History of Western Philosophy.* New York 1946.

The work of this English empiricist endeavors to show the development of philosophy against its political and social background.

History of Periods and Monographs

*E. Zeller: *Outlines of the History of Greek Philosophy*. New York 13th edition, 1951 (Revised by W. Nestle).

A translation of *Grundriss der Geschichte der Griechischen Philosophie,* 13th impr. Leipzig 1928. Contains the essence of the author's well-known complete history of Greek philosophy *Die Philosophie der Griechen.*

John Burnet: *Early Greek Philosophy*. 3rd ed. London 1930.

John Burnet: *Greek Philosophy (From Thales to Plato)*. London 1928.

*Theodor Gomperz: *Greek Thinkers*. 4 vol. London 1901-1912.

A translation of *Die Griechische Denker.*

*B. Fuller: *History of Greek Philosophy*. 3 vol. New York 1923-1931.

W. Ross: *Aristotle*. 4th ed. London 1945.

Léon Robin: *Aristote*. Paris 1944.

A. Mansion: *Introduction à la physique aristotélienne*. 2nd ed. Louvain 1945.

Three works on Aristotelian philosophy. The first two are comprehensive studies of Aristotle's philosophy in its entirety, the last deals more especially with Aristotle's philosophy of nature.

*C. Bailey: *The Greek Atomists and Epicurus*. Oxford 1928.

*Paul E. More: *Platonism*. Princeton 1931.

For the study of Arabic and Medieval philosophy the following may be consulted:

Maurice de Wulf: *History of Medieval Philosophy*. 2 vol. 3rd ed. New York 1935-1937.

*A translation of *Histoire de la philosophie médiévale.* A new translation of Vol. I was published in 1952.

G. Quadri: *La philosophie arabe dans l'Europe médiévale*. Paris 1947.

Étienne Gilson: *The Spirit of Medieval Philosophy*. London 1936.

A translation of *L'esprit de la philosophie médiévale*.

*The following three works contain selections of the great philosophers from the early Greeks to Kant:

*T. V. Smith: *Philosophers Speak for Themselves*. 6th impr. Chicago 1949.

Extracts from Greek, Roman and early Christian philosophers.

*Richard McKeon: *Selections from Medieval Philosophers*. 2 vol., New York 1929.

*Smith and Grene: *From Descartes to Kant*. 6th impr. Chicago 1950.

Introductions to Philosophy

Among the numerous works of this kind we select the following:

*Jacques Maritain: *An Introduction to Philosophy*. New York 1933.

A translation of *Introduction à la philosophie*.

*Ray H. Dotterer: *Philosophy by way of the Sciences*. New York 1933.

*Durant Drake: *Invitation to Philosophy*. New York 1933.

Louis de Raeymaker: *Introduction to Philosophy*. New York 1948.

A translation of *Introduction à la philosophie*. Rather concise, but interesting on account of its extensive survey of philosophic organizations and publications.

*D. Hawkins: *Approach to Philosophy*. London 1938.

Philosophic Trends

Although no philosophic work is without some definite philosophic basis, we will mention here a few books which are especially intended as introductions to some particular system of philosophy. We will limit ourselves to those trends which are connected with the subject of our study.

I. M. Bochenski: *Contemporary European Philosophy.* Berkeley, 1957. Bern, 1947.

A penetrating general survey of current trends.

Dagobert Runes (editor) : *Twentieth Century Philosophy.* New York 1947.

Contains 22 short studies by various authors on different schools of thought. Gives an excellent idea of modern problems in philosophy.

R. von Mises: *Kleines Lehrbuch des Positivismus.* Chicago 1939.

A good introduction to positivistic and empiricistic philosophy.

Bertrand Russell: *Human Knowledge.* London 1948.

A theory of knowledge upon an empiricistic basis but with a realization of its limitations.

A. J. Ayer: *Language, Truth and Logic.* 2nd ed. London 1946.

Positivistic-empiricistic. Emphasizes the analysis of scientific language as the task of philosophy.
*For a critical analysis of this work see C. Joad: *Critique of Logical Positivism.* Chicago 1950.

B. J. Ovink: *Philosophie und Sophistik.* Den Haag 1940.

An explanation of philosophy according to Kantian principles.

*F. Caird: *Critical Philosophy of Kant.* London 1889.

*Harold A. Prichard: *Kant's Theory of Knowledge.* Oxford 1909.

*Martin Grabmann: *Thomas Aquinas.* New York 1935. A translation of *Thomas von Aquin.*

*Hans Meyer: *The Philosophy of St. Thomas Aquinas.* St. Louis 1944. A translation of *Thomas von Aquin.*

Thomism is one of the most important realistic trends in philosophy. These two works are brief introductions to the life and philosophy of Thomas Aquinas.

Philosophy of Nature and Philosophy of Natural Science

Peter Hoenen: *Filosofia della natura inorganica.* Brescia, 1949.

A systematically constructed philosophy of nature with a realistic basis.
*Exists also in German and Dutch editions.

B. Bavink: *Ergebnisse und Probleme der Naturwissenschaften.* 9th impr. Zürich 1948.

An excellent survey of the achievements of the natural sciences and of connected philosophic problems.

A. S. Eddington: *The Philosophy of Physical Science.* Cambridge 1939.

A plea for the *a-priori* tendency of natural science.

A. N. Whitehead: *Science and the Modern World.* 11th ed. Cambridge 1946.

A philosophic evaluation of the development of science.

P. Jordan: *Physics of the Twentieth Century.* New York 1944. A translation of *Die Physik des 20 Jahrhunderts.*

It sketches the latest developments of physical science, to which it gives a positivistic interpretation.

G. Hermann, E. May, Th. Vogel: *Die Bedeutung der modernen Physik für die Theorie der Erkenntnis.* Leipzig 1937.

Three important philosophic studies of the quantum theory and relativity, each from its own philosophic viewpoint.

F. Renoirte: *Cosmology. Elements of a Critique of Sciences and of Cosmology.* New York 1950.

An introduction to the philosophy of natural science. A translation of *Éléments de critique des sciences et de cosmologie.*

*Vincent Edward Smith: *Philosophical Physics.* New York 1950.

A discussion of the philosophy of nature which takes into account modern scientific data, especially in the field of atomic physics.

A. G. M. van Melsen: *Natuurwetenschap en Wijsbegeerte.* Utrecht-Brussels 1946.

A general study of the relationship of philosophy and physical science, and a critical analysis of the consequences of modern physics.

*P. H. van Laer: *Philosophico-Scientific Problems.* Pittsburgh, 1953.

Action at a distance. Causality.

*P. H. van Laer: *Matter and Light.* New York 1939

Modern physics and philosophy.

L. de Broglie: *Continu et discontinu en physique moderne.* Paris 1941.

A philosophical study of quantum mechanics.

*C. F. von Weizsäcker, *The World View of Physics*. Chicago, 1952.

Modern physics and Kantian philosophy.

*Herbert Dingle, *The Scientific Adventure*. New York 1953.

Stimulating essays in the history and philosophy of science.

E. Meyerson: *Du cheminement de la pensée*. 3 vol., Paris 1931.

A richly documented work in which the development of science is taken as the basis of a theory of knowledge.

*Herman Weyl: *Philosophy of Mathematics and Natural Science*. Princeton 1949.

A critical study of man's endeavor to analyze his knowledge of nature.

*Henry Margenau: *The Nature of Physical Reality*. New York 1950.

A discussion of the philosophical implications of modern science, followed by a philosophical synthesis which is partly idealistic and positivistic.

*Philipp Frank, *Modern Science and its Philosophy*. Cambridge, 1950.

NATURAL SCIENCE

The History of Natural Science in General and of the Atomic Theory in Particular

General Works

F. Danneman: *Die Naturwissenschaften in ihrer Entwicklung und ihrem Zusammenhange*. 4 vol., 2nd impr. Leipzig 1920.

W. Sedgwick and H. W. Tyler: *A Short History of Science*. New York 1935.

Charles J. Singer: *A Short History of Science to the Nineteenth Century*. 4th impr. Oxford 1946.

E. Mach: *Die Mechanik in ihrer Entwicklung*. 9th impr. Leipzig 1933.

F. Cajori: *A History of Physics*. 2nd ed. New York 1929.

E. O. von Lippmann: *Entstehung und Ausbreitung der Alchemie*. Berlin 1919.

H. Kopp: *Geschichte der Chemie*. 4 vol., Braunschweig 1843-1847.

H. Kopp: *Die Entwicklung der Chemie in der neueren Zeit*. München 1873.

*Harvey Brace Lemon: *From Galileo to the Nuclear Age*. New York 1946.

*A. C. Crombie, *Augustine to Galileo*. London 1952.

*A. C. Crombie, *Robert Grosseteste and the Origins of Experimental Science 1100-1700*. Oxford 1953.

*H. S. Redgrove: *Alchemy Ancient and Modern*. 2nd ed. London 1922.

*J. R. Partington: *A Short History of Chemistry*. 2nd ed. London 1939.

*Cohen and Drabkin: *A Source Book in Greek Science*. New York 1948.

*W. F. Magie: *A Source Book in Physics*. New York 1935.

*W. Whewell: *History of the Inductive Sciences*. 3 vol., 3rd ed. London 1857.

History of the Atomic Theory

K. Lasswitz: *Geschichte der Atomistik von Mittelalter bis Newton*. 2 vol., 2nd ed. Leipzig 1926.

*F. H. Loring: *Atomic Theories*. London 1921.

A. G. M. van Melsen: *Het Wijsgeerig Verleden der Atoomtheorie*. Amsterdam 1941.

*Joshua Craven Gregory: *A Short History of Atomism*. London 1931.

F. A. Lange: *Geschichte des Materialismus und Critik seiner Bedeutung in der Gegenwart*. 10th impr. Leipzig 1921.

This work indicates also the philosophic background of the various stages in the development of the atomic theory.

*A. Wurtz: *A History of Chemical Theory From the Age of*

Lavoisier to the Present Time. London 1869.

*A. Wurtz: *The Atomic Theory.* London 1880.

Development of the Atomic Theory in the Last Decennia

The number of books on this subject is almost inexhaustible. Many combine a sketch of scientific development with insufficiently founded philosophic considerations. The following works about this difficult subject can be understood even by those who do not specialize in atomic science.

L. de Broglie: *Ondes, corpuscules, méchanique ondulatoire.* Paris 1945.

A. Haas: *Wave Mechanics and the New Quantum Theory.*
A translation of *Materiewellen und Quantenmechaniek.* 4-5th impr. Leipzig 1934.

*Herman T. Briscoe: *The Structure and Properties of Matter.* New York 1935.

*J. D. Stranathan: *The 'Particles' of Modern Physics.* Philadelphia 1942.

*Lord Rutherford: *The Newer Alchemy.* New York 1937.

*M. Born: *Atomic Physics.* London 1945.

*George Gamow: *Atomic Energy in Cosmic and Human Life.* Cambridge and New York 1946.

The Smyth Report. U. S. Government 1945.

F. K. Richtmeyer, E. H. Kennard, and T. Lauritsen, *Introduction to Modern Physics.* New York 1955.

R. S. Shankland, *Atomic and Nuclear Physics.* New York 1955.

H. A. Bette and P. Morrison, *Elementary Nuclear Theory.* New York 1956.

D. Halliday, *Introductory Nuclear Physics.* New York 1955.

I. Kaplan, *Nuclear Physics.* Cambridge 1955.

INDEX OF NAMES

INDEX OF SUBJECTS

235